Anne Cullen

Given to me by my
grandfather Ed - Feb. 16,
1964

A Cavalcade of Horses

A CAVALCADE
OF HORSES

In Fact, Fantasy and Fiction

EDITED BY

Florence K. Peterson and Irene Smith

ILLUSTRATED BY WESLEY DENNIS

THOMAS NELSON & SONS

Edinburgh   NEW YORK   *Toronto*

Acknowledgments

To Holiday House, Inc. for *The Blind Colt* by Glen Rounds. Copyright 1941 by Holiday House, Inc.

To Holiday House, Inc. for *Hunted Horses* by Glen Rounds. Copyright 1951 by Holiday House, Inc.

To William R. Scott, Inc. for *The River Horse* by Nina Ames Frey. Copyright 1953 by owner, Nina Ames Frey. Permission granted by the publisher, William R. Scott, Inc.

To the Copp Clark Publishing Co. Ltd. for *The Black Stallion and the Red Mare* by Gladys Francis Lewis. Permission granted by Gladys Francis Lewis, copyright owner.

To Abingdon Press for "A Battle for Mastery" from the book, *Cowboy Boots* by Shannon Garst. Copyright 1946 by Doris Shannon Garst. Permission granted by Marcia Marshall, copyright owner.

To Bill Hosokawa of the Denver *Post* for *Elijah, the Hermit Horse*. Permission granted by Bill Hosokawa, copyright owner.

To Longmans, Green and Co., Inc. for "The Outlaw Roan" from the book *The Phantom Roan* by Stephen Holt. Copyright 1949 by Longmans, Green & Co., Inc.

To *Scholastic* Magazines, Inc. for "Easy Does It!" by Robert L. McGrath. Copyright © by Scholastic Magazines, Inc. Reprinted by permission.

To *Calling All Girls* Magazine (Parents' Institute, Inc.) for "Trapped" by Arlene Hale. Copyright by publisher, January 1960. Reprinted from *Calling All Girls* Magazine.

To the Macmillan Company for "Lessons from Holley" from the book, *High Courage* by C. W. Anderson. Copyright 1941 by the Macmillan Company and used with their permission.

To Alan Lomax for "Riding Song" from *Songs of the Cattle Trail* by John A. Lomax. Copyright 1919 and used with permission of copyright owner, Alan Lomax.

To Rand McNally & Company for excerpts from *Black Gold* by Marguerite Henry. Copyright 1957 by Rand McNally and Company, publishers.

To Julian Messner, Inc. for *The Good Luck Colt* by Genevieve Torrey Eames. Reprinted by permission of Julian Messner, Inc. from *The Good Luck Colt* by Genevieve Torrey Eames; copyright 1953 by Genevieve Torrey Eames.

To *Reader's Digest* for "Justin Morgan, Vermont Horse Hero," renamed from *The Horse That Became a Legend*, by Harland Manchester. Copyright 1954 by the Reader's Digest Association, Inc. Condensed from *American Mercury*.

To Holt, Rinehart and Winston for "The Runaway from New Hampshire" by Robert Frost. Copyright 1923 by Holt, Rinehart and Winston, Inc. Copyright 1951 by Robert Frost. Reprinted by permission of Holt, Rinehart and Winston, Inc.

To Lothrop, Lee & Shepard Co., Inc. for "The Arabian from Canyon Fury" by Robert Sidney Downs. By permission of Lothrop, Lee & Shepard Co., Inc. from *Canyon Fury* by James Robert Richards © 1952 by Lothrop, Lee & Shepard Co., Inc.

To Doubleday & Company, Inc. for "A Horse Afraid of His Shadow" from *Wonder Tales of Horses and Heroes* by Frances Carpenter. Copyright 1952 by Frances Carpenter Huntington. Reprinted by permission of Doubleday & Company, Inc.

To Curtis Brown, Ltd. for "Alexander the Great" and "Buffalo Bill" by Eleanor and Herbert Farjeon from *Heroes and Heroines*. Copyright 1933 E. P. Dutton and Co. Reprinted by permission of the author.

To Bobbs-Merrill Company, Inc. excerpt from *Jeb Stuart, Boy in the Saddle* by Gertrude Hecker Winders, copyright © 1959 by the Bobbs-Merrill Company, Inc., used by special permission of the publishers.

To the Houghton Mifflin Company for "Mud Pony" from *Red Indian Fairy Book* by Frances Jenkins Olcott. Copyright 1945 by Houghton Mifflin Company.

To Dodd, Mead & Company for "The Nutcrackers and the Sugar-tongs" from *The Complete Nonsense Book* by Edward Lear. Reprinted by permission of Dodd, Mead & Company from *The Complete Nonsense Book* by Edward Lear.

To Julian Messner, Inc. Reprinted by permission of Julian Messner, Inc. from *Baron Munchhausen: His Wonderful Travels and Adventures*, retold by Erich Kastner, translated by Richard and Clara Winston, illustrated by Walter Trier. Copyright © by Julian Messner, Inc. 1957; Copyright 1951 by Atrium A. G., Zurich.

To Abingdon Press for "The Three Horses" from *I Rode a Black Horse Far Away* by Ivy O. Eastwick. Copyright © 1960 by Abingdon Press.

To Farrar, Straus & Cudahy, Inc. for *Comanche of the Seventh* by Margaret Leighton. Copyright 1957. Used by permission of publishers, Farrar, Straus & Cudahy, Inc.

To Lothrop, Lee and Shepard Co., Inc. for "Myles Keogh's Horse" by John Hay from F. E. Clark's *Poetry's Plea for Animals*. By permission of Lothrop, Lee and Shepard Co., Inc.

To Appleton-Century-Crofts, Inc. for "The Old Cavalry Horse" from *The Last Run of Uncle Sam's Fire Horses* by Frances Margaret Fox. Reprinted by permission of the publishers, Appleton-Century-Crofts, Inc.

To Brandt and Brandt—agents for the estate of Stephen Vincent Benét for "Western Wagons" from *Book of Americans*. Published by Farrar and Rinehart 1933. Permission granted for publication by Brandt and Brandt.

To Simon and Schuster, Inc. for From the "Book of Job" from The Bible designed to be Read as Living Literature, edited by E. S. Bates. Used by permission of the publisher.

To Viking Press for excerpts from *Little Vic* by Doris Gates. Copyright 1951 by Doris Gates Hall. Reprinted by permission of The Viking Press, Inc.

To Franklin Watts, Inc. for portions of *Black Beauty* by Anna Sewell and introduction by Noel Streatfield. Copyright by publisher 1959.

THIS BOOK IS DEDICATED TO THE FAVORITE NEPHEWS OF THE EDITORS—

David Travis Smith

AND

John Brett Klauer

Foreword

Horses are old, horses are new. We cannot even imagine how old they are in our history, or how long ago they and man became friends on earth. Yet, nowadays when they are fewer, they seem to be new, and the rarer they are in our everyday lives, the more people find to write about them. And the more that is written, the more young people want to read about horses: trained and wild, aged and modern, fanciful and real.

The storehouse of horse fiction has grown to mammoth proportion in our book collection. Consequently no reader finds all the best stories, and some that should be read widely are too quickly forgotten. To compile this book we searched the list of every publisher and we think that what it holds is worth keeping.

You will find that the selections cover a wide variety. There is a sampling of tales of ancient times: exciting stories of the valor of horses in races and in battle; inspiring stories of their contribution to human progress, and to the building of our country.

Nine parts make up this Cavalcade, each leading in some special direction to the drama and history of horses in the great sports kingdom. If one of these books-within-a-book does not meet your need today, perhaps another one will. This is a big volume, good to open at random and enjoy as you like. Take off in any direction.

Happy reading and riding. May *A Cavalcade of Horses* carry you far and bring you back safe in the saddle.

FLORENCE K. PETERSON

and

IRENE SMITH

Table of Contents

VIII HORSES TO THANK
Faithful services to man and country

IX HORSES TO KEEP
Beloved friends and pets

I

HORSES TO FIND

*Stories about wild horses, captured,
or left to run free*

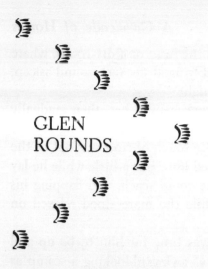

GLEN
ROUNDS

The Blind Colt

IT WAS NEAR SUNDOWN OF AN EARLY SPRING AFTERNOON WHEN THE BROWN
mustang mare left the wild horse band where it grazed on the new spring
grass, and climbed carefully to the top of a nearby hogback.

All afternoon she had been restless and nervous, spending much of her
time on high ground watching the country around her. Now she stood and
stamped her feet fretfully while she tipped her sharp-pointed ears forward and
back as she looked and listened. Her nostrils flared wide as she tested the
wind for any smells that might be about.

The rain-gullied buttes and pinnacles of the Badlands threw long black
shadows across the soft gray and brown and green of the alkali flats below
her. A few jack rabbits had already left their hiding places and were prospect-
ing timidly around in the open, searching out the tender shoots of new
grass. They, too, threw long black shadows that were all out of proportion to
their size.

A few bull bats boomed overhead, and a meadow lark sang from the top of
a sagebrush nearby. Below her the rest of the mustang band grazed quietly
except for an occasional squeal and thump of hoofs as some minor dispute
was settled. Otherwise everything was quiet.

But still the little mare didn't leave the ridge. She stood watching while the
flats grew darker and the darkness crept up the sides of the buttes, until at last
the sun touched only the very tiptops of the highest pinnacles. Then after a
look back to where the rest of the horses were bedding down for the night,
she slipped quietly down the far side of the ridge and was soon hidden in the
darkness.

Next morning she was in a grassy hollow at the head of a dry coulee where the rolling prairie and the Badlands meet. And lying at her feet, sound asleep, was her colt, that had been born during the night.

The early sun touched the top of the rimrock behind her, then gradually crept down until it was warming the grass where the little mustang lay. As soon as the ground had begun to steam and the touch of frost was out of the air, she nudged him with her muzzle and waked him. For a little while he lay there, sniffing around in the grass as far as he could reach, and flapping his tail to hear it thump against the ground, while the mare stood relaxed on three legs and watched him.

But after a while she seemed to figure it was time for him to be up and about; so she urged him to his feet. He was as awkward-looking a scamp as you'd care to see as he stood with his long, knobby legs braced wide apart and caught his breath after the effort of getting up.

His body was close knit and compact and his back was flat and strong. His muzzle was delicately shaped but his forehead bulged as all colts' do. His neck was so short he couldn't get his nose closer to the ground than his knees, and his legs were so long he seemed to be walking on stilts. His ears were trim and sharply pointed but looked as though they should belong to a horse much larger than he.

The mare saw all this but she knew that colts were put together so, and that those extra long legs of his were specially made that way so that by the time he was a day or two old he would be able to travel as fast and as far as the grown horses in case of danger. And besides, she thought that his blue-gray coat was especially handsome.

For a few minutes the colt was busy trying to balance himself on his legs while he sniffed and snorted at everything in reach. As long as he stood still he was all right but when he tried walking he found he was engaged in a mighty ticklish business, what with his being so high in the air with nothing holding him up but those four knobby legs. They had to be lifted and swung just so or they got all tangled up and started him kiting off in some entirely unexpected direction.

But he was hungry, and the only way he could get anything to eat was to go after it himself; so it wasn't long before he was able to scramble around against the mare's side. After a little nuzzling around he found her teats and settled down to sucking noisily, flapping his tail with excitement.

Before long his sides began to stick out, he was so full of milk, and he was quite ready to enjoy the business of having his coat groomed by the mustang mare. She was fair bursting with pride, as this was her first colt. She whickered softly and caressed him with her muzzle every now and again as she scrubbed him with her rough tongue. When she hit a ticklish spot he'd flap his tail and squirm and snort his tiny snorts. When he did that she'd nip him gently with her big yellow teeth to warn him that wild young ones must learn to obey, and he'd better stand still until she was done or he might get worse.

And not an inch of his hide did she overlook. The white snip on his nose, his speckled blue sides and flanks, his legs that shaded down to black shiny hoofs: all got their share of combing and washing. By the time he had been thoroughly polished the sun was warm in the hollow and he practised his walking again, and his smelling, and his hearing.

He started taking little exploring trips, a few wobbly steps in one direction, then another, with much snuffing and snorting as the brittle last year's grass crackled under foot. As he got the hang of operating his walking apparatus more smoothly, he became bolder and extended the range of his explorations until sometimes he traveled as far as ten or twenty feet from the brown mare.

His black-tipped, pointed ears were fixed to turn in all directions, to help him locate the source of sounds he heard. He pointed them forward and back, and the soft wind that springs up on the desert in the morning brushed against them, feeling sweet and clear and smooth. What few sounds he heard at first seemed to float separately through the warm silence as though there was all the time in the world and no need for two noises to be moving at the same time. Meadow larks whistled from nearby sagebrush, and far off he heard the harsh bickering of magpies as they quarreled over a dead rabbit or a gopher.

Later on he discovered that down close to the ground there was a thin blanket of bug sounds. Flies buzzed and grasshoppers whirled. And burier beetles made clicking noises as they busily buried a small dead snake.

Sniffing through his nose, he caught the sharp clean smell of the sagebrush, and the more pungent smell of the greasewood as the sun began to heat it up. Occasionally he got a whiff of wild plum and chokecherry blossoms from the thicket down below the rim of the Badlands.

Of course, these were the big plain smells, easily discovered. Later on he would learn to identify others that had to be searched for with flared nostrils, and carefully and delicately sifted for the story they could tell him of friends, or danger, or the location of water holes in the dry times. But for now the simpler lessons were enough to keep him busy, and the mustang mare was mighty proud of him.

But for all her pride, she was a little troubled, too. For there was something strange about the colt, although she couldn't tell exactly what the matter was.

He was as lively as you'd expect any colt only a few hours old to be. He snorted and kicked up his heels when a ground squirrel whistled close by. And when a tumbleweed blew against his legs he put on a mock battle, rearing up and lashing out with his front feet. When he came back to her from his trips he'd pinch her with his teeth, and pretend to fight, as any healthy colt should. But nonetheless, she felt that something was wrong.

The sun climbed higher, and the colt finally tired himself out and lay down to doze at the mare's feet. She thought about starting back to join the mustang band, but it seemed so safe and peaceful here in the pocket that she hated to leave. By tomorrow the colt's legs would be stronger and he would be able to follow her with no difficulty.

But before the morning was half gone she heard the sound of danger, an iron-shod hoof striking a stone, and looked up to see two cowboys between her and the mouth of the pocket.

It was Uncle Torwal and Whitey out to see how their range stock was getting along. Torwal was a slow-speaking fellow with a droopy red moustache, and a good many of the horses running in the Badlands belonged to him. Whitey, who was probably ten years old or thereabouts, had lived with him on the ranch for several years. Almost since he could remember. He wore a cast-off Stetson hat of Torwal's and high-heeled riding boots from the same source. They lived alone like any two old sourdoughs and were familiar sight at all the round-ups, and in town of a Saturday, Torwal on a crop-eared black and Whitey on a pot-bellied old pinto named Spot. Torwal usually spoke of Whitey as his 'sawed-off' foreman.

The little mare had whirled to face them, keeping the colt behind her. With her teeth bared and her ears laid back, she looked half wolf for sure.

"Spunky crittur, ain't she?" Whitey remarked as they rode carefully around, trying to get a good look at the colt.

"She's a wolf all right," Torwal agreed. "An' if you ain't careful she's agoin' to paste you plumb outta your saddle. Better not crowd her."

They sat on their horses and watched awhile and admired the colt. "Purty as a picture, ain't he, Uncle Torwal?" said Whitey. "Reckon we better take him home so the wolves won't get him?"

"Don't reckon we'll take him anywheres," Torwal told him. "Looks like I'm a-goin' to have to shoot him!"

"Shoot him! Why?" squalled Whitey. "Why he's the purtiest colt on the ranch!"

"Better look him over closer, Bub," said Torwal. "See if you notice anything outta the way about him."

"I don't see anything wrong, myself," Whitey told him, after he'd walked Spot in a circle around the mare and colt again. "He looks to me just like the kind of crittur I'd like to have for a 'Sunday' horse."

"Look at his eyes; they're white." Torwal growled. "That colt's blind as a bat!"

"Aw, them's just china eyes, Uncle Torwal," Whitey said. "Lotsa horses has china eyes. Even ol' Spot has one."

"Them ain't no china eyes, not by a long shot," said Torwal. "If you look close you'll see that they're pure white without no center. He's blind, and we gotta shoot him. Otherwise he'll fall in a hole somewheres or get wolf et."

"Well, even if he is blind do we *hafta* shoot him?" Whitey asked. "Couldn't I take him home an' keep him at the ranch?"

"All he'd be is a mess of trouble even if you got him home, and I doubt that he'd go that far without somethin' happening to him anyways," Torwal told him. "An' besides, he wouldn't be good for nothing."

"Well anyway, do we hafta shoot him?" Whitey said. "Couldn't we just let him go loose?"

"Now quit your squallin'," Torwal told him, patiently. "I don't like it any more than you do, but if we leave him he'll either fall in a hole and starve or else he'll get wolf et. Lookit her tracks where she circled during the night. Fighting off an ol' 'gray,' I bet she was."

While Whitey sat with his lip hanging down almost to his collar, Torwal took another chew from his plug and got his rifle out of his saddle scabbard. But whenever he tried to get near the colt the little mare was there, lashing out with her hoofs and showing her teeth to bite either man or horse that got too near. Before long she was covered with lather and her eyes showed white, and the ground was plowed and trampled in a circle. But still the colt was safe.

Then Whitey spoke up again. "Lissen, Uncle Torwal," he said. "Lookit the way she fights. I don't believe any wolf could get to that colt, the way she uses them heels. If you'll let him go I'll watch mighty close to see if he falls in anything. I'll ride out every day to see that he's all right. An' if he does fall in I—I—I'll shoot him myself!"

Uncle Torwal thought the matter over awhile.

"You want that colt mighty bad, don't yuh?" he said at last.

"Yeah, I sure do! He's the purtiest thing I've ever seen!" said Whitey. "I don't think anything will happen to him, really, Uncle Torwal! He's too smart lookin'!"

"Well, I tell yuh," Torwal said, doubtfully. "Since you feel like that about it we'll let him go awhile. We'll be a-ridin' over here every day for a while, anyways, so we can always shoot him later."

"But don't go gettin' your hopes up," he added. "The chances are he won't last a week. An' if he does he ain't good for nothing except to eat up good grass an' be a gunny sack full of trouble."

"Nothing is going to happen to him," Whitey exclaimed. "You'll see."

"Maybe," said Uncle Torwal, but Whitey could see that he was glad to have an excuse for not shooting the colt. Uncle Torwal put his rifle back in the scabbard, and they sat for a minute watching the colt, and then rode off to attend to their other affairs.

The little mare watched them until they were out of sight, and finally when she could no longer hear them she turned to the colt. She nuzzled him all over to make sure that nothing had happened to him. Then, after letting him suck again, she started down the trail toward the place she'd left the mustang band, with the blind colt following close against her flank.

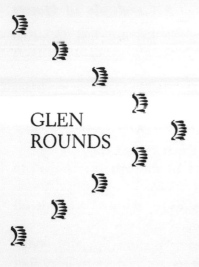

GLEN
ROUNDS

Hunted Horses

Wild Appaloosa

FOR THREE DAYS AND NIGHTS A LATE SPRING BLIZZARD HAD BEEN ROARING and whooping over the high, barren rims and ridges of the wild horses' range. It whipped before it powder-dry snow that swirled in blinding, choking clouds, clogging the eyes and noses of the wild Appaloosa stallion and his band of mares and colts as they stood humped up with their backs to the wind. Standing patiently, braced against the wind that beat at them from all sides, they waited out the storm. The fine snow drifted deeper and deeper around their feet, piled up thick blankets of snow on their backs, and beat its way into the long hair of their shaggy winter coats until they were almost invisible.

While the storm blew there was a sort of truce between the hunting animals and the ones that were hunted, as all took what shelter they could from the snow and bitter cold. But when at last the wind dropped and the air cleared, the stallion began to stir uneasily in the early morning starlight. He rubbed his muzzle against a foreleg to clear the ice and rime from his nostrils, shook himself, and stamped his feet to limber his stiffened muscles. He knew that the meat-eaters, driven by three days' hunger, would soon be moving. All the other animals must be once more alert. Already, far off among the ridges, he heard the thin faint howl of a gray wolf hunting, and from the broken country below another one answered.

When the first faint sign of daylight was touching the high peaks above

him, the wild stallion started moving stiffly through the deep snow toward
the top of the nearby ridge for a look around. The rest of the band, still
sluggish from standing so long in the bitter cold, stayed huddled together
for what warmth they could get from each other. From the ridge, as the
light strengthened, the stallion could see the new snow, unmarked in any
direction. The stunted bushes were hidden, and no track showed anywhere.
The only marks were occasional rocky scarps, too steeep to hold the snow,
that loomed up black and strange, in contrast to the soft muffled white
shapes elsewhere.

The tumbled, broken country below the ridge where the wild horse stood
was still dark when the sky in the east brightened and the first sun struck
the tips of the peaks. It gradually moved down the slopes, past his ridge
and onto the gentle slope where the band of mares and colts were just
beginning to stir.

A whiskey jack came fluttering and beating his way up through the snow
from where he'd been hidden, and started squalling loud complaints at the
blinding white world he found. The noise seemed to shatter the morning
that had been so still. The horses shook themselves and moved cautiously
about, enjoying the sudden feeling of warmth. The stallion still carefully
watched the slopes and ridges in all directions, and sniffed the little air cur-
rents that sprang up with the sunshine.

He cleared his nostrils and tested the air again and again but found no
scent that might mean danger. The only movement he saw was a band of
antelope unhurriedly crossing a ridge half a mile away. They had come up out
of a place that was hidden from him by the ridge between. As long as they
showed no sign of alarm, he felt sure there was nothing threatening there.
However, he watched them carefully as they stopped to look over the country beyond the second ridge, not entirely satisfied until they moved quietly
on again and disappeared into another place he could not see. Then, deciding that no danger threatened from that direction, he took another quick
look around and started down the slope to where the mares and colts waited.

All through this high Red Desert country with its sagebrush flats and
broken, rocky rims and ridges—country that ordinary range stock avoids
because grass and water is scarce—scattered bands of wild horses still hold
their own against their many enemies.

At one time there were thousands of them grazing on the plains below;
but the ranchers, wanting the grass and water for more profitable stock, sys-
tematically shot and trapped them by the hundreds. These last small bands,
driven into the highest, roughest parts of the desert, are all that are left.

Even here they have many enemies to keep their numbers down: snow and rock slides on the treacherous slopes, gray wolves, mountain lions, and even bears. In summer wild-horse hunters often come to capture some of the showier individuals to be broken to the saddle or sold for rodeo stock.

In different parts of this high range country there are horses of various sizes and colors: bay and brown, blue roan and iron gray, buckskin and black. Some are small and compact in shape, others are bigger and more rangy, but all, no matter what their size, are tough and hardy. No others can survive in that rugged country.

Some are probably descended from horses lost by the Indians, who had gotten them by trade or by stealth from the early Spaniards. Others might have come from stock abandoned by wagon trains on the old Santa Fe and Oregon trails. And even now, an enterprising wild stallion sometimes manages to toll a few mares away from the ranchers' herds below.

The mares and colts of the Appaloosa's band were blue roans, mousy grays, and a mixture of nondescript duns and bays. All the colts and most of the younger horses showed the flashy Appaloosa markings of the stallion— the white rump patch with the dark spots, the white stocking feet, and pink nose—markings that the Indians and the wild-horse hunters prized highly.

Where the stallion had come from, nobody knew, for never before had there been any Appaloosas among the wild horses in that part of the country. He'd first been seen by hunters some four or five years before, a young horse with only a couple of mares following him. His handsome build and unusual markings had immediately attracted the horsemen, and any number had tried at one time or another to capture him.

However, he had proved to be as crafty as he was striking in appearance, and year after year he managed to escape the best-arranged traps. Year by year his band of mares had increased until now he had twenty or more. He must have fought many savage battles with other stallions, for it is no simple thing for a lone horse to gather a band of mares together, but he showed no scars or markings.

This morning he moved about the slope where his mares and colts were pawing away the snow to get at the grass, now and then driving back a straggler that seemed to be on dangerous footing. As he moved warily about, he was restless and uneasy.

Not only was he alert for danger that might come from the hidden places behind the ridges, but from the snow itself. It was an enemy. It not only covered the grass and stunted bushes the horses browsed on, but it lay in a smooth, soft blanket that completely hid deep gullies and washouts. What seemed like solid ground could give way without warning and drop an incautious horse into a place where he might be held prisoner until he starved or froze. And along the tops of the high rims were great overhanging snow cornices that might break loose at any time, burying anything below under tons of snow.

Later in the morning, as the sun warmed the south slopes, the Appaloosa began to hear more and more frequent crashes as the huge masses broke loose and fell into the canyons below. Sometimes long low rumblings told of whole slopes loosening and sliding to the bottom at express-train speed, carrying hundreds of tons of snow and rock that sheared off trees or anything else in their path.

As he listened to these sounds the wild stallion became more and more uneasy, and when he began to feel small creakings and shiftings in the snow underfoot he bunched the band and started moving them cautiously across the slope toward flatter ground not far away. Most of the horses had gotten safely out on the flat, when one of the younger mares turned back up the slope a few steps, and tried to reach a bunch of grass that stuck above the snow. As she stretched her neck and gave it a great yank with her powerful jaws, the snow where she stood cracked loose and started to slide gently downhill.

Before she could turn, the snow above her also began to move. All the way to the top of the ridge it heaved and rippled, slowly at first, then faster and faster until it was piling up around her knees and threatening to carry her feet out from under her. Behind her, the stallion had also been caught by the moving snow. Snorting with terror, the two horses fought their way across the slide.

It was only a short distance to firm ground, but they were being carried rapidly down slope at every lunge. Once they lost their feet they'd be carried over the edge of the canyon below, where already they could hear the roar of the snow pouring over the sheer cliff. Luckily, the outer edges of the slide were moving slower than the middle, so they came to comparatively firm footing while they were still several yards from the drop-off. They made their way out to the safety of the flat where the rest of the horses were already grazing. It was some time before they stopped their sweating and panting. On the flat they were safe, although they still heard, now and again, the roaring of slides on the other slopes.

Strange Stallion

For several weeks the Appaloosa stallion and his band of wild horses stayed quietly in the rough country around the Haystack Buttes. Now that spring had reached even the highest parts of the range, they found grass coming up rich and green in all the draws, and snow water still standing in all the little hollows. The ragged patches of their long winter hair were rubbed off, and they looked sleek and glossy in their new summer coats. It was still too early for the flies that would plague them later.

Nearly every day one or more of the mares drifted stealthily away from the others to search out some hidden spot, and returned hours later with a wobbly-kneed colt at her side. A few came back without their colts, for a crafty old mountain lion had taken to hanging around the Appaloosa's territory. The stallion had caught his scent several times, but the cat never came in close, preferring to prowl around the rims waiting for a mare to leave the safety of the band and the watching stallion.

Gray wolves bothered them some, too, for there were pups in the dens among the washouts, and their appetites made great demands on the hunters. Several of the wild horses showed festering gashes where they'd been slashed by wolf fangs.

As always, the Appaloosa spent much of his time on high points and ridges, keeping watch on the country in all directions. Far off, he sometimes saw other wild-horse bands moving as though they were being driven, and a time or two he saw horsemen, but they didn't cause him any particular worry. Long before they could have found their way into this rough range he would have taken his band and disappeared in one of the hundreds of twisting canyons behind him.

The kind of men he knew never came into this country for pleasure, nor did their range stock ever drift this far, so any rider was pretty sure to be after horses. As long as the snow water held out, the wild-horse band could stay hidden far back in these rocky pockets. So the hunters waited, fixing up their traps and looking over the country, knowing that the hot dry weather would force the horses out onto the long water trails where they'd be easier to come at.

Meanwhile the Appaloosa kept them in mind, as he did the prowling wolves and mountain lions. He had escaped from men many times, and felt he knew their hunting methods well enough. More than once they had set out to "walk him down," using the old Indian trick of posting riders and fresh horses in a great circle, the relays of fresh riders keeping the wild horses moving day and night so they had no chance to rest or graze. Such a chase might go on for days before they wore the leader down so that a man on a fresh horse could, in a sudden burst of speed, overtake and rope him.

Many times the Appaloosa had seen riders suddenly come, whooping and swinging ropes, out of some side canyon to try to stampede him into the wide wings of a horse trap. But so far, his alert craftiness had saved him.

The Appaloosa had a different kind of trouble at hand now. A lone black stallion had shown himself several times lately on high places in the neighborhood. So far he'd made no attempt to challenge the Appaloosa, but more than once, when the mares were scattered out grazing, he'd come in close to try to run one or more away from the fringe of the band. Each time, however, when the Appaloosa had come roaring out to fight, the strange black had quit the mares and galloped off.

Sometimes for a day or two nothing would be seen of him. Then suddenly he'd appear again on some high ridge, where he'd stand watching until the Appaloosa moved out to drive him off. The Appaloosa redoubled his watch over his band, moving constantly around them as they grazed, driving back stragglers. He moved from ridge to ridge when the black wasn't about, to be sure that the stranger wasn't hiding.

As the days went on, the black grew bolder and bolder, sometimes grazing all day in plain sight, a couple of hundred yards off. When the Appaloosa moved threateningly out toward him he'd go away, but each time he went less willingly and came back sooner, making it plain that sooner or later he'd make up his mind to fight.

The Appaloosa grew irritable and short-tempered from the strain. He was forced to stay alert both day and night, for often in the moonlight he found the black moving stealthily nearby. There was no telling when he might try to slip in and drive off some of the mares.

Meanwhile, the first of the hot winds had begun to blow across the desert, and before long the grass started to turn brown and the smaller water holes dried up. The wild horses had to travel greater and greater distances to water.

One evening the Appaloosa was leading his band to water, and, as he always did, left them grazing part way up the last ridge while he went on to the top to scout the place before letting them come on. When he looked out over the flat below, he saw a strange brown mare not far from the water hole, and nearer by, the black stallion. The mare whinnied and the black answered her, bowing his great neck. He moved toward her at an exaggerated trot, lifting his feet high and snorting proudly.

The Appaloosa's first intention was to go roaring down the slope to fight it out with the wild black stallion, to settle the matter once and for all, and then collect the brown mare for himself. But even as he gathered himself, an uneasy feeling made him hesitate. He stood instead, shifting his feet and looking carefully all around the flat for sign of something wrong. He examined the place foot by foot, and still could see nothing that looked suspicious. But the uneasy feeling was still strong, and so he went down the slope, drove his mares and colts back down the trail a few yards, and bunched them up ready for quick flight.

That done, he went back to the ridge again, where he stood with his head thrown high and his nostrils spread wide to test the air in all directions. Several times he bowed his neck and started down after the black intruder, but each time something vaguely threatening about the place disturbed him. After a few steps he turned back to the top.

Meanwhile, the black had seen the Appaloosa on the ridge. After trumpeting one shrill challenge and getting no reply, he turned back and zigzagged his way closer and closer to the mare, showing off his paces. His long mane and tail waved like flags in the sun, his eyes rolled to show the whites, and bright red showed in his distended nostrils. He made a proud appearance.

This was an old, old challenge to the Appaloosa, this stranger strutting in his territory, but still he hesitated on the ridge, angrily shifting his feet and throwing his head. He was still unable to rid himself of the feeling that there was an unseen danger down there. He had no fear of the strange stallion, but he had been hunted a long time, and more than once this feeling of danger when there was nothing suspicious to be seen had saved him. There would still be plenty of time to settle the black stranger when he felt it was safe to go down after him.

The brown mare whinnied again and the black curvetted closer, stopping now and again to whistle shrilly, and to look arrogantly all around him. When he came close the mare whirled and let fly at him with her heels, then turned to whinny coyly again. But all this time she had hardly moved her own length from the place the Appaloosa had first seen her.

Perhaps that was what had bothered him, for even a tame ranch mare would ordinarily have made at least an appearance of flight from a strange stallion. However, the black seemed to sense nothing wrong, and continued his prancing courtship performance.

The Appaloosa's mares had edged up the slope behind him, anxious to go on to water, so he turned irritably and drove them back down the trail, again bunching them compactly before he went up to his lookout. Snorting and blowing, the black had moved up again to within a few feet of the mare, stretching his muzzle toward her. He got a squeal and her heels in his face for his pains. He whirled gracefully, knowing well he made a handsome picture, and came down with his feet bunched in the middle of the trail. And then the unseen danger struck!

The Appaloosa saw a spurt of dust at the black's feet, and the sudden movement of a dark and snakelike thing whipping up around the bunched hoofs, entangling them in a loop that tightened and jerked him to his knees. The black horse fell heavily, with a wild scream of terror. A man jumped out of a hole where he'd been hidden close by and whipped a couple of turns of the rope around a short post set firmly in the ground beside him.

The black had been caught by an old horse-hunters' trick of staking a mare out to toll a wild stallion up to where he'd put his feet in a hidden loop. The Appaloosa didn't wait to see any more. He whirled about, and drove his band back along the trail the way they'd come. When they watered, it was the next day at a water hole thirty miles away. They never saw the strange black horse again.

NINA
AMES
FREY

The River Horse

Arana

I<small>T WAS EARLY EVENING IN A LITTLE VILLAGE ON THE SHORE OF ONE OF THE</small> beautiful lakes in central Guatemala. The quick dark of the tropics had already fallen, and the mountains that rose in majesty behind the groups of adobe huts, were black shadows against the dark sky. Inside one of the thatched-roof, windowless houses, an Indian boy sat on a mat and watched the smoke from the cooking fire rise and swirl out through the open doorway.

The firelight touched the face of the boy's mother, Maria, intent on her weaving. It cast shadows on the hunched forms of his grandfather and three men of the village. It flickered over a sleepy brown thrush in its cage on the wall, and sent a gleam into the dreaming eyes of the boy, Arana. He was hardly aware of it, so absorbed was he in his thoughts.

"A wild horse," he was thinking to himself, intent on the sleek image in his mind, "as swift as the wind over Lake Atitlán." He sighed heavily and looked up at the small bird sitting so still in its cage, its head tucked under a wing. "Like you, little *cenzontle*," he said gently. "A horse who will feed out of my hand and belong only to me." He chirped loudly at his pet.

Startled, the bird awoke. Its bright eyes fastened on the boy and a short lilting melody from one of its beautiful songs filled the room. Arana laughed and whistled back at him.

* * *

17

He was secretly very happy to be going into the forest with his father. At ten he had already learned to do the work of a man, and usually his days were spent in hoeing corn, picking coffee beans, or helping to cut down cedar and avocado trees to be made into the blunt-ended dugout canoes that were used on the lake. It was almost a holiday to be going on the mountain trails with his father. Might he not see a deer or a wildcat? Perhaps he would catch an iguana, the timid lizard that was so good to eat. He had not tasted iguana meat in a long time. Arana decided to take his rope noose and try to snare something to bring back to his mother for dinner.

He looked up at his father. "If we go into the far forest," he said, "perhaps we may see one of the wild horses."

"There are no wild horses," Maria said harshly. "Only on the plains, perhaps, there might be some. Certainly not in the forest. You dream too much, Arana."

"A mule we may have one day," José said kindly. "It eats little. If we had a mule, he would carry as much as I have in the *cacaste*, and then I could walk along with a load beside him. Or, if we had oxen and a cart, they could carry even more. But a horse . . . ," he shook his head.

Maria was very practical. "We have no mule and no oxen," she said. "Yet we do well enough. I do not have shoes such as the *ladino* women wear in the cities." She paused and shook her pleated skirt and looked down at her bare toes. "I would not want them," she said. "Not even sandals do I want."

The old grandfather had been standing listening quietly. "Beads for your neck and ribbons for your hair and perhaps a silver ring, though, you do want," he said gently.

"Well," Arana's mother said tossing her head. "A silver necklace, of course. Who would not?" But she smiled a little.

"Let the boy dream then," the grandfather said. "Maybe he will find your necklace in the forest."

Arana was astonished. Necklaces in the forest? Sometimes he did not understand his grandfather.

They went back to the hut quickly, and José took down the *machete*, the long knife that was used for many purposes, and placed it in his belt. Arana retied his sandals, pulling the thongs closely around his ankles. Soon he would have to make himself another pair. These were worn and full of holes.

At last they were ready to go. They were starting out when the sun was high in the sky. It was hot in the village, even with the breeze that came off the lake. Perhaps on the forest paths it would be cooler. Often Arana had gone with his father to hunt in the very early morning. Walking along the narrow, well-worn pathways, his feet would be drenched with the dew from the grasses. He would see the stars wane with the coming of the sun, and even in the half light of the forest with its deep blue shadows he could feel the splendor of the dawn.

*   *   *

Abruptly they came to an open space, and the marsh was before them. Buzzards were hovering over one end of it, and a large pink heron stood calmly on one leg looking for its dinner. A wild turkey was roosting on a branch nearby, and the tall grasses around the border of the swamp were moving as though an animal were wading carefully through them.

Suddenly a little creature about the size of a young fawn stepped through an opening and stood motionless before the man and the boy.

Arana stopped. "What is that?" he whispered to his father.

There was a silence. The little animal did not move, and José did not answer at once but looked intently at the small creature.

Arana saw that it was a young animal, of a pale fawn color, covered with soft brown spots and white stripes that ran from its brown mane to its brief tail. He had never seen anything like it before. "What is it?" he asked softly again.

José motioned to him to be quiet. At that moment the late sun, slanting in over the trees onto the marsh, bathed the little creature in a stream of golden light. Its dark mane and strong head showed up clearly. Arana's breath caught in his throat.

"It looks like a small horse!" he said, his voice husky with excitement.

Arana and his father stood at the edge of the marsh and looked at the little animal. It was about three feet high and almost four feet long. It seemed to be blinking in the late afternoon sunlight, and it looked around the open space as though it were lost.

The boy stood completely still. He hardly dared breathe.

José shaded his eyes. "It must be . . ." he started to say. And then he said, "But no, it is too unlikely." He stood quietly beside Arana.

The small creature now came out of the underbrush completely, and timidly ate a few mouthfuls of marsh grass.

"What is it?" Arana whispered again. "Can it be a sort of wild horse? Let me throw my noose around its neck."

"Without doubt the mother is near," his father said, "and we have no hours to waste. It is perhaps after all the animal I first thought it to be, called a *danta*. It is a somewhat similar creature to the horse. We do not often see the *danta*, as it is an animal of the night and generally sleeps by day. Our ancestors, the Mayas, carved it in stone and used the figure in so many ways that it was thought for a long time that the Maya people must have had horses. If you remember your grandfather's stories, however, the Mayas had never seen a horse until the Spaniard, Alvarado, and his men rode down from Mexico into Guatemala. The *danta* resembles the mule somewhat, too, but unlike the horse and the mule it lives near rivers and swims in them. That is why we sometimes call it the little river horse. It prefers the night, too, like the deer."

"Why have I never seen one before in the forest?" Arana asked. "I have seen the deer many times."

José started along the path again with a purposeful, fast walk. He did not look back, but Arana kept turning his head to watch the little animal at the edge of the marsh until they had entirely left the place. The *danta* was still there, standing and feeding quietly. It had not noticed them.

"Why is it . . . ?" Arana began again excitedly.

"You have never seen one," his father said, "because the *danta's* life is spent in the densest part of the forest. It lives, always, near water, and runs into it if frightened. The priest once told me of these animals. They are gentle and easily trained. It is believed that at one time they lived in many parts of the world, but now they are found only in Guatemala and in one other place across the world from here."

"How large is the mother, if this animal we saw is only a young one?" Arana asked. "Is it as large as a horse? Could it be trained to carry a pack to market?"

José considered this carefully, while still keeping to his fast walk. "They do not grow quite as large as some horses," he said, "but the grown animal is large enough to carry a load and can be trained. It is brown, with a black mane, and it eats the leaves and berries and tender shoots of trees. In some forest villages the people hunt these animals for their flesh, which is supposed to be quite good, and for the hide which is used in making whips."

Arana walked on, so lost in thought that he did not see the fat iguana, hiding behind the glossy leaves and white flowers of the *madroño* tree. Even if he had looked directly at the lizard, he might not have seen him, so similar was the iguana to the color of the tree itself. The noose hung idly at the boy's belt. He saw nothing.

The forest was very thick and luxuriant here. The branches of the trees, the tall *conacaste*, the *guayacan* with its purple flowers, the *madre cacao* of delicate pink flowers and poisonous roots, the feathery palms and the straight pines all twined together over their heads, shutting out the light of the sun. But on the forest floor there was reflected a sort of liquid green color as though one were looking at it all through sea water.

Bees and butterflies in swarms were probing the many-colored blossoms of the forest orchids, and everywhere birds were gorging themselves on the juicy jungle fruits and berries, spitting out the seeds that pattered down with a sound as of light rain. The tall flowers and bushes that bordered the path brushed against Arana's face, they scratched his arms and legs, but he did not feel them. In his mind a plan was forming.

*   *   *

The Search

Arana awoke to the cry of a flock of *azacuán*, the falcon, whose flight to the north in the spring always meant the opening of the rainy reason to the Quiché. There must be hundreds in the flock, the boy thought, from the sound of their beating wings and the harsh resonance of their cries. It meant that the rains would be plentiful and the crops abundant, and it seemed to Arana a good omen for his plans this morning. He got up quietly and threw off his blanket.

In the darkness he found his belt and searched with careful probing fingers for his knife. It would have to be sharpened on the road, there was no time now to look for a stone for that purpose. He picked up his sandals and his noose and went cautiously over to the cooking fire. Its embers were still warm, and on a flat baking dish there were a few *tortillas* left from the night before. Arana took some and placed them in a small fiber mesh bag which he hung from his belt.

Soundlessly the boy went around the sleeping forms of his father and mother, wrapped from head to foot in their blankets, and out the door with no more noise than the brush of a bird's wing. In spite of all his care, however, he stepped on a sleeping chicken. She gave an indignant gasp and rose up, flapping her wings with such suddenness that Arana nearly fell headlong over her. His heart almost stopped beating. Had they heard him? He listened, scarcely breathing, but there was no sound from the inside of the hut. Chickens' noises in the night were commonplace. Often the fowl slept inside on the floor companionably with the family.

Arana ran now, out through the patio and down the village street. At the church steps he stopped to sit down and tie his sandals. There he said a short prayer for a safe journey and a safe return.

"Go with God," the priest would have said to him and, seeing a candle lighted in the church, Arana hesitated. Should he go in and tell the good *padre* about his journey and his mission? He knew that the priest was often awake and at the altar at this hour. His kindness and understanding could be taken for granted, his advice might be valuable. However, since it was the duty of his grandfather to pray daily in the church for his people and as it was nearly time for that ceremony to take place, Arana decided to go on. He wanted more than anything to surprise his grandfather with his adventure.

The stars were beginning to fade from the sky now. It would not be long before the first pale fingers of morning light would creep over the mountain tops and splash gold upon their steep sides. When he had found the small *danta* and had captured him, providing that were possible, then he would display his prize to his grandfather and to the priest as well. He climbed the steep hill that led out of the village and soon found himself on the trading route which he had traveled the day before.

The branches of the low bushes beside the path bathed him in a ceaseless shower of dew, so that in a few minutes he was drenched and cold. He shivered a little and cut a short stick to beat at the branches in front of him and rid them of moisture. The result was that the gourd-like leaves above him emptied a quantity of water down the back of his neck, wetting him completely. He wished for a brief moment that he had waited until the sun was high and had dried out the forest. But then, if he had delayed, he might never have been allowed to come at all.

It was darker on the trail as he went along, not black like the night, but dim, as though he were looking at the trees through a fog. It was also exceedingly quiet. The birds, the monkeys, the parrots, the parakeets and the macaws, all the noisy voices of the forest were asleep. Only the owls hooted softly. The little rustlings of the leaves, the soft sighing noise the light wind made in the underbrush, now seemed almost loud and somewhat startling. Some hidden creature near Arana kept making a sort of small sneeze, sometimes almost beside him, sometimes a little distance away, but always unexpected. It made his heart beat faster.

After a while the boy became conscious of a kind of light rustling that seemed to go along with him. It stopped when he stopped and then started up again quietly when he went ahead. He held his breath and heard it distinctly.

Suddenly there was a small piercing scream, a shriek that was cut off in the middle with a long gasp. Then, finally, complete silence.

Abruptly a fox darted across the path in front of Arana. It was carrying a small limp rabbit in its jaws. For one startled moment the fox looked at the boy, and then it was gone in an instant, leaving a trail of blood on the underbrush.

"Murderer!" Arana shouted, waving his stick. It caught on a branch and a small waterfall came down and drenched him completely. He rubbed his wet face with the sleeve of his *camisa*. For the first time he wished that his father's tall form strode ahead of him.

It was slightly lighter now. The stars had gone completely from the small patch of sky that Arana could see, and the miracle of a new day was taking place in the forest. The trees seemed to turn green at once, and the flowers returned to their brilliant color. The butterflies crawled out from under the leaves where they had spent the night and opened and shut their wings in swift motions like sails in the wind. The birds shook themselves, preened their feathers, and said cheerful good mornings to one another. A lark sang somewhere in a treetop, and a monkey came down, hand over hand, to look at Arana. It kept pace with him in the branches, swinging from limb to limb with careless ease.

Increasingly the upper forest was filled with a noisy activity. It sounded almost as though a large crowd had come suddenly into an empty room. Where there had been silence, broken only by a single bird call, now there were shrill alarms that resounded from the earth to the tree tops. Hundreds of tiny sharp eyes were watching Arana's progress.

The monkeys chattered, "There's a stranger in the forest. Beware! Beware!"

The parrots shouted, "The branch he carries at his side. Watch out for that!"

The birds shrilled, "Stay away. Away."

The excitement traveled. It reached the innermost parts of the forest. The rabbits scampered to their certain hiding places. The weasels, the porcupines, and the armadillos hid themselves, each in his own fashion. All the hundreds of small animals near the path remained motionless, their sensitive noses sniffing the air. The deer stood up and trembled in their glades, their flanks close, their muscles taut, ready to spring in any direction. The jaguar and the mountain cat, the tapir and the wild boar were alerted. Their ears pricked, but they alone had no fear of an intrusion. They settled down again in their lairs. They slept. A small creature was in the forest. What of that?

It seemed an endless time before Arana reached the borders of the swamp. He approached the high grasses with caution and looked out first over the expanse of marsh from behind the trunk of a huge tree.

There was nothing to be seen this morning but a few small birds. The buzzards had gone. The heron had floated on graceful pink wings to another swamp, another feeding ground, for his breakfast.

The boy crept cautiously through the tall marsh grass, parting the rushes with the utmost care until he came to the place where he had seen the young *danta* the day before. There were the small footprints in the mud, still clear and distinct. But now there were others. They led to the far curve of the marsh. He followed them.

The water moccasins were sluggish this morning. The warmth of the sun had not yet loosened their muscles and they moved through the water slowly. As Arana parted the branches of a small overhanging tree, a viper darted away, hissing.

The boy drew a long breath. A snake bite was something to fear. He could be bitten and die here alone in the forest. No one would know where to look for him.

"Where there are known snake places, walk confidently," his father had always told him. "Make noise with the feet. Snakes are cowards. They will run. All but the rattlesnake, perhaps, and he gives warning."

Arana did not feel confident, nor could he thrash his stick about or stamp on the mud. He did not want to frighten the *danta* should it be near.

There was a foul smell here in this place and soon he came upon its source. A large creature lay on its side, its lolling head partly in the water. The stiff black mane was tangled in the bushes and the shaggy hide was ripped open, showing the bare flesh, stripped in places from the bone.

Arana did not have to look long to realize that this was the mother of the small creature he had seen the day before. The buzzards had been waiting for her to die and had feasted on the body already. He turned away. Had the little one died too? His heart was sick. Perhaps he had come all this way for nothing. He walked around the swamp to the other side. There was no sign of anything there. He sat down under a towering *conacaste* tree, discouraged and sad.

Something was moving in the bushes beside him! His heart stood still and his breath caught in his throat. With quiet caution he took the rope noose from his belt. Whatever it was, he would be ready.

Suddenly a shaft of brilliant sunlight came piercing through the branches of the trees. A head peered out of the low bushes. Without turning Arana could see the tawn-colored body with its white stripes and brown dots. The little creature was poised for flight. Quicker than thought the noose flew out of Arana's hand. It caught the startled little *danta* fairly around the neck and tightened on the small stiff mane. Bounding away with high agonized shrieks, it jumped high over the bushes into the forest.

Arana was unprepared for such strength. Holding the rope tightly, he was flung headlong into the base of a tree. His head hit the trunk with the force of a hammer, and he fell unconscious to the ground. The rope pulled through his nerveless fingers. The *danta* disappeared.

How long Arana lay at the base of the tree he did not know, but when, finally, he opened his eyes the sun was high in the sky and for a moment dazzled him. A flock of birds was peering at him from above, two monkeys had come down to have a closer look, and a fat turkey cock with four hens was walking by unconcerned and unalarmed.

At first Arana thought he was on the hard dirt floor of his own hut. He thought he could hear his mother grinding corn. It must be time to get up and bring in the morning wood. He sat up abruptly. His head ached. Where was he?

Gradually his eyes focussed in the strong sunlight. He saw the marsh, his mind cleared, and the events of the morning came back to him. He remembered seeing the *danta* and throwing his noose around its neck. That was the last that he knew. The little creature must have leaped away. Time had gone by. By the look of the sun, several hours had passed and he had lost what he had come so far to find. If it had been possible for him to cry, he might have done so, but Arana never cried. Seldom, even as babies, do the Quiché Indians cry.

He clamped his jaws together and stood up. His legs were stiff and his head pounded, but that did not matter. What worried him most was the position of the sun in the sky. If he were to get back to his village before dark, he would have to start soon. Night closed in suddenly here in the forest. What should he do? Go back without the small creature he had so nearly captured?

Suddenly he had a thought.

"There should be tracks," he said aloud.

At the base of the large tree the boy knelt down on the soft moist earth and looked carefully around him. The sprawling footprints of the turkey cock and his hens were easy to recognize, but there were no footprints of the *danta*, so distinct, so different from all others. Arana sat back on his heels and looked about him. There, over on the other side of the tree, what was that? The bushes were broken down, leaves torn. The boy was exultant. He remembered now. The *danta* had taken a flying leap and had vaulted over the bushes away from the marsh.

Arana forced his way through the thick growth. Thorns tore at his face and ripped his *camisas*, but on the far side of the bushes he saw something. Four small hoof marks, clear and distinct! Four footprints deep in the soil! Wild excitement gripped him.

"He's here!" Arana shouted, and ran forward.

At once he had lost the trail. There were no more footprints. He forced himself to go back to the marsh, to start again at the big tree and go forward slowly and cautiously. The boy tried to be extremely quiet now. It would not do to frighten the small animal. Softly he parted each bush, examined the ground for footprints, and looked for broken branches. Finally he found another set of hoof marks. From there he followed the trail even more slowly. Here was a patch of hair clinging to a thorn. Beyond it, a few yards away, he found a shred of rope from the noose. At that place he lost the trail again in the dense undergrowth.

Arana stopped. He took out his knife from his belt and cut a cross in the tree trunk beside him, making a large white gash that would be easy to see. From there he walked in circles around the tree, keeping his eyes alternately on it and on the ground. He went in larger and larger circles until at last he found what he was looking for. On a hard bit of ground he saw two small imprints from the front hoofs. The little creature must be jumping and bounding about like a young deer. The boy pushed aside the heavy entangling vines and stumbled over roots he could not see. Now, however, he was going in the right direction. Soon he discovered another set of marks. Following them and other signs of the *danta's* flight, he was led finally into a sort of clearing far from the swamp. Tall pines spread their boughs high above the dark mossy ground. They made a thick canopy through which the sun hardly penetrated. It was a glade full of shadows.

Arana stopped for breath and leaned against the bark of a giant *conacaste* tree for a moment. The little *danta* was not here. He would have to look carefully for the trail out of this place. He rested his stick against the tree and felt the string bag at his belt slap against his thigh. He had forgotten the *tortillas*. There were five in his hand when he drew them out. Arana ate two and felt much better. He was about to start to eat the others when he hesitated. He might need more food later. He thought of his mother and of the village he had left that morning. It seemed a long way off. Would he be able to find his way back there? He looked anxiously toward the tops of the trees. It was difficult to tell here where the sun was in the sky, but he reasoned that there were several hours yet before darkness should creep over the forest. He took a long breath. Which way now?

Without warning two men appeared in the clearing. On the backs of each were huge bundles of split *pinabete* wood for the making of hand looms. They stopped short in astonishment when they saw Arana.

"Boy," one of them said finally, "are you lost here in the forest?"

Arana shook his head. "I came from the swamp," he said briefly, "near the *ceiba* trees."

The second man leaned on his staff heavily. The leather band that supported the heavy bundle of sticks pressed deeply into his forehead. He looked fierce, but when he spoke his voice was kind.

"I have a son such as you," he said slowly, "maybe taller and somewhat older perhaps. But he does not come alone into the depths of the forest. Have you no father?"

"My father weaves mats," Arana said. "We are from San Pedro La Laguna. I came from there this morning, alone," he said proudly, "before the stars had left the sky."

"There is a trail near here," the first man said, "but it is far from San Pedro. The stars will be in the sky again before you are there. Come with us to Santiago Atitlán. Tomorrow perhaps someone will be going by boat to San Pedro. That way you will reach home safely."

Arana hesitated. Should he go back like a small child with these two men? How would he feel tomorrow? He took a long breath and shook his head. Now that he had come so far, he must find the small *danta*. There was no other course. Nothing else could be considered.

"Thank you," he said to the men, "but I do not go with you to Santiago Atitlán. There is a small creature here in the forest that I have come all this way to find. Its mother is dead. It wanders alone, I think, and it must not be far from here. Already my noose is about its neck. When I have found the little animal I shall go back to the trail near the swamp. The trail is . . ." He hesitated. Where was the swamp? He pointed uncertainly. "Over there," he said.

The first man shrugged his shoulders. "With God," he said kindly but indifferently.

The second man scowled. His eyes looked fiercer than ever. He hesitated, started toward Arana as though to compel him to go with them. Then he stopped. "A child in the forest," he muttered. "Look well, little one. Go before the night has come." He seemed to be thinking for a moment. "There was an animal back a way by a great pine," he said slowly. "You can see the pine from here. It is not far. Perhaps it is the creature you follow. I did not look carefully, thinking it was a fawn. It had spots . . ."

"That's it!" Arana leaped to his feet with sudden energy. He turned to look for the pine where his fierce friend had pointed.

"Go with God," the man said.

"With God," Arana called back over his shoulder. The men had gone. He was alone again.

He could see the huge pine, but it was quite a long time before he was close to it. The trail the men had been following was faint and overgrown with vines. Great grey drifts of moss hung down from the branches here, and brilliant orchids covered the cypress and walnut trees. With every muscle tense, he pushed slowly through the brush that came to his waist and tangled his feet, making as little noise as possible. He must not startle the *danta*. It was his last chance. If the small creature escaped from him again and disappeared into the forest depths, there would be no time to follow him further and return to the trading route before night. His heart beat uncomfortably fast as he advanced step by step toward the pine. He held his breath and parted the bushes carefully and soundlessly. There was the *danta!*

All in one motion Arana jumped and caught the rope in his hands. The little animal gave a surprised desperate gasp, shot up with a high bound, and came down on four fiercely straining hoofs. The boy held on. He braced his feet and clung with iron fingers to the rope. The *danta* shook suddenly and violently all over and then abruptly stopped and stood still. Arana approached it with gentle hands. He patted the quivering sides softly.

"You are mine now, little one," he said. His voice was choked. He could hardly breathe, he was so excited. Finally he had a thought. He reached into the bag at his belt and brought out a *tortilla*. He crushed it with his fingers and held it out in his hand.

"It is good," he said softly. "Eat."

The little creature sniffed the corn cake, pawed the earth with its feet, and shuddered away. Arana held on to the rope, his fingers clamped around its end. The other hand still held the *tortilla*.

"Eat it," he said again. "We will be friends then." He offered the food a second time. The *danta* stood still. It stopped shaking. Its small ears close to its head went straight up. Its eyes were very soft and bright. This time it put its nose down on Arana's hand and licked the food from his fingers. The boy's heart overflowed with a sudden love. He patted the stiff mane with cautious hands. "No jaguar will get you now," he said.

The boy and the *danta* stayed there in the glade beside the tall pine for a while longer. Arana patted the animal's spotted sides until they no longer quivered at his touch. "They are like sunlight on pine needles," he thought, "and they feel like pine needles, too, soft and smooth and yet stiff somehow." He wished he could stay here in this place for a long time until the little creature knew him better, but it was growing late. They must be starting back.

II

HORSES TO TAME

Training, mastery, and bronco riding

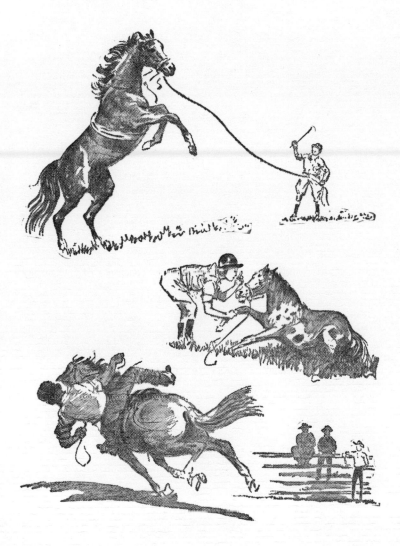

GLADYS
FRANCIS
LEWIS

The Black Stallion and the Red Mare

At FIRST DONALD LAY STILL. SCARCELY A MUSCLE MOVED. THE BOULDERS and the low shrubs screened him from view. Excitement held him motionless. His hands gripped the short grass and his toes dug into the dry earth. Cautiously he raised himself on his elbows and gazed at the scene below him.

There, in his father's unfenced hay flats, was the outlaw band of wild horses. They were grazing quietly on the rich grass. Some drank from the small hillside stream. Donald tried to count them, but they suddenly began moving about and he could not get beyond twenty. He thought there might be two hundred.

Donald knew a good deal about that band of horses, but he had never had the good luck to see them. They were known over many hundreds of square miles. They had roamed at will over the grain fields and they had led away many a domestic horse to the wild life. Once in that band, a horse was lost to the farm.

There in the flats was the great black stallion, the hero or the villain of a hundred tales. Over the far-flung prairie and grass lands there was scarcely a boy who had not dreamed of wild rides, with the great body of the stallion beneath him, bearing him clean through the air with the sharp speed of lightning.

There was the stallion now, moving among the horses with the sureness and ease of a master. As he moved about, teasingly kicking here and nipping

33

there, a restlessness, as of a danger sensed, stirred through the band. The stallion cut to the outside of the group. At a full gallop he snaked around the wide circle, roughly bunching the mares and colts into the smaller circle of an invisible corral.

He was a magnificent creature, huge and proudly built. Donald saw the gloss of the black coat and the great curving muscles of the strong legs, the massive hoofs, the powerful arch of the neck, the proud crest of the head. Donald imagined he could see the flash of black, intelligent eyes. Surely a nobler creature never roamed the plains!

Off-wind from the herd, a red mare came out from the fold of the low hills opposite. She stood motionless a moment, her graceful head held high. Then she nickered. The black stallion drew up short in his herding, nickered eagerly, then bolted off in the direction of the mare. She stood waiting until he had almost reached her; then they galloped back to the herd together.

The shadows crept across the hay flats and the evening stillness settled down. A bird sang sleepily on one note. Donald suddenly became aware of the monotonous song, and stirred from his intent watching. He must tell his father and help send news around the countryside. He was still intensely excited as he crept back from the brow of the hill and hurried home. All the time his mind was busy and his heart was bursting.

Donald knew that three hundred years ago the Spaniards had brought horses to Mexico. Descendants of these horses had wandered into the Great Plains. These horses he now was watching were of that Spanish strain. Thousands of them roamed the cattle lands north to the American boundary. This band now grazed wild over these park lands here in Canada—four hundred and fifty miles north of the boundary.

His father and the farmers for many miles around had determined to round up the horses and make an end of the roving band. As a farmer's son, Donald knew that this was necessary and right. But a certain respect for the band and the fierce loyalty that he felt toward all wild, free creatures made him wish in his heart that they might never be caught, never be broken and tamed. He, who was so full of sympathy for the horses, must be traitor to them!

There had been conflicts in his heart before, but never had there been such a warring of two strong loyalties. He saw himself for the first time as a person of importance because he, Donald Turner, had the power to affect the lives of others. This power, because it could help or harm others, he knew he must use wisely.

When he stood before his father half an hour later, he did not blurt out his news. It was too important for that. But his voice and his eyes were tense with excitement. "That band of wild horses is in the hay hollow, west of the homestead quarter," he said. "There must be close to two hundred."

His father was aware of the boy's deep excitement. At Donald's first words he stopped his milking, his hands resting on the rim of the pail as he looked up.

"Good lad, Donald!" he said, quietly enough. "Get your supper and we'll ride to Smith's and Duncan's to start the word around. Tell Mother to pack lunches for tomorrow. We'll start at sunup." He turned to his milking again.

The other men were in the yard shortly after daylight.

Donald afterward wondered how long it would have taken ranch hands to round up the band of horses. These farmers knew horses, but not how to round up large numbers of them as the men of the ranch country knew so well. The farmers learned a good deal in the next two weeks.

Twenty men started out after the band as it thundered out of the hay flats, through the hills and over the country. The dust rose in clouds as their pounding hoofs dug the dry earth. The herd sped before the pursuers with the effortless speed of the wind. The black stallion led or drove his band, and kept them well together. That first day only the young colts were taken.

At sunset the riders unsaddled and staked their horses by a poplar thicket, ate their stale lunches and lay down to sleep under the stars. Their horses cropped the short grass and drank from the stream. Some slept standing; others lay down.

At dawn the herd was spied moving westward. With the coming of night, they, too, had rested. For a mile or more they now sped along the rim of a knoll, swift as bronchos pulled in off the range after a winter out. The black stallion was a hundred feet ahead, running with a tireless, easy swing, his mane and tail streaming and his body stretched level as it cut through the morning mists. Close at his side, but half a length behind him, ran the red mare. The band streamed after.

After the first day's chase and the night under the stars, Donald had ridden back home. Not that he had wanted to go back. He would have given everything that he owned to have gone on with the men. But there were horses and cattle and chores to attend to at home, and there was school.

The roundup continued. Each day saw the capture of more and more horses. As the men doubled back on their course, they began to see that the wild horses traveled in a great circle, coming back again and again over the same ground, stopping at the same watering holes and feeding in the same rich grass flats. Once this course became clear, fresh riders and mounts in relays were posted along the way, while others drove on from behind. The wild band had still to press on with little chance for rest and feeding. The strain of the pursuit took away their desire for food, but they had a burning thirst and the black stallion would never let them drink their fill before he drove them on. Fatigue grew on them.

As the roundup continued, the whole countryside stirred with excitement. At every town where there was a grain elevator along the railroad, people repeated the latest news of the chase. On the farms the hay went unmown or unraked, and the plows rested still in the last furrow of the summer fallow. At school the children played roundup at recess. Donald, at his desk, saw the printed pages of his books, but his mind was miles away, running with the now almost exhausted wild horses.

Near the end of the second week of the chase, Donald's father rode into the yard. Donald dropped the wood he was carrying to the house and ran to meet his father.

"Dad, they haven't got the black stallion and the red mare, have they?" Donald could scarcely wait for his father's slow reply.

"No, Donald, lad," he said. "Though those two are the only horses still free. They're back in the flats. We'll get them tomorrow."

Donald felt both relief and fear.

In the yellow lamplight of the supper table his father told of the long days of riding, of the farms where he had eaten and rested, and of the adventures of each day.

"That was a gallant band, lad!" he said. "Never shall we see their equal! Those two that are left are a pair of great horses. Most wild horses show a weakening in the strain and grow up with little wind or muscle. But these two are sound of wind and their muscles are like steel. Besides that, they have intelligence. They would have been taken long ago but for that."

No one spoke. Donald felt that his father was on his side, the side of the horses. After a long pause, Mr. Turner continued.

"With his brains and his strength, that stallion could have got away in the very beginning. He could have got away a dozen times and would now be free south of the border. But that was his band. He stayed by them, and he tried to get them to safety. This week, when his band had been rounded up, he stuck by that red mare. She is swift but she can't match his speed. It's curious the way they keep together! He stops and nickers. She nickers in reply and comes close to him, her nose touching his flank. They stand a moment. Then they are away again, she running beside him but not quite neck to neck. Day after day it is the same. They are no ordinary horseflesh, those two, lad!"

There was a lump in Donald's throat. He knew what his father meant. Those horses seemed to stand for something bigger and greater than himself. There were other things that made him feel the same—the first full-throated song of the meadow lark in the spring; ripe golden fields of wheat with the breeze rippling it in waves; the sun setting over the rim of the world in a blaze of rose and gold; the sun rising again in the quiet east; the smile in the blue depths of his mother's eyes; the still whiteness of the snow-bound plains; the story of Columbus dauntlessly sailing off into unknown seas.

These things were part of a hidden, exciting world. The boy belonged to these things in some strange way. He caught only glimpses of that hidden world, but those glimpses were tantalizing. Something deep within him leaped up in joy.

That night Donald dreamed of horses nickering to him but, when he tried to find them, they were no longer there. Then he dreamed that he was riding the great, black stallion, riding over a far-flung range, riding along a hilltop road with the world spread below him on every side. He felt the powerful body of the horse beneath him. He felt the smooth curves of the mighty muscles. Horse and rider seemed as one.

A cold dawn shattered his glorious dream ride. With his father he joined the other horsemen. From the crest of the slope from which Donald had first seen them, the pair of horses was sighted. They were dark moving shadows in the gray mists of the morning.

They had just finished drinking deep from the stream. Not for two weeks had the men seen the horses drink like that. Thirsty as they were, they had taken but one drink at each water hole. This last morning they were jaded and spent; they had thrown caution to the winds.

At the first suspicion of close danger, they stood still, heads and tails erect. Then they dashed toward the protecting hills. There the way forked.

It was then Donald saw happen the strange thing his father had described. At the fork the stallion halted and nickered. The mare answered and came close. She touched his flank with her head. Then they bounded off and disappeared in the path that led northwest to the rougher country where the chase had not led before.

Along the way the horses had been expected to take, grain-fed horses had been stationed. These had now to move over northwest. But the men were in no hurry today. They were sure of the take before nightfall. The sun was low in the west when two riders spurred their mounts for the close in. The stallion and the mare were not a hundred yards ahead. They were dead spent. Their glossy coats were flecked with dark foam. Fatigue showed in every line of their bodies. Their gallant spirits no longer could drive their spent bodies. The stallion called to the mare. He heard her answer behind him. He slowed down, turning wildly in every direction. She came up to him, her head drooped on his flank and rested there. In a last wild defiance, the stallion tossed his magnificent head and drew strength for a last mighty effort. Too late!

The smooth coils of a rope tightened around his feet. He was down, down and helpless. He saw the mare fall as the rope slipped over her body and drew tight around her legs. It maddened him. He struggled wildly to be free. The taut rope held. The stallion was conquered. In that last struggle something went out of him. Broken was his body and broken was his spirit. Never again would he roam the plains, proud and free, the monarch of his herd.

Donald saw it all. He felt it all. His hands gripped the pommel of the saddle and his knees pressed hard against his pony's side. Tears blinded his eyes and from his throat came the sound of a single sob. It was as if he himself were being broken and tied.

The sun dipped below the rim of the plains. The day was gone; the chase was ended. The men stood about smoking and talking in groups of two's and three's, examining the two roped horses. Donald's father knelt close to the mare, watching her intently. Donald watched him. His father remained quiet for a moment, one knee still resting on the ground, in his hand his unsmoked pipe. Donald waited for his father to speak. At last the words came.

"Boys," he said, without looking up, and with measured words, "do you know, this mare is blind—stone blind!"

A week later, Donald and his father stood watching those two horses in the Turner corral. They were not the same spirited creatures, but they were still magnificent horses.

"I figured," his father said, turning to the boy, "that they had won the right to stay together. I've brought them home for you, Donald. They are yours, lad. I know you will be good to them."

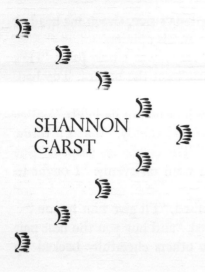

SHANNON
GARST

A Battle for Mastery

(Bob is spending the summer on his Uncle John Benton's cattle ranch in Wyoming, and learning to ride the range. Unwisely, the day before, he had gone out alone. His ideal cowboy is the top hand, Montana.)

WHEN THE MEN CAME IN TO DINNER, THEY WERE ARGUING FIERCELY. At first Bob could not make out what it was about. He could see that Montana was defending himself and that the other men all seemed to have taken sides against him.

"You're so doggoned sure of yourself," Crowbait was saying sarcastically. "You're supposed to be a top hand. You have quite a reputation for hoss sense. I reckon then that you're willing to back up your reputation in this matter by something worth-while."

"You can be sure of that," Montana said positively. "I'll give you my silver-mounted rodeo saddle if I don't ride that hoss."

Bob gasped, then held his breath. He knew that, next to his favorite horse Silver, Montana treasured above all his possessions the handsome saddle he had won as prize in the rodeo the year before. It was a finer saddle than any of the other men owned.

The conversation continued, growing louder and more serious. Still Bob did not discover what it was all about until Montana burst out hotly, "I'll not only ride Dynamite but I'll bust him, too."

At this all the other cowboys broke into loud and jeering laughter.

39

Shorty, who had seemed to be partly on Montana's side, shook his head at this statement. This was evidently going too far in his opinion.

"Success has gone to his head," Bob heard Shorty say to Uncle John. "He's plumb loco. Thinks there isn't any animal he can't get the best of. Too bad. When a top hand gets that notion, he's headed for the dust. Dynamite will throw him so high the birds'll build nests in his hair before he lights."

"I'm so sure I can bust Dynamite," Montana said calmly, "that I'll throw in Silver along with my saddle if I don't do it." The cowhands gasped. "But this whole thing is pretty one-sided," Montana went on evenly. "I ought to have some sort of prize if I succeed."

"If you break Dynamite," John Benton promised, "I'll give him to you."

"And the rest of us will pitch in," Shorty cried, "and buy you the best pair of cowboy boots Ted Russel can make." The others cheerfully backed up Shorty's offer.

"I'm glad you fellows are making the ride worth my while," Montana drawled. "I'd do it anyway, just for the fun of it, but such fine prizes make it more interesting."

Everyone broke into excited talk. They all agreed that Dynamite was an outlaw horse. One that could never be ridden, much less broken. They also agreed that probably he was a killer.

Bob felt shivers run up and down his spine. He knew that the other men were experienced in the ways of horse nature, too. It did seem that Montana was being pretty reckless to risk his life this way. He felt all tied up in knots of tension. He looked inquiringly toward the head of the table, wondering if his uncle would allow him to go to the corral.

"Go ahead," John Benton nodded, and relief flooded Bob's heart. Evidently nothing more was going to be said about his misadventure of the previous day.

Bob followed the men outside and climbed to the top rail, his heart beating hard.

Montana said nothing as he walked toward the corral. But he strode ahead of the other Circle K hands with the air of self-confidence that Bob admired. Three of the cowboys went to the large corral to cut out Dynamite and force him into the chute that led into the smaller corral where the horses were gentled.

The commotion in the big corral was terrific. It was evident that the other horses there considered Dynamite a killer, for they squealed with terror and scattered in all directions every time he came their way. And when the maddened animal threw himself, pawing and wild eyed, against the sides of the corral, Bob wondered if the poles would hold.

Montana was saving his energy for the great contest ahead. He sat on the top rail and laughed at the perspiring cowboys who were trying to get Dynamite into the small corral.

"I reckon I'll have to come and help you," he drawled.

"Save your steam," Crowbait puffed. "You're going to need every ounce of it or I'm a spavined hunk of hoss meat."

"I reckon you are," Montana grinned. "But do get a move on. I'm getting bored with this inaction."

"You won't be that way long," Shorty called to him, as Dynamite was finally cornered in the narrow chute between the corrals and the gate dropped behind him.

When the horse found himself imprisoned, he went crazier than ever. He squealed and battered the poles with his forefeet until Bob could feel the corral tremble. Then Shorty swung the gate leading from the chute into the small corral, and Dynamite came into it like a ton of his namesake.

Bob involuntarily drew up his legs as the enraged animal came his way. But Montana only continued to gaze at the horse with quiet amusement.

"A hoss with that much spirit will be a good animal after I take the spook out of him," he drawled.

"Huh!" grunted Crowbait, who was now sitting on the top rail beside Bob. "You're as crazy as popcorn on a hot stove. Ice will melt at the North Pole before you get the spook out of that boy. He's a killer or I never saw one."

Bob glanced quickly up at Montana and was surprised to see a look of tenseness on the foreman's face in spite of the grin. In a flood of understanding it came to him how much this contest meant to his friend. It meant not only his most prized possessions—his fine horse (and Bob knew that a cowboy's horses were like members of his family) and his saddle, the finest in the whole range country—but he was also staking his reputation as the best horsebreaker in the country. And perhaps, Bob thought with a sudden start, he was even staking his life.

"What are you waiting for?" Crowbait called, a jeering grin on his face. "Ain't scared, are you?"

"Scared of that amiable creature?" Montana drawled. "Naw. I've just got to give my dinner a little time to digest before I let him begin tossing it around."

"Huh, you're hoping he'll get himself all worn out," Crowbait scoffed.

Bob didn't like the tone of Crowbait's remarks. The cowboys, although they teased each other constantly, were usually good-natured about it. But there was always an undercurrent of meanness in Crowbait's teasing remarks to Montana. Bob wondered again if Crowbait envied Montana's top ranking in the Circle K.

But Montana paid no attention to Crowbait. Deliberately, he untangled his long legs from the top rail, jumped down into the corral, and commenced to twirl his rope.

At sight of this hated, two-legged enemy, Dynamite stopped his wild prancings. Then, with a squeal of fury, he threw himself at the man, rearing high into the air, forelegs pawing. At the same time Montana's rope snaked out.

Bob almost stopped breathing. Would his friend waste his loop and not have time to form another before those sharp hoofs would be upon him?

But miraculously the loop settled neatly around Dynamite's neck. Quick as a thought, Montana wrapped the other end around the snubbing post. His high heels plowed the dirt as he tightened the noose that was choking the meanness out of the horse. Then he yelled for someone to bring a blindfold and for someone else to hold the end of the rope while he lifted the saddle to throw on Dynamite's back.

"Well, I'm a spavined hunk o' hoss meat," cried Crowbait. "If he don't aim to ride that ornery animal without trying to gentle it first!"

And that did seem to be Montana's aim—to get along without any of the usual preliminary motions of letting the animal become accustomed to the man smell or to the feel of first the blanket, then the saddle, on his back. Swiftly Montana threw the saddle blanket on, then the saddle. Then, while Shorty and Crowbait twisted the animal's ears and held the blindfold in place, he leaped into the saddle. Crowbait jerked the blindfold and along with Shorty clambered to the top of the fence.

For a moment the horse stood still as though unable to believe that the weight on his back was real. Then he exploded all over the corral.

"Jumping Jimminy!" Shorty exclaimed. "He has all the mean tricks of all the mean hosses I ever saw rolled into that ornery carcass of his. He can wrinkle his spine, highroll, weave, sunfish, swap ends, jackknife, and everything else."

Bob did not see how any human being could remain seated on the leaping, twisting animal. Most of the time Dynamite's back formed a peak in the middle and his head was between his forelegs. Time and again he swapped ends, as Shorty called it, so suddenly that it seemed a miracle that Montana stuck in the saddle. He had a dozen different motions of the terrific, jerky sort that make a talented bucker.

"I'm beginning to wish we hadn't started this," Shorty gasped. "I'm too fond of Montana for this sort of thing."

"But Montana's riding him!" Bob cried. His hands gripped the top pole of the corral until his knuckles showed white. He ached all over, outside and in, with his concern for his friend and the intensity of his desire to have him triumph.

Shorty shook his head soberly. "That ornery devil hasn't used up all of his tricks yet," he said. "If he does throw Montana, he'll likely paw him to death before the fellow can get up. Or he's likely to start rolling if he can't get rid of him any other way." The cowhand drew a long sigh. "As for me," he concluded, "I'm willing to call it a day. But it's too late now. Montana's got to ride, or else . . ."

Bob gripped the rail and breathed a silent prayer. "Oh, stick on, Montana! Stick on!"

Around and around the corral they went. The spectators were silent now, lost in admiration for both horse and rider. They had been witnessing daring and skillful riding for most of their lives, but never had they seen anything like this. And never had they seen so tireless a horse. Long before this time an ordinary horse would have collapsed. Dynamite was covered with foam and at every leap his breath was forced from him with an agonized grunt, yet he would not give up. But finally the leaps became less wild and at last the horse's head came up. This, Shorty explained to Bob, was a sign that the bucking was over, for a horse cannot buck unless its head is between its legs.

Montana slid to the ground. Instantly Crowbait snatched the saddle and bridle from the horse, before it could find energy for more tricks.

Everyone slapped Montana on the back as he walked toward the bunkhouse. Even Crowbait seemed sincere in his admiration over the ride. And that night at supper no one could talk of anything else.

"You won your prize with interest," John Benton said. "That ride was worth a lot. What do you say, men? Has Montana earned the right to keep his saddle and his cow pony?"

The men gladly agreed with Mr. Benton's generous suggestion. Bob heaved a sigh of relief. Montana certainly should not be required to do any more, to risk his life again after such a wonderful ride. Perhaps luck would not be with him another time. Besides everyone believed that it was impossible to break Dynamite.

Montana looked up from his plate. "What's the matter?" he asked coolly. "Are you men trying to back out of your offers?"

"No," said Shorty. "It isn't that, and you know it. We're only trying to do the square thing by you. We know and you know that you can't break Dynamite. We don't hanker to have you risk your hide, trying a fool stunt like that."

"You've never known me to back out of anything, have you?" Montana asked.

"No," cried Shorty in exasperation. "And you aren't backing out now. We're asking you as a favor to us not to risk your fool neck again. We're shorthanded on the Circle K as it is. We can't spare any top hands."

"I made a proposition and I'll stick to it," said Montana quietly. "Either I'll break Dynamite in a week's time or you fellows get my saddle and my cow pony."

The men shrugged and went on with their eating. Bob wished that Montana would not be so stubborn. Oh, why wouldn't he quit now!

"You'll have to break Dynamite on your own time, Montana," Bob's uncle said. "I'm inclined to agree with Shorty and the other boys that there's an unbreakable horse. I don't think he's worth taking time to work with. I planned to save him for a rodeo horse. But if you want to work with him in your spare time that's your business."

"I reckon he'll be the top horse in my string one of these days," said Montana with a broad grin.

"Don't go countin' your hosses until they are broke," Crowbait warned.

That night Bob took his flashlight and wandered out to the breaking corral. Dynamite was to stay there until the end of the week, because the cowboys had refused to risk their necks cutting him out from the cavy and getting him into the chute again.

At the sound of Bob's footsteps Dynamite let out a fierce whinny. Bob heard his hoofs hit the poles. "Steady, boy, steady," he said soothingly.

"Steady, boy, yourself," he heard, and jumped at the sound.

"What do you think you're doing out here all by your lonesome?"

Bob recognized Montana's familiar voice. "Oh," he laughed, "you scared me more than the horse did! I just came out to talk to Dynamite a little. I thought it might help you if I talked to him a bit and sort of got him used to people."

"Thanks, pal." Montana chuckled. "You have the makings of a real cowboy. You and I had the same idea. Climb up here to the 'opery rail' and we'll have a little powwow and let Dynamite in on it."

Bob perched beside his friend contentedly.

"You know," Montana went on, "I believe he is beginning to understand already that we're meant to be friends."

But if Dynamite had such an understanding, he was very backward about showing it. For two days the men watched Montana each time he gave Dynamite his workout, then they tired of it. By now the horse was able to throw his rider once in a while. He had the advantage of not getting worn out in the battle of changing corrals and he was bursting with energy. But Montana was as agile as a panther. Almost as soon as he hit the ground he was on his feet and back in the saddle again, letting Dynamite feel the bite of the spurs after each victory. Finally the horse began to understand that the short triumph was hardly worth the punishment.

Only Bob knew that Montana went out every night and worked with Dynamite. Talking to him soothingly. Roping and tying him to the snubbing post. Rubbing his neck. Letting him wear the saddle for an hour at a time.

When the night before the end of the week came, Montana said to Bob, "S'pose you can get up before daylight tomorrow?"

"I reckon I can," said Bob, who would have slept standing on his head if Montana had requested it. "Why?"

"Well, I aim to get up before the birdies myself," Montana drawled. "Tomorrow is the day for me to collect my prize. So I want to give friend Dynamite here a bit of a workout before the sun rises. Take some of the spook out of him before the boys are up. When they come out, I want you to open the gate so I can come riding out on a hoss with his head up."

"I'll sure do that," Bob told him with delight.

That night Bob set his alarm for three o'clock, the time when Montana said he was going to begin the workout. Dynamite had never given up bucking whenever Montana first got into the saddle. But now it was more like the game of a mischievous child than the determined meanness of a killer horse.

Bob had seen Montana ride Dynamite around the corral after several of his bucking sprees. The horse acted promising enough then, but Montana had not yet attempted to ride him out in the open. After all, that would be the test. Dynamite might have learned the uselessness of fighting his heart out in the prison of the corral, but when he saw the wide open spaces the urge for freedom might prove to be stronger than the brief mastery Montana had managed to attain.

It was with considerable uneasiness the next morning that Bob called down to his friend, from his lookout on the top of the corral, that the men were coming from the bunkhouse.

"Open the gate then," Montana called, "and keep your fingers crossed, pal."

Dynamite stepped between the poles of the gate with head high and ears perked up.

"Steady, boy, steady!" Montana said quietly, his hand firm on the rein. Dynamite jerked his head as though in an attempt to get the bit between strong teeth, but Montana was prepared for just such a trick.

"No you don't, boy," he said. "Just remember that I'm boss, and we'll get along fine."

The spirited animal made two more attempts to bolt for the beckoning freedom of green meadows and blue hills. But the grip on the reins remained firm and the suggestion of spur against flank reminded him that the two-legged creature astride him was still determined to be master.

Bob held his breath. Would Dynamite bog his head and use his tremendous energy to rid himself of the burden on his back? There was plenty of room for the horse to put his strength to the test if he happened to take the notion.

But the horse trotted around the buildings with beautifully arched neck and high steps.

The men stood speechless, their mouths open with amazement. Cookie came out to whang the triangle and froze midway in the motion. John Benton appeared at the door, half his face clean-shaven, the rest covered with lather.

No one said a word as the handsome horse continued to high-step around the yard. Bob's heart, however, was still in his throat, for Dynamite's nostrils were dilated and he threw walleyed glances about.

Montana was the only one who seemed undisturbed. "How do you like my new hoss?" he called as he trotted by the men. "Isn't he a handsome brute? Don't you wish you had one as good?"

"Well I'll be a hornswoggled hunk o' hoss meat," Shorty cried. "If Montana didn't go and do it again. I never saw his like!"

Several times Dynamite tried to get his head down, but the alert, strong hand on the reins reminded him who was master.

After riding around the buildings for several minutes, Montana signalled Bob to open the corral gate. The foreman rode inside and removed the saddle.

As he came out, John Benton called, "That's a splendid new horse you have there, Montana."

The cowboy grinned. "I reckon he is," he drawled. "And my silver-trimmed saddle will look mighty fine on him."

"Right today," Shorty promised, "we'll get the order off for those new boots. You've really earned them."

"He sure has," the other cowboys echoed.

Bob looked down at his brown oxfords. "I wish I could do something to win a pair of cowboy boots," he thought. Then quickly forgot his desire in his joy over Montana's triumph.

III

HORSES TO RESCUE

Dramatic stories of threats and dangers

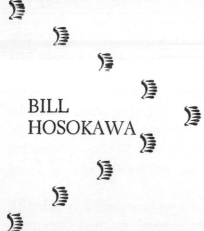

BILL
HOSOKAWA

Elijah, the Hermit Horse

ONE CLEAR, COLD DAY LAST FEBRUARY, WALLACE POWELL, A YOUNG COM-
mercial pilot, was jockeying his single-engine plane over the massive Collegiate Range of the central Colorado Rockies. Suddenly he saw a pair of
horses where no horses should be. Tails to the frigid wind, hemmed in by
huge snowdrifts, they were standing forlornly on the desolate ridge that connects the peaks of Mount Harvard and Mount Yale. Powell estimated the
elevation of the ridge at 12,800 feet, far above the timber line.

At his home base in Gunnison, 40 miles southwest of the ridge, Powell
told his boss, Gordon "Rocky" Warren, what he had seen. "They'll starve
to death," Warren said. "Guess we'd better see if any ranchers are missing a
pair of horses."

Eventually the news reached Gunnison's Mayor Ben H. Jorgensen, who
had been a volunteer officer of the Colorado Humane Association for 16
years. He hurried down to the airport. "Rocky," he said, "I want those horses
fed. The Humane Association hasn't funds for this kind of thing so I'll take
care of the bills myself. What will you charge?"

"The least I can do is take the job at cost," Warren answered. "I'll fly hay
up there for $12 a bale."

"Fine," said Jorgensen. "Let's get going."

When Warren flew over the ridge with the first load, only one horse was
there; apparently the other had died and been buried under drifting snow.
The survivor, a bay, was in pitiful condition, barely able to totter around.

Warren dropped the hay as close to the horse as he could. The bay was munching away when he headed back to Gunnison.

Warren and Powell took turns flying the haylift, making two trips a week. "When the air was smooth," says Warren, "we could come in 15 or 20 feet above the ground. But when the wind was high we'd have to stay a hundred feet off the ridge and drop the hay with a hope."

Soon delivering the hay got to be a personal thing. The horse would be waiting for them. "We hated to disappoint that old boy," says Warren. "Several times Wally and I flew up there when 100-mile gusts were bouncing our tiny plane all over the ridge. That horse was getting the kind of flying out of us that money can't buy."

Early in April, six weeks after the haylift had been launched, Ray Schmitt, a Colorado Air National Guard pilot, happened to touch down at Gunnison. Schmitt saw pictures of the hermit horse which Warren had snapped, and borrowed the photos for a friend, George McWilliams, Denver *Post* reporter. McWilliams excitedly telephoned Warren for details. "Incidentally," he asked, "have you a name for the horse?"

"No," Warren replied. "If you can think of a good one you're welcome to tag it on him."

McWilliams turned to a fellow reporter and said: "What was the name of that fellow in the Bible who was fed by ravens?"

"Elijah," the reporter said.

"That's the perfect name." McWilliams turned to his typewriter and hammered out the story of Elijah, the hermit horse.

The response was immediate. Ivan Thomas, manager of Centennial Race Track on Denver's outskirts, suggested a "Hay for Elijah" fund, started it off with a $100 check, and offered oats and a stall for life. Dozens of youngsters sent letters offering Elijah a home. One boy wrote, "I love horses next to my family and relations. If you are wondering how he would eat, I would mow lawns in the summer and shovel snow off the sidewalks in the winter." Next day some 30 horse lovers, mostly youngsters, sent in a total of $67 for Elijah's hay.

Newspapers all over the country picked up the Elijah story. The pilot of a New York to Los Angeles airliner requested the horse's position so he could point it out to passengers as he flew over. Letters came from virtually every state and from England, Portugal, Switzerland, France, Holland, Germany, Canada and Japan. The London *Daily Mail* correspondent in New York interviewed Mayor Jorgensen by telephone. The Army offered helicopters for hay transport, if needed.

One day while piloting a television crew over the site Warren saw what he described as a pair of winter-gaunt wolves stalking Elijah. Hurrying back to Gunnison, he picked up a shotgun and Wally Powell as co-pilot. The animals were still on the ridge when they got back. Warren shot and killed one, chased the second down the ridge. The American Humane Association in Denver announced silver medals would be presented to Warren and Powell.

Meanwhile, in Colorado Springs Bill and Al Turner, brothers who during the summer and fall guide pack trips in the mountains, read about Elijah with more than ordinary interest. Studying the photos, Al Turner said, "That horse must be our Bugs, the one that got away from the pasture last November."

Bugs had been born in the shadow of the Collegiate peaks and ran wild until he was four years old. He was captured by a wrangler, from whom the Turners bought him in 1946 for $50. He turned out to be one of the best animals in their pack string. When Bugs disappeared through a break in the pasture fence, taking a gray horse named Smokey with him, the Turners hired a cowboy to look for the runaways. The cowboy made nine trips into the high country before snows forced him to quit. The horses were given up for lost.

"If Elijah is Bugs," they now wrote Mayor Jorgensen, "he has quite a history. He hates parked cars and women in skirts, which would certainly be motive enough for heading for the high country."

Entry of the Turners into the picture aroused new public interest. The *Post* published a straight-faced editorial which called the attention lavished on the hermit horse "a hideous invasion of privacy. If Elijah," the editorial continued, "is an unclaimed nag of uncertain history, then rescue efforts must continue. But if Elijah is really Bugs, leave him alone. He's using his good horse sense in seeking solitude away from a noxious civilization."

A newscaster wrote a song about Elijah, and a disc jockey sang it to the tune of the Davy Crockett ballad.

But efforts to rescue Elijah, regardless of his feelings about the matter, continued. The Turners led a party on snowshoes up the seven-mile climb to Elijah's hermitage. When they reached the wind-swept ridge, Elijah regarded them nervously.

"Come here, Bugs," Bill Turner commanded. The horse waited motionless as the Turners approached close enough to drop a halter over his head. It was Bugs, all right, and thanks to the haylift he was in good shape. But taking him down across the snowdrifts, where he would bog down to his belly, was out of the question.

A month later the Turners made two more attempts to bring Elijah down.

The last time, accompanied by two friends and equipped with shovels, they cut a path through drifts 10 to 20 feet deep, working hours for yards of progress. Elijah was led down these paths, but darkness overtook them several miles short of the road. The men staked Elijah out and returned to town for the night. Next morning the Turners found him wandering a mile up the mountain. But now that he had had his last fling at freedom, Elijah took amiably to being rescued.

The welcome that was touched off as Elijah rolled into nearby Buena Vista aboard a trailer was fitting tribute to one of Colorado's most famous sons. The high-school band led a parade down Main Street. There was a float depicting the haylift and behind it came Elijah himself. More floats followed, and then marchers and cars with horns honking.

It was a great day for Buena Vista, population 783. More than a thousand persons watched the parade.

That afternoon Elijah enjoyed a trailer ride to Denver for the opening of Centennial Track. While 7000 spectators cheered, Mayor Will Nicholson of Denver presented him with a red blanket bearing his name in white letters. Later there were radio and TV interviews.

Elijah even visited the famous old Brown Palace Hotel. He was met at the entrance by the manager, led over a red carpet to the reception desk, and escorted to a straw-filled enclosure set up in the lobby—the first horse to be thus housed.

After two weeks of high living Elijah went home to get in training for the summer's labors—carrying fishermen and dudes into the high Rockies. Bill and Al Turner were astonished by an offer of $1500 for Elijah, but they aren't selling. "Elijah is a simple mountain critter, just like us Turners," Al told me. "He has five or six more working years ahead of him. After that, I'll let him retire to pasture—and not on top of a mountain, either."

STEPHEN
HOLT

The Outlaw Roan

(Glenn Barnes' beloved horse, Roy H, had just died. The boy wanted to be a veterinarian, but his foster parents, Abbie and Luce, were having money problems, and Glenn was giving up his dream of a life devoted to saving animals because of Ames College costs. He knew that Dr. Crane, a famous local veterinarian, needed an assistant, but the temptation to apply for the job had to be sternly resisted. Instead, Glenn was on his way to begin a dull city job. This last night he found a place to sleep under the stars, indifferent to the warning that a manhating outlaw roan, a rodeo cast-off, was loose in the river bottom.)

H OW LONG HE SLEPT GLENN DID NOT KNOW. WHEN A NOISE WAKENED him, there remained only the dull glow of the coals of his wood fire. The moon, high in the sky above him, shone clear and bright. He turned to the sound that had roused him, staring questioningly off into the thicket of willows to his right, then rubbed his eyes and stared again.

A horse stared back at him. In the bright moonlight he seemed ghostly, unreal, almost a phantom horse. Partly hidden by the trees, he stood silent, specterlike.

"The outlaw!" Glenn breathed, his eyes racing to follow the sprawling C, the cropped ears, of the horse before him. Glenn gathered himself to spring from a charge, for the horse hated him. He could tell.

The roan stood, head up, nostrils quivering, eyes red by the moonlight.

But suddenly Glenn caught his breath with pity.

55

The outlaw made a move to charge him, then, because one leg did not touch the ground, swung his muzzle down to it. He made a second dive for Glenn, making a feeble effort to strike. But the agony in his foot stopped him cold.

Glenn moved instinctively to help the horse, but checked himself. He was going to Lethbridge.

"After all, he's not mine," he said, turning back to his saddle.

But the roan waving his foot back and forth in ceaseless pain was something he could not ignore. The wind, low and soft, came whispering along the ground bringing the roan's nicker of anguish to Glenn.

It broke something down within him.

"Oh well," he said, and swinging around, moved cautiously toward the outlaw.

The horse, with the memory of a thousand enemy riders searing his mind, laid back his cropped ears and bared his teeth. But a deep instinct suddenly checked his third charge for Glenn. Something within him seemed to prompt, "Here is help!"

Some of the defiance went out of the roan and he waited.

Glenn moved close to lift the injured foot. For a second the odor of the wound rocked him. Then he looked more closely, put the foot down and moved to build up the fire.

"Now," he said, leading the roan by his mane close to the fire and once more lifting the foot. "I thought so," he muttered at length, gingerly pushing at the frog now swollen almost beyond recognition. "It's a rock in the frog."

He pulled a pocketknife from his levis and, opening the largest blade, held it deep in the fire coals to sterilize it. Letting it cool, he steadied the roan's foot.

"Now," he said. "Let's see, boy."

He worked swiftly. Sweat stood out on his forehead. He gagged with the odor. But he worked steadily, forgetting something of his anguish over Roy H and the hateful prospect of his bank job in his absorption. Talking soothingly all the time and working swiftly, he probed for the rock and after a struggle pried it from its imbedded pocket in the roan's foot.

It came free, a three-cornered jagged piece of granite, picked up along the river bed.

"There," Glenn said in triumph, then catching himself. "It was just a rock, just a rock that any kid could have dug out with his pocketknife."

He took his hat and moved down to the river to scoop water in its wide brim to flush out the wound.

"That will clean it out, and now beat it," he said, slapping the roan's flank.

Washing his hands at the river, he came back to his saddle and lay down once more.

But the roan did not move away. He stood there and the pain seemed to die out of his eyes. The fury of hatred was less too.

Glenn turned away from the roan, trying to forget his exhilaration in helping an animal in pain.

"Skip it, Glenn," he said to himself, and closed his eyes tight.

But the roan's presence haunted him, and again came that old dream of his and Abbie's, that he become a veterinarian. And he sat up, recalling that he'd forgotten about Roy H in his concern for the outlaw's foot.

For a long time he sat there, running his hand through his mop of dull-red hair and staring fixedly into the firelight.

Suddenly the roan hobbled to his side.

Glenn, his heart thudding, pulled the feverish head to him. It was a beautiful head, he knew then, small and broad. There was little rust spots of dun-color against the blue of the hide that was like the blue of a late-afternoon Alberta sky. There was a star on his forehead.

"Horse," he said, shakily. "Your coat's the color of blue sky." He pulled the roan's head closer and something within him softened, then hardened with purpose.

"Sky, Sky," he whispered, trying the words on his lips. "That's what I'm going to call you." His voice stopped, then went on, filled with decision. "When I get you into the barn at Doctor Crane's and land that job!"

He lay down, staring into the dying fire.

He'd found himself now, and he knew that he had found his horse. A sense of belonging to each other and of being alike filled him. Hadn't Luce found him on the doorstep? And hadn't he found the roan down here in the river bottom? They'd both been foundlings.

Glenn knew then that, above all else, he had to hold the faith of this outlaw and make him well. Together they would help each other.

But the roan's again moving his foot in anguish told Glenn that the help he'd given him wasn't enough. If the roan were to live he would need real care—and soon.

He put out a hand to touch the foretop of the suffering outlaw. With his fingers entwined in the horse's hair, he lay staring into the firelight, impatiently waiting for dawn.

At daybreak, Glenn rolled from beneath his Navajo blanket, his thoughts all on the roan. Pulling on his boots and his windbreaker, then putting on his hat, still wet from last night's soaking, he moved quickly down to the river to wash. The roan stood there, not far from where he had left him, miserably swinging his foot back and forth, back and forth.

For a moment, Glenn, as he came up, caught his breath and wondered if this horse would ever look like anything again. He was skin and bones. A chill dawn wind ruffled his blue-roan coat showing spur scars along his lean belly, quirt welts along his jaws and a jagged scar along his bony shoulder. But worst of all was the way he'd forgotten what had been done for him the night before and now looked evilly at Glenn, his ears back, his fever-laden eyes glaring.

Glenn knew he must save this horse. In some way this outlaw was part of his plan. Under his rough coat and in those eyes glazed with pain lay the makings of a horse who had to be kept alive. One who would be his companion and help him, taking the place of Roy H.

He walked up to the roan, laying a gentle hand on his rough hairy shoulder just above the scar. Something of the struggle that lay ahead communicated itself to them there, with the river rushing by, the sun lightening the eastern sky and the chill wind blowing down from the Rockies. He started to talk to the roan then as he had always talked to Roy H.

The horse suddenly moved away, but the pain of his foot forced him to stop. He began to tremble, and put his muzzle down to touch this terrible hurt.

Glenn thought for a moment that he couldn't stand to see how the roan suffered. A wave of compassion swept him, and his eyes caught the old jagged shoulder scar.

"Cougar claw you when you were a colt?" he asked softly. "And those spur scars," he went on, his voice shaking, "I'll bet you've been in a thousand rodeos."

The roan just stood, unable to move, his eyes alight with hatred for Glenn, whom he could only recognize as another rider to battle.

Glenn began once more to talk to him as he was wont to do with Roy H. "Sky," he said. "That's your name, now. Sky, I'm going to cure you, fatten you up sleek. You'll be my horse and never hit a rodeo chute again." It was a promise.

Talking softly, he moved the few steps to his saddle, sacked it up, rolled the blanket and stuffed it in beside the saddle, then shouldered them both.

"I'll be back," he promised, taking a deep breath. "With the job all sewed up with Doctor Crane and with his ambulance to take you in."

The inside of the waiting room was as Glenn had expected, but cleaner. Glistening with white paint, it fairly shone. The floor, laid with green and brown linoleum, had a new coat of glossy polish, in which Glenn might have seen his anxious face had he leaned over.

"No one can please Doc Crane," came some remembered voice. "He's got a bug on cleanliness."

Glenn surveyed the walls and the rattan furniture covered with crisp flower print.

"Just like I'll have some day," he whispered.

Through the door marked PRIVATE came a fox terrier's high shrill bark. Other dogs' voices, deeper in tone, chimed in.

A faint odor of carbolic acid filled Glenn's nostrils, making him tingle clean to his toes. A dull pounding ache for the job took possession of him, sending blood up through his neck to suffuse his face.

*   *   *

"I've got to tell you," he said, with Doctor Crane's eyes upon him. "Before you decide about me, I've got a horse."

The corners of Doctor Crane's thin mouth twitched.

"Most boys have," he said. "You could ride him on your inspection trips if you wished."

"You don't understand," Glenn explained, a dull feeling through him. "This is a rodeo outlaw. He's been beaten up and is sick with an infected foot. He's a cast-off down along St. Mary's River and about to cash in."

Doctor Crane's eyes narrowed.

"An outlaw! A rodeo killer, and you want to bring him here. You'd want me to treat him. You'd want the ambulance to bring him in?"

Glenn could see no other way. "That's right, sir," he said. "It's urgent."

Glenn stood, hardly daring to breathe, in the silence that fell. The fox terrier's barking sounded like chattering.

Doctor Crane turned to him then. "You can have the job if you forget this outlaw."

"Forget Sky?" Glenn blurted.

"Sky?" Doctor Crane's eyebrows raised.

"The outlaw. It's the only name that would fit his blue coat," Glenn explained.

"Humpf!"

Glenn steadied himself by the table. He couldn't believe that Doctor Crane would hinge the job on Sky. A sickness filled him.

"Well, young man?" Doctor Crane demanded.

The smell of the hospital came tantalizingly to Glenn once more. The wonderful feel of the place that was so much what he wanted. Alan Roak's soft voice drifted through the door, close and cozy, as he moved the dogs out to their runs for the morning feed and water.

But then the picture of the roan crowded all else out. Sky was sick and a part of himself. Sky trusted him.

"I—I can't give up Sky." Glenn blurted, then watched in concern the way Doctor Crane's eyes narrowed and his long veined hands clasped the arms of his chair.

"As you wish," the doctor said stiffly and turned away. "Good-bye, Mr. Barnes."

There was no place to go but back to town to flag a ride to Sky. And there was Doctor Crane's sign squeaking out a doleful "So long."

Glenn moved down the bank, carrying his saddle and suitcase with him. Maybe the roan was down in the water. Sometimes a horse fell and drowned trying to get a drink to assuage the fever raging within him. He reached the flat and moved toward his old camp site.

A chicken hawk fled from the high branches of a cottonwood. A covey of Hungarian partridge, brown and fast as bullets, fled along the riverbank, then with a wide curve flew up and out of sight across the flat prairie.

Glenn kept thinking of the star on the roan's forehead that was so much like the one Roy H'd had.

He swallowed and felt a wave of faintness creep over him. "Take it easy," he whispered and reached the dead ashes.

There was no roan. No sight of him met Glenn's searching eyes. There was nothing but the cold embers of the fire and the flat mashed-down place among the weeds where Sky had lain.

Glenn gulped and felt then that he should never have left the horse.

After a moment, he bent to unsack his saddle enough to get his lariat. Straightening, he began a wide circling of the flat lands along the river.

But there was still no sign of the roan.

At a bend in the river he paused. "He couldn't have gone any farther than this. Not on three legs."

He stood staring at the swirling water flowing past. He moved along the bank, his heart beating fast, his eyes scanning each eddying pool as he passed.

It wasn't until he had gone past the camping place and on up the river a hundred yards that he found a trace of the horse.

"Here's his track," Glenn whispered, staring down at three hoofmarks and the blur of a fourth. "Get goin'," he breathed and followed the track to the water's edge, where a big eddying pool cut under the bank in a deep swirling current of roily water.

At first it seemed as though there were no horse there. But suddenly, almost at Glenn's feet, came a faint nicker. He looked down and there, right at the edge of the bank, swimming to keep afloat, his head drenched, his eyes glazed with fever, was Sky.

For a moment Glenn could not move.

"He's done for," swept through his mind. "He won't fight."

Glenn thrust the thought aside. With swift sure hands he uncoiled his lariat and tossed the rope toward the drowning horse's head.

But Sky, schooled by the rake of spurs along his neck, the whirr of the cutting quirt along his flanks, thought all men enemies. He had forgotten Glenn's gentle aid. Laying back his ears, he dodged his head from the loop and slipped downstream and out into the eddying current.

Glenn pitched after him, sobbing in his throat.

"He'll drown!" he cried. "Drown right here in the river."

And it seemed as though the roan horse would drown. His head went under. His muscled, scarred body whirled over in the water and disappeared from sight.

Throwing off his windbreaker and grasping his lariat in his hand, Glenn plunged wildly into the river. With powerful strokes he swam toward the place where the roan had sunk from sight.

The horse would have to surface some time.

Then suddenly, right at Glenn's side, the roan split the surface of the water. Coming up with a surge, breathing air into his tortured lungs, he showered Glenn with water.

Glenn dog paddled.

"Sky, Sky," he pleaded. "Let's get out of here."

Sky turned on him, ears back, head thrust forward. With a rush of his body he lunged over Glenn, forcing him beneath the water.

Fighting free of the roan's body, Glenn surfaced.

The roan again plowed over him.

Glenn's wind failed. His mouth filled with water that rushed down into his lungs. A buzzing filled his head.

He fought to the surface once more.

Sky was there, attacking, bearing him down and under.

The past filled Glenn's drowning mind. Roy H, Abbie and Luce, and even the roan.

Glenn gave up. He knew that he was through. But just to try one last time. Make one more effort to come to the surface and save Sky. With feeble arms, he pushed his way to the river surface.

The roan again!

But suddenly a voice came from the bank. A familiar voice, that of Doctor Crane, and behind him a swift flash of the ambulance and Ricky Clements, the Law-and-Order man.

Again Glenn found himself thrust under.

But a courage filled him. It lent strength to his arms. The doctor was a good guy after all. There would be a chance for Sky to recover, and beyond that a job for Glenn as assistant—Ames, and maybe his name on that shingle with Doctor Crane's.

With his last strength, Glenn forced his body to the surface, took a deep breath, rolled from the roan's path and struck out for the bank.

"Give me the rope," Doctor Crane said, dragging Glenn up the bank. "Give it to an old chump."

"No, I'll take it," Glenn said. Fighting for wind, he coiled the stiff manila rope and, with a fling, sent it over the roan's head and jerked it taut.

"Wonderful!" Doctor Crane said. "Now, we'll pull him to shore, and I'll tell you that you're hired."

The two men, with Law-and-Order lending a hand, pulled the roan to the edge of the water.

"Let him get his breath," Crane said. Then he turned to Glenn. "You know, I had a sick horse when I was a boy. It started me on the road to Ames. I'd forgotten it until you left the office. I'm sorry."

Glenn could scarcely believe that the doctor stood here, and the ambulance that must have been skillfully threaded down the bank and through the trees to the river edge. It had all been something like a roller coaster, getting this job, Doctor Crane's brushing him off and now, right here, putting it in the bag.

Warmth filled Glenn and thankfulness, and an urge to get Sky moving toward the hospital. "Skip it," he said, with a grin, "I was young once myself."

In the laugh that followed, they got the roan to hobble to the dry ground. Sky stood, weaving with weakness, his right foot upheld.

Glenn looked the horse over critically, seeing his strong short-coupled back, the small head, the slender powerful legs and firm well-knit body. Again, as it had last night, came the feeling that blue's future was his future; that they were all tied up together.

But that foot?

Doctor Crane took one look at it, and said, "There's no time to lose. We'll have to get him to a stall at once."

Glenn took hold of the rope and tried to lead Sky toward the ambulance, while Ricky, from behind, tried to shoo him with a willow branch.

"No, don't do that," Doctor Crane said. "Never hit a horse or scare him into doing anything. They are nervous. They take on the mood of the master and do things for him from kindness."

Suddenly, as Sky came at the doctor on three feet, the doctor stepped nimbly aside.

"Like that?" Ricky laughed.

Doctor Crane smiled, and Glenn thought, he's certainly human after all.

They got the roan to the ambulance. Glenn let the ramp down, but Sky balked at walking up the cleated incline.

"Let's do it this way," Glenn said. Taking the end of the lariat he passed it through the front slat of the trailer, then bringing it around Sky's rump. "Now, all together."

The three pulled, forcing Sky up the ramp and inside. Once there, he seemed to grow weaker and, as the ramp closed behind him, sank to the floor trembling.

"He's having a chill," Doctor Crane said. "He's a sick horse."

Glenn made no answer. He could only think of getting Sky to the hospital barn.

As Doctor Crane climbed into the Dodge and, with Ricky beside him, started the engine, Glenn piled horse blankets on the shaking roan.

"I'll drive as fast as I can," Doctor Crane called.

Glenn beside Sky nodded, leaning into the motion of the starting ambulance.

It climbed out of the river bottom to the prairie, weaved along the grass to the road, and hitting gravel ran swiftly back to town and into the hospital yard.

Pulling into the barn runway, Glenn got out to let down the ramp, as Doctor Crane came up.

Glenn's eyes met those of the doctor, swung to the trembling roan, then came back to the veterinarian once more.

"Do you think you can save him?" he whispered.

Doctor Crane paused, then, with a slow look at Sky, turned grave eyes to Glenn.

"If I do, it will be a miracle," he said.

Glenn turned and made ready to lift the horse from the ambulance with the derrick. Sky's recovery seemed all tied in with this magic world of healing that he had entered.

Letting down the ramp, he said, "Guess he'll never make it under his own steam. We'll have to hoist him into the stall."

Doctor Crane, brusque again, nodded, then moved toward the barn door.

"I'll get my instruments and send Alan out to help," he said. It seemed that he'd suddenly began to regret entering into this plan.

Glenn nodded, wondering, then moved in beside Sky.

Alan, slight and quiet, came grudgingly through the barn door.

It was natural, Glenn decided, for Alan to be a little suspicious. Here was a new assistant coming on. He might be no good, or he might be good enough to take first place with the doctor.

"Sorry to be so much trouble," Glenn began.

Alan waved his hand, then scowled. "Don't you know we'll have to work the bands under his belly?" he demanded. "It's the only way we can hoist him up and run him along the track to his stall."

Glenn took the bands Alan handed him.

"Okay, Sky," he said, bending down to whisper into the roan's ear. "We'll sling you up in a jiffy."

Sky did not move. He lay with his head limp on the bedding of the trailer, his eyes closed and his breath coming sharply. Glenn thrust the bands under his side.

"Don't you know we'll have to turn him on his side?" Alan groused, coming in to help. "Then we roll him back so we can get the bands under him to connect with the pulley hook."

Together, they rolled the sick horse on his side, slipped the web bands under, then rolled him back.

"Okay, now to connect the rings in these belts with the pulley hook," Alan snapped.

Glenn couldn't help noticing how resentful the boy seemed. He sensed that things weren't going to be too easy here.

"All right, Alan," he agreed. "Here goes." Adjusting the four ends with the rings through the hook, he grasped the pulley chain along with Alan, and together they began slowly hoisting Sky to his pins.

"Easy," Glenn cautioned, standing close to the horse. "Okay, Sky," he said. "We must get you into your stall."

The chain rattled through the pulleys, tightening on the hooks, the web under the roan tightened slowly, easily lifting him to his feet.

"Now, run the ambulance out from under him," Alan ordered, as the roan's feet left the ambulance floor.

Glenn, with a quick glance at Alan's set face, slipped into the Dodge seat and, starting the motor, ran the car ahead its length.

"Okay, now to let him down," Alan said. Slipping the chain through the pulleys, he dropped the roan so that his three good feet touched the plank floor. "Now, into the stall. And take him easy."

Glenn grasped Sky's body, and together the two boys pushed the roan along the runway to a division in the track, then into the third stall on the left. In the fourth stood a sleepy buckskin gelding. The horse, Glenn sensed glumly, he would probably ride on his range inspection trips; if he lasted here long enough to make one. Glenn thrust the thought from him and turned back to Sky.

Sweet mountain hay lay in the iron feed rack. Bright golden straw lay underfoot. Within a neck's length, clear water ran through a porcelain bowl.

"There you are," Glenn said, touching Sky's neck. "Home at last." The words had a hollow sound to him, with Alan's unexpected glowering and Doctor Crane's sudden shift of mood.

Buck, in the next stall, opened his eyes, nickering softly, then chewed lazily on a timothy stalk that stuck from his muzzle.

Sky did not open his eyes, but stood quietly sagging on the web bands, his right forefoot moving uneasily back and forth, back and forth.

Glenn swung, wondering where Doctor Crane was, just as the tall gaunt doctor came through the barn door. A flood of gratitude filled Glenn. Watching the doctor take Sky's pulse, then run his hand down to lift his injured forefoot, he vowed he'd work his head off to stick here.

But his heart sank at the doctor's grim stare at Sky's rowell-marked sides, the quirt scars along his jaws and the way Crane flinched away from Sky who stiffened at his touch.

"An old outlaw who'll never, never be any good," he grumbled. Then he bent to examine the foot.

Glenn thought otherwise, but kept discreetly silent.

"You dug this out?" the doctor's eyes raised.

Glenn, expecting he'd done the wrong thing, nodded. "I'm sorry. I had only a pocketknife and the light of a campfire."

"A good job, and possibly saved his life, worse luck for him. The roan will probably find his way back into the arena," the doctor said. "What did you find in it?"

"A piece of granite," Glenn watched the doctor's face for some sign of relenting. "It was imbedded in the frog."

"A thrush," Doctor Crane said, bending once more to the foot. "Hard to cure and often leaves the foot disfigured. I'll have to go a little deeper to get bottom drainage."

Glenn, watching the doctor get his farrier's knife and once more pick up Sky's foot, couldn't help but think of his words: "The roan will probably find his way back into the arena."

"Never," Glenn breathed. He grew silent and thrilled watching Doctor Crane's deft hands probing the wound, bringing out bits of gravel, then paring down the wound till it bled clean blood.

"Wonderful," Glenn whispered to himself. "I don't blame him for being short. He's seen a lot of horses and a great many poor assistants." He drew a deep breath, watching Doctor Crane wash out the wound with lysol water brought by Alan, then skillfully pack the wound with sulpha.

In ten minutes the roan was as comfortable as his foot would allow for the time being.

Glenn watched the doctor straighten from his work, and waited for some sign of his relenting.

The doctor turned to Alan.

"Clean up, sterilize the instruments," he said, then moved to go.

*   *   *

Iron filled Glenn then. It straightened him.

"Sky," he whispered, coming close and laying a hand on the roan's hot body. "We'll stick it out here. You'll get well, and I'll make the grade with the doctor. I don't care how abrupt he is. We'll go places."

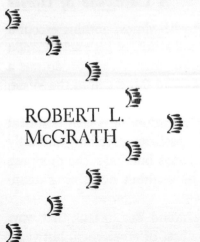

ROBERT L.
McGRATH

Easy Does It!

Rod mc lean slowly picked himself up out of the dirt of the corral, the laughter of the Diamond Bar hands echoing in his burning ears. At the far side of the enclosure, the young bay horse—Rod's horse—stood still now, trembling with the excitement of what had just happened. "Too soon," Rod said to himself. "I tried to ride him too soon."

"Try 'im again!" urged Hub Watkins, the foreman, from his place on the fence. "Don't let 'im think he can get away with it."

"No," Rod said. "He's not ready."

"Better let somebody else ride 'im that can," the foreman said with a sneer. "He'll never be any good this way."

Rod stopped in the middle of the corral and turned to face the others. "You know what Uncle Caddo promised me, Hub," he said quietly. "I break Lucky my own way. He's not getting any more riding today."

"Told you he was chicken," Rod heard the foreman say, and it hurt—more than being thrown from Lucky had hurt. But Rod chose to ignore it.

He took a long time to unsaddle the bay horse, talking quietly and soothingly all the while, and rubbing the horse down carefully after taking the saddle off. It gave him time to think about all this—time to wonder if maybe he was trying to do something that just wouldn't work.

It all started about a year before. Everything was fine then, or so it seemed. Rod was in high school in a large Eastern city—plenty of friends, plenty of activities, everything smooth. And then, just like snapping your finger, everything changed. An auto accident. Mom killed outright. Dad lingering for a week, and then he too passing on. And Rod left with almost nothing except a will that said he was to be placed under the guardianship of his uncle, Caddo McLean, whom Rod had seen only once in his 16 years. Uncle Caddo was a sort of dream to Rod, who had heard of the Diamond Bar ranch in the West, but had never seen it. Not until a year ago, that is.

It wasn't exactly the way he'd pictured it. In his mind, he'd seen beautiful white buildings, well-kept wooden fences, green pastures stretching endlessly across the plains. And when he saw the squat, faded buildings, the drooping barbed-wire fences, the sun-scorched prairies, he couldn't help being disappointed.

Of course, there was good reason for the Diamond Bar to look that way. In his day, Caddo McLean had been one of the best of ranch men, but years ago he'd taken a bad fall. He'd been a semi-invalid ever since—handling the affairs of the ranch from his wheel-chair, but having to depend on others to do the work. And so the proud Diamond Bar had lost some of the luster it once wore.

Rod McLean thought about all of this now, rubbing down Lucky and getting him gentled again after the incident in the corral. It had been a hard year for Rod—a year filled with harder work than he'd ever dreamed possible. But it had its rewards, too. Lucky, for instance. He'd earned ownership of the colt, same as the other hands earned their wages. And long before Lucky was actually his, he'd begun gentling the horse the way he thought an animal ought to be handled.

"Why can't a horse be trained by being kind and gentle to him?" Rod had asked his Uncle Caddo. "Looks like you'd get lots better results."

Uncle Caddo was gentle and kind himself, always a square shooter. "Guess it's one of the traditions of the West," he said mildly. "Bronc bustin' is something that's been done ever since the first time a man ever straddled a cayuse." He pulled at his pipe thoughtfully. "Reckon you could try it, though," he said. "You pick the colt you want out of that string in the south pasture, and you break him any way you want. You can work out his price."

And that was how it had been. Now, Lucky was his—all his—and it was time he was being broken to ride, the same as the other colts his age. But they were broken by the time-honored bronc-busting routine of being ridden and reridden until they accepted the load.

The worst of the past year had been Hub Watkins. Hub was a good range boss—no doubt of that. But he didn't have much sympathy for the city boy who'd been thrown on the ranch. To Hub, a man not born to the range just didn't fit.

But, even though Hub gave him all the unpleasant jobs that nobody else wanted, Rod knew he was learning more every day about how a ranch is run.

One Sunday he was driving Uncle Caddo out across the range in the pickup truck to check the stock. They suddenly came up to the ten palomino mares —the most valuable animals on the ranch.

"Aren't they beauties?" Rod exclaimed. "Just look at those cream-colored manes and tails!"

"Makes life worth livin' to see critters like that," Uncle Caddo said. "Be some more before long, too."

"You mean you're taking some more in for pasture?" Rod asked. The mares, like much of the other stock on the Diamond Bar, belonged to other people, who paid Caddo McLean to look after them.

The old man smiled, a twinkle in his eye. "Wait and see," he suggested.

"Oh—you mean more colts," Rod said. "Boy, isn't Golden Lady a honey?" He pointed to a mare walking toward them.

"Sure is," Uncle Caddo agreed. "Ten thousand bucks worth of horse there, son. Might' near worth her weight in gold."

The rich tan of her body, the slender sturdy legs, the quiet friendliness in her eyes made Golden Lady something out of a picture book as she approached.

"See," Rod said, as she nuzzled his arm. "She likes the way I treat her."

Caddo McLean nodded. "She trusts you," he said. "That's mighty important, sometimes."

On a Saturday afternoon about a month after Lucky had first thrown Rod, he stayed at the ranch instead of tagging along to town with the hands. Putting saddle and bridle on Lucky, he headed for an open pasture some distance from the ranch house, where he could work with the horse by himself. Lucky accepted saddle and bridle without protest, and followed Rod without hesitation. In the middle of the open field, Rod gently tested the horse by putting his weight on the stirrup, talking soothingly all the time. Lucky looked around, but seemed not to mind.

Keeping a tight rein, Rod slowly eased his leg over the saddle, keeping his weight on the left stirrup. Lucky looked around again, but with Rod's reassuring hands along his withers, he gave no sign that he intended to buck, bolt, or pitch. In fact, he just stood stock-still, waiting.

"Good boy!" Rod said. "We made it!"

Gently he nudged the horse to a walk, keeping the reins tight lest Lucky suddenly decide to put his head between his legs and lose the weight on his back. But the horse never faltered. Rod urged him into a lope, reined him to both left and right, and let him stretch into a run along the well-worn path back toward the house. And when he pulled back on the reins to slow the bay, Lucky slowed to a walk as though he'd been ridden for years.

Not noticing the darkened clouds scudding across the sky, Rod rubbed his horse down and then rushed into the house to see his uncle. He was unable to conceal his excitement, and old Caddo McLean sensed something unusual at once.

"What is it, boy?" he said. "What's happened?"

"I did it!" Rod fairly shouted. "It worked—just like I thought it would!"

"Now hold on a minute," the old rancher said. "What worked—what did you do that's so all-fired remarkable?"

Panting for breath, Rod explained in quick bursts. "Lucky—I rode him," he said. "Didn't buck! Gentle as a lamb! See, it worked!"

Caddo McLean leaned back and smiled, his mane of white hair giving him an unusual appearance of dignity. "And not the first time," the old man said. "You'll never go wrong by handling any animal with kindness."

Rod started to say more, but the door was flung open and Hub Watkins, his face clouded with anger, burst into the room. "You leave the big gate open?" His words were directed at Rod.

"Why—I—I don't know," Rod faltered. "I had Lucky down in the south pasture. But I—"

"I thought so," the foreman interrupted. "Now we've got a mess on our hands!"

"Just a minute." It was the stern voice of Caddo McLean. "What kind of a mess?"

"Golden Lady," Hub said. "She's due to foal any time, and I had her in the barn lot." He looked meaningfully at Rod. "Now she's gone—and there's a winger of a storm brewin'!"

Rod's heart sank. The pride and joy of the whole ranch—Golden Lady—missing, because he'd left the gate open. And worst of all, she didn't belong to Uncle Caddo. That made her an even bigger responsibility—she and her unborn colt!

"No tellin' where she'll head," Hub went on. His words were punctuated by the distant rumble of thunder rolling across the sky. "Reckon I got a job on my hands now, tryin' to find her an' get her back before the rain hits."

"All right." Caddo McLean was sober, his brow wrinkled in a frown. "Better take Rod with you."

"Ain't no horse in but mine," the foreman said.

"I'll ride Lucky," Rod said quietly. "He's in."

"That good-for-nothin' bronc!" Hub Watkins snorted. "I need help—not a millstone tied on my neck."

"Take the boy along," Caddo McLean said. "Better check those draws by the creek. She might head there."

Without a word, Hub Watkins turned and stalked through the door, with Rod at his heels. The less said the better, Rod thought to himself. I made the mess—now maybe I can help get us out of it.

Stopping only long enough to get his oilskin slicker from his room, Rod went to the barn where he'd left Lucky, and carefully re-saddled the bay horse. Hub, he noticed, was not wasting any time, nor was he waiting for Rod to get ready. He was astride his horse, already cutting across the rolling land east of the ranch house, by the time Rod had Lucky ready to go.

He swung carefully to the bay's back again, uncertain what to expect, but Lucky stood still and waited. Rod spent a moment rubbing the horse's withers, then clucked him to a start and followed after Hub Watkins.

He had barely started across the rolling prairie on Hub's trail when the first giant drops of rain began to pelt down on him, and he knew that if the rain lasted any time at all, Golden Lady could very well be in grave danger. Water running off the slopes of the gullies in the far-flung ranch could create flash floods that would sweep animals or anything else along with them.

Rod nudged Lucky into a gallop, anxious to overtake the Diamond Bar foreman. The rain came faster, with more lightning and thunder, and as he rode, Rod slipped into the slicker. Lucky galloped smoothly along, as though he'd been ridden all his life.

When Rod came abreast of Hub, the foreman said nothing for a time, merely throwing Rod a grim glance through the spattering rain. They rode side by side for a time, and then Hub suddenly veered off to the left.

"Come on," he shouted through the rain. "She probably came off down this way."

Hub was wise in the ways of the range and its animals, Rod knew, and he followed without question. They rode for what seemed an age when Lucky suddenly whinnied and threw his head up and down. Hub pulled his mount to a stop.

"I think we're close to the crick," he announced. "You see anything?"

Rod tried to force himself to see through the heavy rain, but it was no use. Despite frequent flashes of lightning, there was too much water falling for him to see ten feet in front of his nose. Then, through the gloom, came an answering nicker, faint but unmistakable, and Lucky shook his head and neighed again.

Hub looked at Rod. "Looks like she's over there somewhere," he said. "Come on!"

But they had gone only a few yards when both horses shied back away from the torrent of water that rushed across their path. "Crick bed," Hub stated. "She's on the other side—got to get her back or we'll lose her sure!"

Rod nodded, uncertain what to say or do.

"Here!" Hub handed Rod the loop of the spare lariat hanging on the back of his saddle. "Hook this on your saddle horn, so I can find my way back."

"Okay." Rod fastened the loop securely and watched while Hub urged his horse toward the churning waters of the creek. But the horse, fearful of the uncertainty of the flooding torrent, backed away. Hub brought his lariat down on the horse's rump, he kicked and scolded, but the horse would not step into the current. At last, Hub reined back beside Rod.

"No use," he said. "No horse in his right mind will tackle that stuff. Reckon we better head back up to the bridge."

The only bridge across the creek, Rod knew, was several miles from here— miles that might mean the difference between saving Golden Lady or losing her.

"Let me try it," Rod said quietly. "Maybe Lucky will go across."

The foreman looked skeptical, and for a moment, Rod thought he'd be denied the chance to attempt the crossing. Then, "Won't hurt to try," Hub drawled, and Rod unfastened the lariat from his saddle horn, exchanging the loop for the other end of the rope.

"Come on, Lucky boy," he said, and reined the horse toward the raging waters of the creek bed. How deep it might be, Rod did not know. Normally, the creek was only a trickle. Now, fed by the slashing rain, it was deep, wide, and treacherous.

The horse went willingly to the edge of the water, and there he stopped. "Come on, Lucky," Rod urged. "Come on, boy, we can make it!" Gently, he nudged the bay's ribs with his boots, rubbing the horse's withers with his hands and talking quietly all the time. "Easy, boy, easy does it."

Gingerly, the horse put his left foot into the water, found solid footing, and moved forward. It was slow going, and in only a moment, Rod could feel the water swirling around the horse's legs. Still Lucky moved on, guided by Rod's confident voice. The water deepened, washed over Rod's boots, and filled them with the chill of the flood.

Then, when a blinding flash of lightning crashed nearby, Rod saw a splotch of tan ahead of him, and he knew they'd found Golden Lady. Lucky whinnied again, but moved steadily forward through the water. Then, abruptly, he scrambled up the side of a small island where Golden Lady stood. Beyond lay more of the raging flood waters. There would be no choice but to take the palomino mare back across the way they had come.

And then Rod saw something else. A small, whitish figure nestled at Golden Lady's front feet, and Rod's heart thrilled with surprise. For there were not one, but two animals to return across the churning waters. Golden Lady had foaled, and this tiny object she was licking was her colt. Rod swung to the ground.

Carefully, talking softly, Rod rubbed the palomino mare, gently soothing her and getting her used to him here in the driving rain. He took the lariat hanging from the pommel of the saddle and, shaking out a loop, carefully placed it over the mare's head. Then, using all the care he could there in the wet of the storm, he scooped his arms under the spindly-legged colt and lifted it up.

The colt, for all its small size, was heavy, and Rod wondered for a moment just how he'd get the tiny new life back across the water. But there would be only one way. Somehow, he'd have to get the colt up on the saddle in front of him. He'd have to trust Lucky to carry both him and the foal back across the creek.

He felt a nudge in his ribs, and he spoke softly and reassuringly to the palomino mare watching his every movement. "Easy, Lady," he said. "Everything's okay. Easy now. Whoa, Lucky—whoa, boy."

Thinking about lifting the colt and getting it on the saddle were two different things, Rod found now. It took an almost superman effort for him to get the spindly legs up and across the saddle, and Rod was fearful that Lucky might shy away from this new burden. The horse stood his ground, however, and with the colt safely straddled over the saddle, Rod himself swung up, putting his feet in the straps holding the stirrups.

He was thankful then for the lariat that stretched back across the driving rain and the churning creek to where Hub Watkins waited. Carefully, he nudged the bay horse back the way they'd come. There was little need, he found, for the lariat around Golden Lady's neck. The mare would follow her colt, no matter where it went.

Afterward, Rod saw the ride back through the creek as a bad dream. Halfway across, in the deepest part, Lucky slipped and went down. But with the colt to protect, Rod stayed astride the horse, even though the plunging water threatened to tear him and the colt in his arms away from each other and from Lucky. Then the horse found footing again, and moments later Rod saw Hub Watkins loom up out of the murk ahead of him.

"Good work!" Hub said. "Here, let me take the little guy."

"He's all right," Rod said. Now that the worst was over, he wanted to keep Golden Lady's foal himself—to give Lucky all the credit due for the rescue.

They stood there a moment, while Golden Lady nuzzled her colt and satisfied herself that her firstborn was all right. Then, Hub reined away from the creek, and the trek back began.

The rain lasted all the way back, and more than once Hub Watkins led them up on ridges to avoid the chance of more flash floods down the gullies. But the wet didn't bother Rod now. Lucky had proved himself to be everything Rod had expected—everything and more.

After bedding down the mare and the colt and rubbing them dry, during which time Hub Watkins said not a word, Rod and the foreman saw to their own horses, and then, still without speaking, headed for the ranch house.

The rain had let up some now, and Rod could see the weather-beaten buildings around him with a new sense of pride. This was his life, this was where he belonged—on the Diamond Bar—whether Hub Watkins liked it or not.

They reached the house, and they went directly to the big room Caddo McLean used as an office. Then, for the first time since Rod brought back the colt and the palomino mare across the creek, the foreman spoke.

"Reckon you can send that wire, Caddo," he said quietly. "Lady's got a mighty nice stud colt—and both in fine shape, thanks to my partner here."

My partner! The words echoed in Rod's ears.

"Trouble?" Caddo McLean asked.

"Oh, just a mite," Hub Watkins said. "Nothin' serious." He turned to Rod McLean. "Any time you and that horse of yours—Lucky, or whatever you call him—want to ride with me, you hop to it," he said. "Takes a lot more than bein' lucky to do what you did!"

He turned and walked out, and Rod's happy smile followed him. "Reckon I better go change my duds," he drawled, and his voice sounded strangely like Hub Watkins'. "Got a mite wet."

"Reckon so." Caddo McLean grinned. "Reckon you'll be one of the regular hands from now on."

IV

HORSES TO RIDE

The rewards and ideals of
good horsemanship

ARLENE
HALE

Trapped!

(Samantha, in her first ruse to divert the badmen, yanked the reins and forced her horse to rear on his hind legs, a trick she had taught him. The confusion which followed allowed her to leave a clue which was to be her salvation.)

THE DESERT WAS PEACEFUL AND THE CACTI LOOKED LIKE SLEEPY SENTINELS. Samantha Roland galloped her horse at a good pace down the lonely trail and grinned at her friend, Carrie Nelson, riding beside her. Little did she know they were riding straight into trouble.

"How much farther is Dover's Bend anyway, Sammy?" Carrie asked. "It seems like we should have been there hours ago."

Sammy grinned.

"Another five miles. Are you getting saddle sore again?"

Carrie nodded.

"A little. Remember I'm still a tenderfoot."

Carrie was new in these parts for her father had just bought the old Bar X ranch.

"We'll rest awhile in town," Sammy said. "A wagon or a stage coach must be ahead of us. Look at all that dust down the trail. They must be trying to run their wheels off."

The girls reined up their horses to a slow trot. There was no wind so the dust was a long time in settling. Crack! Crack! It was gunfire!

"Indians!" Carrie gasped.

Sammy laughed.

"No Indians for fifty miles. Somebody's in trouble though. Come on, maybe we can help!"

Sammy touched her spurs to her horse and galloped on. Sounds traveled far and clear on the desert and Sammy estimated the shots had come from

77

somewhere near Willow Creek Canyon. When they drew near, Sammy motioned for Carrie to slow up. Then they rode on cautiously.

The dust stifled the air. Sammy heard another shot and horses galloping, the turning of wheels spinning over the ground, the hoarse shouts of a man. It must be a stage coach. But why had they stopped and then raced away?

She eased her horse farther down the trail and then abruptly came to a halt. As the dust cleared she saw two men pulling handkerchiefs from their faces. Another shot rang out and Sammy saw that they'd blasted off the lock of a Wells Fargo box and were scooping out small canvas sacks. Gold dust! They'd robbed the stage!

"Let's get out of here, Carrie! If they see us—"

They dug in spurs and slapped the reins. Sammy's heart was thundering hard and Carrie was deathly pale, hanging onto the saddle the best she could.

"They're after us!" Sammy shouted.

"Sammy, oh, Sammy—"

Carrie had disappeared right off her horse's back! Sammy reined up and jerked around. Carrie was spilled in the middle of the trail.

"Get up!" Sammy yelled. "Ride double with me."

She reached a hand for Carrie but she was too late. Pounding hooves bore down on them and they were looking straight into the barrels of two rifles.

"All right, you two," a short, fat man growled. "Just where do you think you're going?"

"Oh, let them go," the other man said. "They're just kids, Flint."

"We can't have any witnesses, Tex. You know that."

"Yeah?" Tex asked with a scowl. "Just what are you aiming to do with them?"

Flint scratched his whiskered face.

"We'll have to take them along. We can't turn them loose."

"We wouldn't tell, Mister," Carrie said. "Honest!"

"Yeah?" Flint scowled. "With a reward on our heads?"

"Shut up, Flint," Tex snapped. "You talk too much."

Flint poked Carrie in the back with the end of his rifle.

"Get on your horse."

Sammy bit her lip and looked around her. Not a soul had seen what had happened. Where would these two evil men take them? How could anyone ever find them and rescue them?

"Follow me!" Flint ordered.

Deliberately, Sammy yanked on the reins and forced her horse to rear up on his hind legs, a trick she'd taught him. In all the confusion that followed, she quickly stripped off her leather gloves and tossed them to the side of the trail. Someone would find them, maybe even Dad, for he was certain to come looking for them when they didn't return home.

Flint led the way at a brisk pace. Carrie followed, then Sammy with Tex bringing up the rear. Carrie hung precariously to the saddle, her eyes wide with terror.

They wound upward through the rocks, riding hard. They were going into part of the hills that Sammy had never seen before. It was rugged and forlorn. Once they stopped at a gurgling stream and watered their mounts. Sammy and Carrie cupped some of the clear water in their hands and drank, too.

"What will we do?" Carrie asked in a scared whisper.

"Wait," Sammy replied. "Maybe tonight we can make a break for it."

Sammy tried hard to make her voice sound hopeful. These men were obviously outlaws with a price on their heads. Anything could happen. When neither was looking, Sammy jerked a button from her shirt and dropped it.

They rode on, passing through rugged rocks, leaping draws, fighting the brush and mesquite. Whenever she could manage it, Sammy broke a branch to mark the trail. Tex seemed too busy watching behind them to take notice.

Then they were following the stream again and riding up an impossibly steep hill. Poor Carrie couldn't make it. Sammy snatched her horse's bridle and helped her up. At the top, barely visible, was a shack. From here the surrounding country was in open view.

"Get down!" Flint ordered. "Get in there. Start fixing some grub."

Tex led the horses away and tethered them in some brush so they, too, were hidden. Inside the lean-to, there was a dirt floor, a wobbly table and two chairs. There were supplies though, enough to last the men several weeks. This was evidently their hideout.

"You can build a fire outside," Flint said. "There's a stream in back for water."

Fortunately, Sammy had been a cook on some of her father's round-ups and knew her way around a skillet and a coffee pot. In record time she had the meal ready and set on the wobbly table. Flint ate noisily and greedily.

"Good idea, bringing them along, Tex," he said. "They cook better than you."

"They'll only bring us trouble!"

"I'm still boss!" Flint snapped. "No one will find us here. It's a perfect hideout."

A quick glance at the sun told Sammy it was past noon. By now Dad would be looking for them. When morning came he and a posse would probably start trailing them. But this place looked impossible to reach from below. They might miss them! Someway they had to escape.

When night came, the girls curled into a corner under a dusty blanket. Flint snored while Tex stood guard.

"If Tex goes to sleep, we'll try to escape," Sammy whispered to Carrie.

They lay there stiffly, waiting. It seemed hours before Tex began to snore too.

"Now!" whispered Sammy.

They crept for the doorway, reached it and crawled out past Tex. They got to their feet and ran for the horses. Bullets whizzed past them and whined off the rocks.

"Stop!" Tex shouted. "Get back in here! The next one won't miss you!"

The girls skidded to a stop and went back. Tex shoved them back into their corner with a snarl. They lay there shivering. Sammy knew they were trapped. It was hopeless. They could never escape. She would have to think of something else.

When the sun streaked the desert sky red, Flint poked Sammy in the ribs with his boot and ordered her to fix breakfast.

It was mid-morning when he gave the girls another order.

"Get the horses and walk them around. Don't try nothing," he said, rubbing his rifle with a grimy hand. "I'm a real good shot. I won't miss like Tex did last night."

Sammy and Carrie began exercising the horses. It gave them a chance to talk.

"Have you got any ideas?" Carrie asked with a worried frown.

"Just one," Sammy replied. "Dad and the posse are sure to be on their way."

"Oh, Sammy, they'll never find us."

"They will if we help them," Sammy answered. "When we finish this, go along with me whatever I want to do."

"All right," Carrie nodded.

They finished walking the horses and tied them back in the brush. Then they went back to the shack.

"Would you cut us a couple of branches, Tex?" Sammy asked.

"What for?"

"Well, as long as we're cooks, we might as well be housekeepers too. This place could sure stand some cleaning."

Tex frowned.

"All right."

He cut them two long, leafy branches and, while they made a crude broom, it was better than nothing.

The girls were quite thorough and raised so much dust that eventually Flint and Tex had to go outside in order to breathe.

"Get that lamp and reflector down from the wall," Sammy said quickly.

Carrie took it down with shaking hands. They gathered the men's bed rolls, too, and took them outside.

"What are you doing?" Flint asked.

"Cleaning," Sammy said patiently. "These blankets haven't been aired in months from the smell of them."

"Real sanitary, ain't you?" Flint growled. "What about the lamp?"

"Look at it!" Sammy replied. "It's no wonder it doesn't give any light. The glass is all smoked, the reflector is dingy and the wick needs to be trimmed!"

The girls moved away from them and went to the stream. There they hung the blankets on bushes and went to work on the lamp. With water and sand and a piece of old burlap they'd found, they worked diligently. For awhile Tex stood guard over them, decided they weren't up to anything and moved away.

"Quick, the reflector," Sammy whispered.

It had already been polished and it glistened in the sunlight. Sammy had her directions well in mind and knew the posse would come riding from the east and north. Once Dad had learned Morse code and worked as a telegrapher. He'd taught Sammy the alphabet.

If she could catch the sun on the reflector for just a second for a dot and a bit longer for a dash, there was no reason why she couldn't send a message. Dad's alert eyes would see it and decipher it.

Nimbly, Sammy tilted the reflector and began painstakingly sending the message. Three dots for the letter "O" and a dash and a dot for the letter "N." The message spelled out, "On top of ridge; surprise attack only chance."

She sent the message twice before she heard footsteps behind her and dropped the reflector quickly.

"What's taking you so blamed long?" Flint demanded.

Sammy scowled at him, her heart jumping wildly. Had he seen her? Did he know?"

"This lamp hasn't been cleaned for a year."

"Get back here. Forget about the lamp! You're giving me the willies."

The girls had to obey. Sammy wondered desperately if the message had been seen. There had been no answer and she was certain Dad would have sent a reply if he'd seen it.

The hopelessness pressed down on her. They were trapped here. Carrie was near tears, knowing their last chance hadn't worked, for there was nothing else they could try. The outlaws might keep them here for weeks! Then when they decided to move on or hit another stage—Sammy shivered thinking about it!

When night fell, the girls curled up in their corner, but Sammy couldn't sleep. Flint was snoring and Tex was nodding where he sat guarding the doorway.

Suddenly, Sammy sat up straight. Had she heard something? Could it have been a boot striking a rock? Maybe she had only imagined it. No! Tex had stiffened, jerked to attention. He'd been sleeping with one ear open.

What if it was Dad out there? Any minute, Tex might shoot him down. She had to do something! Quietly, she ripped the blanket off of Carrie. She doubled it and grasped one end tightly. She got to her knees and crept toward the doorway. Tex was listening intently to the sounds outside.

There was another sound and Tex jerked to his feet. His rifle was ready and aimed. Sammy swung the blanket and it dropped over Tex's head. He swung his arms wildly, fighting it off.

The doorway filled with the dark form of a tall man and a heavy blow sent Tex sprawling. Carrie was on her feet, leaping for Flint's gun, snatching it out of his reach just as he awakened with a start.

"On your feet, both of you!" a voice said into the dark. "You're covered from all sides."

"Dad!"

"Sammy, is that you? Are you girls all right?"

"We're okay," Carrie answered.

"That was good work," Dad said. "If you hadn't swung that blanket, I'd have been a goner."

Quickly, the lamp was lighted and the posse came pouring in. The Sheriff handcuffed the two outlaws.

"There's a jail cell waiting for you," he said.

"How'd you find us?" Flint growled. "This was a perfect hideout."

"Not quite perfect enough," Dad said. "Sammy outsmarted you. Sent us some signals."

Flint sent her a dark, angry glance.

"So you saw my message after all!" Sammy grinned. "But you didn't answer me."

"Too risky," Dad answered. "They might have seen us and known we were around. It was hard enough staying under cover. You marked the trail just fine, Sammy. We didn't have any trouble finding your trail. And once I saw your message you sent by code, our biggest problem was sneaking up here so that those outlaws wouldn't spot us."

"Well, you didn't get here too soon for me!" said Carrie. "I was beginning to think we'd never get away."

"There's a big reward for these two," the Sheriff said. "Part of it rightly belongs to you girls."

"Just to get home will be reward enough for this tenderfoot," Carrie sighed. "I've had my fill of adventure!"

"Tenderfoot!" Sammy exclaimed. "Not any more. I saw you get Flint's gun away from him!"

Carrie grinned proudly. Sammy laughed tiredly, glad their nightmarish adventure with the outlaws was over at last.

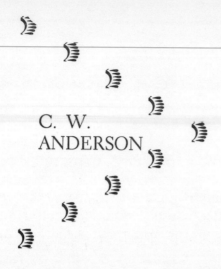

C. W.
ANDERSON

Lessons from Holley

(Tall, black, wide-shouldered and soft-voiced was Holley. He was gentle with people, gentler with children, gentlest with horses. His early life had been spent around racing stables at the big tracks and he lived much in the past, for this had been the high point in his life. In Patsy he had a perfect audience for his reminiscences; she could never hear enough of the deeds of the great horses Holley had seen and known.)

Hands Light

HOLLEY HUMMED TO HIMSELF AS HE BRUSHED THE SLIM BAY MARE THAT was crosstied near the big open stable door. Her coat shone in the slanting rays of the early-morning sun and she nuzzled Holley for sugar as he worked on her forelegs. He stepped back and looked with approval at her sleek, shining coat.

*   *   *

"When a horse is feeling extra-fine an' fit his coat gets an extra shine. It's like when you're feeling good your cheeks are red an' your skin has good color."

"Lady must be feeling fine then, Holley. She shines like satin," Patsy agreed.

"Yeah, she's fit all right. Time your mother took her out or she'll feel too good."

84

"Couldn't I help you, Holley? I could clean Lucky."

"That's a good idea. He'll know you better an' like you more if you take care of him. You can't ever get to know your horse too well. Lots of folks never come near their horses except when they ride, an' then they expect the horse to be glad to see them an' make a fuss just because they own them. Horses don't know who paid for them. They think they belong to the person who waters them when they're thirsty an' feeds them when they're hungry an' cares for them when they're sick. That's the one they'll do most for.

"I remember a woman who thought she owned a horse called Night Hawk. She paid for him, sure enough, an' he raced in her colors. On race days she'd come out dressed up in about everything she could find that was flashy. She'd dash over to Night Hawk in the paddock to pat him—just to show she owned him an' hoping some newspaper photographer would take her picture, prob'ly. He'd always lay back his ears an' jerk back his head when he saw those long red claws coming at him suddenly. Funny how some people never learn not to make a sudden move 'round a horse." Holley paused and shook his head disapprovingly.

"But she didn't own that horse," he continued. "No sir! A colored boy with only one shirt to his back an' never a dollar in his pocket owned him, every hair of him. He slept in the straw next to Night Hawk's stall an' they could almost talk to each other, those two. That horse knew if he wanted anything, day or night, he only had to whinny. He was a high-strung horse; sometimes it took two men to handle him, but he'd follow that colored boy around like a dog. Folks never realize how much a horse can learn if you spend time with him. Some say a horse is dumb compared to a dog, but how much time do you spend with a pet dog? He's around with you all the time, usually, an' most folks never spend more than an hour or two a day with their horse. A boy that goes to school once a week can't learn as much as one that goes every day. No sir!"

"I'm afraid Mother wouldn't let me sleep down here, Holley, but can't I feed Lucky every morning and clean and brush him?"

"It would be pretty early for you to get up if you're going to feed him, Honey," said Holley, smiling at her eagerness. "Horses are up as soon as it's light, so I feed them around five o'clock. But if you come down an' make a fuss over Lucky—bring him an apple or a carrot an' brush him when you have time—he'll be glad to see you. If a horse likes you he gives you a better ride. Same as you'd rather do something for a friend than a stranger."

Patsy was working strenuously on the pony. "He keeps jerking his head away when I try to brush his face, Holley."

"That brush is too stiff. Lots of horses are fussy around their heads. Use a rag an' he won't mind. You wouldn't like a stiff brush on your own face. Treat a horse like you would yourself an' you get along better with him."

"Shall I brush his teeth too, Holley?"

Holley looked over severely. "Any jokes 'round this stable, I make. You brush."

"I'm sorry, Holley. It just popped out. I wish Lucky would shine like Lady." Patsy's face was red from her exertions. Although the pony was very clean his coat looked like an Airedale's.

"He just ain't got the kind of coat that shines. The hair is too coarse an' long. He's mighty clean, though."

"But how will I ever know if he's in fine condition, then, Holley?"

"That Lucky's always in fine condition," laughed Holley. "Comes a day when he don't try to turn back to the stable with you, then you start worrying. Something wrong then, sure enough."

East Is East and West Is West

"Whoa, there! Easy now!" called Holley. "Don't ever trot a horse downhill unless you're looking for a fall."

"But, Holley, in those Western pictures the cowboys ride down the steepest hills at a gallop."

"A gallop's different. A horse is more sure-footed at a gallop than at a trot. An' those Western ponies are different from our horses. Sure-footed as burros. No hunter could gallop down the kind of hills they do out there. But then the Western pony couldn't jump these big fences. Each one has been trained for what's he's meant to do."

"Why do the cowboys ride so differently from us, Holley? Their knees aren't bent at all and they sit so straight in the saddle."

"They're in the saddle ten or twelve hours a day. It's more comfortable to ride with long stirrups when you've got to ride all day. An', of course, the saddle's a lot different—high in front an' behind so you don't need so much knee grip. It's wonderful how those ponies do it, though. They ain't more than fifteen hands, usually, an' have to rough it on feed that would have a thoroughbred starved in a week, an' still they can carry a big man an' a forty-pound saddle all day. They're wonders."

"George Fenley, a boy at school, was out in Montana on a ranch last summer and he brought back one of those big Western saddles. He says only
sissies use English saddles."

"Each thing has its place, but some folks just can't leave it be that way.
Once I worked for a riding stable in New York for a spell. Used to take
beginners out on the bridle paths in Central Park. There was a fellow used
to ride there who wore chaps an' a big cowboy hat. He rode in a big Western
saddle with a horn that could have held a steer that weighed a ton. He was
sorta fat too, an' all in all that poor horse must have been carrying two hundred an' fifty pounds. He'd prob'ly spent a summer on a dude ranch, that fellow. It sure made me laugh. Those chaps he was wearing were meant to keep
the sagebrush from tearing your pants, an' the big heavy saddle was for roping
cattle." Holley paused thoughtfully. "Give you my word, Miss Patsy, I never
saw a steer in Central Park all the time I rode there."

Patsy grinned. "I'm going to tell George Fenley about that. Did you ever
ride a bucking bronco, Holley?"

"No, I never did; an' from what I've seen I don't think I'd care to. Course,
I've broken young horses; but we take it a lot slower than they do out West.
There it's a fight an' it's all over. They haven't time to go slow. Here it's
different. If you got a colt that's worth several thousand dollars you don't
want to take any chances of its getting hurt. An' horses have long memories.
Be too tough with a high-strung thoroughbred an' you're apt to have a tough
horse on your hands afterward. You'll never see a horse that's always been
treated gentle that's head-shy or jumpy, an' one that's been mistreated takes a
long time to forget it—sometimes they never do.

"Once we got one like that at a stable where I worked. He was a big, grand-
looking horse but nervous as a cat. If you walked by his stall an' he saw you
suddenly, he'd give a start an' a jump; often he'd bang himself against the
stall, an' that made it worse. I was always sort of good with nervous horses,
so they told me off to try to quiet him down. You'd have laughed to see me
when I worked around that horse. It was like in the movies when they show
things in slow motion. It sometimes took me an hour to clean him at first,
but it worked. In about a month he was galloping an' jumping for me as nice
as could be. An' he could jump! Every now an' then when he'd come up to
some big fence just right he'd let go an' sail over with a foot to spare. I sort
of think that was his way of doing something nice for you because you'd been
good to him.

"Finally he was going so nice an' looking so fit they decided to start him in
a jumping race. The jock was told just how to handle him, but I was wor-

ried all the same. There ain't too many jocks that use their heads if something goes wrong, an' this horse couldn't have any mistakes made with him. Well, he gets off well an' goes mighty nice for the first three fences; then there's a little crowding at the next jump an' he pecks on landing an' loses ten lengths. Instead of pulling him together an' letting him get going smooth again, the jock gets excited an' starts driving him at the next fence. Well, sir, that jock cleared the jump nice, but the horse didn't. He swerved sharp an' cut across the infield an' jumped the rail an' the outside fence an' tore for his stable. Nobody could come near him till I got there. He was dripping wet an' trembling all over. Six weeks' work was spoiled in just two minutes. We never could do much with him after that. Finally they sold him to a man who wanted to try to make a hunter of him. I sure hope it worked out; he was an awful nice horse."

"Why didn't they have you ride him in the race, Holley?"

"I never was a jock, Honey. I was always too big, even for a steeplechase rider. I wouldn't have been much good anyway. I'd always be thinking more of saving the horse than of winning the race. I never liked to see a jock go to the bat when he was on a horse I knew. Sort of soft I guess. Never could think of a horse as just an animal; all of them seemed like friends of mine, each one with some funny little tricks an' way of doing things. A lot more human than most folks, horses are. Always seemed so to me, anyway.

"There you got me talking again," said Holley after a pause. "You ask too many questions, an' I guess I like to talk. A man shouldn't talk so much. Getting so I'm always chattering."

"How am I going to find out things if you don't tell me, Holley? I want to learn about horses and you know more than anybody. I've got to be ready so I can help you when we get that horse we're going to train."

Holley looked over at her earnest face with its flushed cheeks, at her tangled curls. "Maybe we've got something, Honey," he said. "If we ever got a horse that had it in him I think we might do a job. You can't love horses like we do an' not get something back."

Display

The mist was almost gone from the lower meadows when Patsy came into the stable. Holley was working on Bobcat. He had finished grooming him and was about to clean his hoofs.

"Let's have this foot, boy," said Holley as he stooped over.

Bobcat made no move.

"He don't like to have his feet messed with. Must have been a blacksmith he didn't get along with, sometime. Looky here, boy." Holley held out a piece of carrot. Bobcat reached for it, but Holley put it back in his pocket. "Not now; after you let me clean your hoof," he said.

The horse stood as if thinking for a moment, then raised his foot.

"I don't ever like to fight a horse," said Holley. " 'Specially when he's as big an' strong as this fellow. It don't get you anywhere. Just sort of sets it in his mind that here's something he don't want to do. When he first came he didn't like to take the bit. Kept raising his head higher an' higher an' clenching his teeth tighter. If I'd forced him, next time would have been harder. So I just showed him a carrot an' wouldn't let him have it until he took the bit. It was a little while till he got the idea, but he's smart. The second day he knew he wouldn't get a carrot till he'd done what I asked him.

"An' with his hoofs, now. He knows he gets a piece of carrot for each hoof. Sometimes I forget an' do two or three hoofs before I give him anything. Do you think he don't know how many pieces I owe him? He can count, that Bobcat; he sure can."

Just then Bobcat reached down and nipped Holley and, quickly raising his head, looked down at him with a rim of white showing in his eye.

"Look at the ole devil!" said Holley, rubbing his shoulder. "He's laughing at me. I'd be black an' blue from him if I wasn't black already. He never bites you; he knows he should be gentle because you're small an' a girl, but he like to play rough an' he thinks I'm his dish. Sometimes he reaches out when I ain't looking an' grabs my hat in his teeth an' throws it on the ground. Then he looks so pleased with himself—he's put something over on me. If I don't pretend to be mad an' cuss him he's disappointed. He's got a lot of old Display in him; only gentler. His dam was by Display, you know."

"You were Display's groom, weren't you, Holley?"

"Yes. An' man, oh, man, what a job!"

"Was he as bad as they say, Holley?"

"He was an' he wasn't. Some say he was mean, but I never found him mean; only tough, awful tough. Like he was born with a chip on his shoulder. He wasn't exactly looking for trouble, only expecting it; an' he always met it halfway. He was never bad with me, but then I was never bad with him. When I went in his stall I never slapped him an' said 'Move over,' like to the others. No siree! I'd say, nice an' polite, 'Would you please move over, Mister Display?' He'd stand still, looking at me for a while to make sure I wasn't trying to force him. An' then he'd move over slow, like it was his own idea."

Patsy smiled. "He does sound sort of like Bobcat."

"He was lots tougher," said Holley. "How the starters and ground crews hated to see him coming, and what a fight there was before they got him in line! He had just as much fight left for the stretch—he never asked favors from horse or man. I remember one day he was 'specially bad; there was a big tough assistant starter who decided to tame him an' they battled for ten minutes, an' Display with top weight up. When the start finally came this starter gave Display a jerk that pulled him sideways, an' when he got straightened out an' running he was twenty lengths behind. The pace was fast; a couple of speed horses were fighting it out for the lead, an' there wasn't much chance to make up ground. The jock saw he couldn't wait for the stretch to make his run—they were too far back—so he put Display to a drive the middle of the far side. For half a mile Display stood a drive that few horses could carry for a quarter, an' he got up in the last strides to win by a head.

"Oh, but he was a tired horse when I led him to the winner's circle! His nostrils were big as saucers an' his sides were heaving an' covered with lather. He wasn't even holding his head up; the only time I ever saw that.

"There was some big politician who was going to present the cup, a blustering, red-faced, important-feeling sort of a man who didn't know one end of a horse from the other. He came shoving out there in his fancy shoes an' white pants an' walked around behind Display. Well, Miss Patsy, Display left the neatest hoofprint on those white pants you ever saw. Then he turned to look at me out of the corner of his eye, an' if ever a horse winked he did.

"They don't often come like Display. Somehow I miss him more than the nice ones. He was *somebody!*"

Shooting High

Holley was grooming Bobcat under Patsy's admiring eyes the next morning when a roadster drew up outside the barn door. A slim boy of twenty, with his arm in a sling, slid out from under the steering wheel.

"Morning, Patsy. Morning, Holley," he called. "How's the champ today?"

"He's just fine, Jack," answered Patsy, and Holley grinned.

"You could have knocked me over with a feather—or at least a riding crop, Patsy. You and Holley have certainly done a job. I'll take back everything I said. You bring 'em back alive, all right. It's just as well that I was laid up with this shoulder. It saved my horse a beating."

"Do you really think Bobcat can beat Black Raider, Jack? Why, he was a good third in the Maryland Cup last year."

"I hate to admit it, but I don't think he'd be close if your horse was going his best. What do you think, Holley?"

"Black Raider's a nice horse, Mister Randolph," said Holley, "but this Bobcat—well, I sorta think there ain't going to be many beat him when he's going kind."

"Is he that good?" asked Patsy excitedly. "I hoped he was, but I didn't want to fool myself. Everybody always thinks their own horse is wonderful. Is he really that good?"

"He's so good that I came over to see if you'll let me ride him in the big races next spring. I think you've got a good chance to win the big one."

"Not the Maryland Cup?" asked Patsy breathlessly. "You don't mean that, do you, Jack?"

The boy nodded. "Give him a season's hunting and let me work with him a bit through the winter and spring, then let him get a good race or two under his belt and I don't know a horse I'd rather ride in the Maryland."

"Oh, that's wonderful, Jack. I know you'd get along with him. He's still headstrong, but he's much better than he was. Don't you think he would go kindly for Jack, Holley?"

"I b'lieve so," answered Holley. "I took him out the other day an' he went as nice as could be. Clowned around a little, but he's always that way with me. You get used to him, Mister Randolph, an' go easy till he gets to know you an' you'll get along with him. He still won't take any pushing around, that Bobcat."

"I know, Holley. Black Raider was something like that when I first got him and I had to go slow with him. Don't worry, I won't try to fight him. Not this baby!" And he patted the big horse's powerful neck.

"I'll be at Beverly Hall this year," said Patsy, "so I'll get home to hunt on week ends and holidays. Holley can take him out other days and when your shoulder is better I wish you'd hunt him as often as you think he needs it."

"Fine. It won't be any chore to take him out. I'll be the envy of the valley. I promise you I'll treat him as if he were my own. I'll be able to hunt again in a month, the doc says, and before I hunt him I'll go out hacking a few times so we get to know each other. We'll keep him in top shape and in the spring we ought to go places." He looked at his watch. "I'll have to run. Remember you promised him to me for the races. Don't change your mind if some of the other boys come around. Lots of people are talking about your horse and news gets around. See you later." And he drove off.

"That's a real break, Miss Patsy. Ain't a boy among the riders I'd rather have up than Mister Randolph. He's got mighty nice hands an' a way with horses. I don't think there's many riders could have gotten Black Raider up as close as he did last year. That horse wanted to refuse the last three fences an' it took a mighty heady ride to get him home. He'll fit Bobcat like a glove. Looks to me like we're on our way—" Holley jumped back with a grunt.

"You ole devil, that hurt. Look here, now! Fun's fun, but don't take hold like that." Bobcat put his head over and nuzzled Holley apologetically. "That Bobcat, he's mad because we ain't been paying him any attention," said Holley in a mollified tone. " 'All this talk,' says he. 'I'm the one who done it, but nobody pays any attention to me.' You were good, boy; you were mighty good. Look at him now, Miss Patsy. He's proud as Punch. That's what he wanted. I b'lieve he likes praise and attention more than carrots. He sure eats it up."

"He certainly does, Holley. You'd almost swear he understands what you say, sometimes. I suppose it's the tone of your voice when you tell him he's good. I talked to him all through the race and he kept cocking first one ear and then the other as if he understood every word. You know, Holley, I don't think he would have run out on the turn if I hadn't gotten him excited by asking for an extra-big jump. He let out a notch then, and we were going too fast to make the turn."

"It's a pretty sharp turn for a big striding horse. Prob'ly a man could have pulled him down enough to make it; anyway, they don't have anything as sharp as that on most courses. Everything else he did just right. I was afraid that he might go too fast, but he set a nice pace an' didn't rush his jumps. He ain't got all that width between his eyes for nothing. He's got about as much sense as he has spirit."

"I'm so happy, Holley. At last we know we've got a real horse. He's *somebody*, isn't he?"

"He's good," said Holley cautiously. "So far he's real good. Come spring an' he comes along like he should, we might be sort of proud of him. He could be quite a lot of horse."

By Six—Going Away

The winter was a mild one and hunting had been good. Bobcat had distinguished himself on many occasions when hounds were running, and his reputation as a fast horse over country was spreading beyond the valley. Jack Randolph made no secret of the high regard that he had for the horse, and no one now remembered that Bobcat had originally been cast for the villain and not the hero. He was still a handful of horse when hounds were flying, and the shrill "Gone away" on a frosty morning made him a mount for none but a bold and skillful horseman.

Young Randolph seemed to have found the key to the big horse, restraining him as little as possible to avoid making him fretful and giving him his head when possible so that he could ease himself of some of his pent-up energy and spirit. Since both horse and rider gloried in speed and felt the same surge of excitement when a run was hottest, it was natural that they got on well together. For a timid, careful rider Bobcat would have been a problem; for a fearless, reckless one he was ideal. For the first time in his life Jack Randolph had a horse after his own heart. Hounds never ran fast enough or far enough to lose the big chestnut, and his rider's cheers were often carried back to the ears of riders following.

"Let's show 'em how to take this one, baby," he would cry. "That's swell. You're great, boy. You're wonderful! You're a bear cat!"

Many a rider, following, found himself putting his horse at a big fence instead of looking for a gap as he had intended.

As early spring spread over the Maryland hills and meadows Patsy found that under Jack Randolph's dashing riding Bobcat had become such a dynamo of speed, power, and surging excitement that she confined herself to hacking him and jumping only when they were out alone. She did not have the strength to hold him when the excitement of hounds and horn was in his blood. This was not a disappointment to her, because she realized that he was being keyed up for a supreme effort and she thrilled to the feeling of power and speed that his every movement gave. Later, when racing was over, she knew she could gradually quiet him.

Both Holley and Randolph felt that one good race would be enough to get Bobcat on edge for his top effort. Almost every week they had tested him against Black Raider over several miles of fences, and the way the big chestnut pulled away from the black on the flat as well as over the jumps left no doubt in their minds that they had a real horse.

The Harkaway Cup, a race of three miles over timber, was selected as the best one for their purpose. As it was held at a course only twenty-five miles distant, the problem of vanning the horse over was simple. It gave an interval of two weeks before the Maryland Cup and they felt it would tighten the horse up for the big race and still give time enough to bring him up fresh for the four-mile test.

Patsy's excitement was so great that she failed to notice a soreness through her jaws and cheeks at first. The day before the race her face was noticeably swollen and her mother called in a doctor.

"Has she ever had the mumps?" asked the physician after a brief examination.

"No, she never has," answered Patsy's mother.

"Well, I'm afraid that's what it is. When it comes this late you must be very careful. She had best stay in bed until the swelling has gone."

Patsy burst into tears and buried her head in the pillow, sobbing.

"Now, now," said the doctor, "it's not that serious. Nothing to worry about."

"It's the race tomorrow," explained her mother. "Her horse is running and she's been looking forward to it for weeks, poor child."

"That's too bad. I'm sorry, but I feel it would be dangerous for her to go out. I'll be over again in a day or two to see how she's getting along. We'll have her up very soon."

Patsy's eyes were red when her mother returned, but she had stopped crying. Her mother leaned over and stroked her tousled hair.

"Mumps!" said Patsy bitterly. Her mother smiled sympathetically. "All my life has been like this," added Patsy darkly.

"Why, darling! Your life has been very happy."

"Yes, but all my life people have treated me like a child and now, when I'm owner of a grand horse and people are beginning to treat me like a grown person, what happens? I get mumps! It couldn't be appendicitis or pneumonia or gout. No, it had to be mumps! Can't you see the papers? 'Miss Patricia Allison was not present to see her horse win or to receive the cup, as she was confined to her bed with mumps.' " Patsy buried her head in the pillow. "And I so wanted to see Bobcat run."

"You'll see him in the Maryland Cup, darling. That will be much better."

"How do you know, Mother?" said Patsy bitterly. "How do you know that I won't have the whooping cough or colic? Unless maybe I'll be cutting a tooth." Her mother smiled and put an arm around her shoulders. "I'm sorry, Mother. I didn't mean to be like that, but I'm so disappointed."

"I know, darling. But I'll ask Jack to send a wire as soon as the race is over, and when Holley comes back he can come up and tell you all about it. You know how you've always loved to hear Holley tell about races. It's almost as good as seeing them."

The day of the race was clear and bright, with a scattering of fleecy clouds that made the sky seem even bluer. Patsy could hear the bustling around the stable and Bobcat snorting as he was led into the van. Then everything was quiet and nothing remained but to count the hours until racetime. Jack Randolph and several friends phoned their sympathy, but to Patsy's oversensitive ear there seemed to be an undercurrent of amusement in their condolences. The fact that her illness had no dignity added to her cup of bitterness.

The afternoon wore on and racetime came and passed and still no word had come. The phone had rung several times, but it was merely friends calling to give their sympathy. Had something gone wrong that Jack didn't want to let her know about? Perhaps Bobcat had fallen and been injured.

The telephone beside her bed cut in sharply on her fears.

"This is Western Union," said a voice. "I have a telegram for Patricia Allison. Shall I read it to you?"

"Yes, please," said Patsy in a weak voice.

"It's from Greenvale, Maryland. 'Bobcat by six lengths, going away. Make room on your mantel for the Maryland Cup.' Signed, Jack."

"Thank you," said Patsy. "Oh, thank you very much."

ANONYMOUS

Riding Song

Let us ride together—
Blowing mane and hair,
Careless of the weather,
Miles ahead of care,
Ring of hoof and snaffle,
Swing of waist and hip,
Trotting down the twisted road
With the world let slip.

Let us laugh together—
Merry as of old
To the creak of leather
And the morning cold.
Break into a canter;
Shout to bank and tree;
Rocking down the waking trail,
Steady hand and knee.

Take the life of cities—
Here's the life for me.
'Twere a thousand pities
Not to gallop free.
So we'll ride together,
Comrade, you and I,
Careless of the weather,
Letting care go by.

V

HORSES TO CHEER

Success on the race track

MARGUERITE
HENRY

Black Gold

(Al Hoots lived among the Osage Indians and his wife Rosa was an Osage. This true story begins in 1909, when Al—who knew a good horse when he saw one—bought the little thoroughbred mare U-see-it. The price he paid was eighty acres of his Oklahoma farm.)

U-SEE-IT WAS HIS YOUNGEST, HIS FAVORITE, AND HE FOUND HIMSELF planning for her the way a parent plans for the child who is handicapped by littleness or plainness. He would have to get a trainer for her, a good one—a trainer who would recognize and be so excited by her possibilities that he would be willing to work the clock around—a man who would love her for her eagerness as Hoots himself did.

For a few months he decided to baby her with no work at all, so he turned her out to roll and romp with the other horses. She seemed as pleased as a child let out of school—playing all day in sun and rain, and in snow, too. There was, of course, a big roomy shelter where she could come and go as she liked. But she seldom used it! She liked weather, all kinds. With her tail to the slanting snow, she let it pile up on her back until she looked like a race horse under a white blanket.

As for her diet, there was delicious bluestem grass in summer and corn and hay in winter. And there was the clear-flowing Hominy Creek to drink from.

Life at Skiatook was good! On twilit evenings Rosa came out on the porch

99

and cranked her music box. The tinkly notes made U-see-it and all the other horses come flying across the meadow. Once at the gate, U-see-it remained very still, her head resting on the top rail, her delicate ears pricked sharply to pull in all the melody.

Rosa's eyes laughed. "When they come galloping in," she told her husband, "the other horses, they *lumber* alongside her."

It pleased Al the way Rosa loved U-see-it. As for him, he was building the filly's whole future on the look in her eye. The eagle look will make up for littleness, he thought.

"Yes!" he told U-see-it. "You may have to take two strides to the other horses' one, but I know you can do it."

One sleepless night, as Al Hoots lay listening to the wind in the cotton-wood tree, a happy idea came to him. The very man to train U-see-it was none other than old Hanley Webb. Good old bald-headed, bow-legged Hanley Webb, who had lost two fingers in a 'coon hunt. He had neither chick nor child to care for. Why, Webb had complained as recently as the last race meeting: "Al, sometimes I get mighty tired being County Sheriff and coming home to no one but me. Yuh, I get mighty tired of it. Sometimes I think I'd like to turn in my silver star and quit the constabulary for good."

"But what would you do?" Hoots had asked him.

The answer had come without hesitation. "What I'd like," he had said, "what I'd really like is to be nursemaid to a good smart horse—to walk him cool, to groom him, and to train him up until he'd be *my* handiwork to take a pride in!"

And so, in less than a month Hanley Webb arrived, bag and baggage, eager to begin. The first thing he did was to grade a track in the field behind the shed. Then he hired an old wizened Indian, named Chief Johnson, to be U-see-it's exercise boy. Now each day, rain or shine, she was put to work. First she had to run clockwise of the track, then counterclockwise, until she began to sense that running was her business in life. Even in winter there was scarcely any let-up. Hanley Webb threw straw on the frozen track to cushion it, and schooling went on just the same.

The combination of work and freedom after work and friends, both four- and two-legged, agreed with the little mare. By the time she was three years old her whole appearance had changed. The wispy look was gone! Now she had developed into a well-formed mare, round and solid as an apple. And her eyes, always beautiful, became so full of health and liquid light that one was stopped by their brilliance. Even the brownness of her coat had taken on a nice shine, like a plain brown boulder made glossy by the water that flows over it.

But most remarkable of all was her spirit. She *wanted* to race! First she won on little straightaway tracks hewn out of the wilderness. Then on half-mile tracks at county fairs. Then she was entered at the big race meetings—at Tulsey Town, at Enid, at Oklahoma City. And at last she was too fast for Oklahoma! She was shipped to New Orleans and Chicago and to far-away places, like Juarez down in Mexico, and Calgary up in Canada.

With each race she earned a new nickname—Twinkle Toes, Hummingbird, Comet, Sandpiper.

On and on she went, winning from quarter horses and from Thorough-breds. Al Hoots was in an ecstasy of pride over his mare that looked so little and raced so big. He beamed at the gentle joshing about her. "How's the light o' your life?" he was asked. "How's the apple o' yer eye? Ain't Rosa jealous?"

There was only one racing mare that spelled defeat for her. She was Pan Zaretta, known as the Queen of Texas, and of pretty nearly everywhere else. She was big-going as the state itself, with no less than a twenty-foot stride.

Old Man Webb took a sharp dislike to her. "I wouldn't trade our Twinkle Toes," he said loyally, "for all the Pan Zarettas in Texas!"

The years of racing and travel went by. Good years for everyone at Skiatook. One night when Webb and U-see-it had gone on ahead to Juarez, Al Hoots was trying to figure up the number of times his mare had finished first. He and Rosa were sitting at the supper table, just the two of them, and he was jotting down the names of cities on the back of an old calendar. Rosa was spooning up second helpings of boiled hominy with pork, while Buster, their bob-tailed pup, looked on hopefully.

"Rosa!" Al pronounced between mouthfuls. "Think on it! As near as I can figure, U-see-it has won thirty-four races for us! That's meant enough money to mend fences and buy feed for our whole string of laggards."

Rosa stopped in the midst of stirring her coffee. She laid down her spoon quietly in the saucer. Slowly, thoughtfully, she said, "Now, Al, now would be the time to bring her back to the Home Place. Now—while she is the winner."

The house suddenly went quiet. Outside in the cottonwood tree a bluejay whistled, "G'night! G'night!" And the red puppy spoke for a piece of meat.

Al looked at Rosa beseechingly, thinking of her Indian wisdom. Was it a foreboding she had? "I wish somehow you hadn't said that, Rosa."

"I think not only of my love for U-see-it."

"No?"

"I think you need to come home, too, Al."

"*I* need to come home?"

She named the reasons slowly, with a pause after each. "Yes. The long grind of the circuit . . . the traveling . . . the dust worsening your cough . . . the long hours . . . the cold food served to you warm and the hot food served cold. No squash and hominy. None of the good things the Osage eats. And"—after a long pause—"I miss you . . . both."

Al Hoots looked at his wife and nodded. Everything she had said was true. But his plans were made. U-see-it and Hanley Webb were already on their way to Juarez, and he had committed himself to go, too. It was the last race meeting of the season and he was leaving in the morning.

He could not answer her. He took a marrowbone from his plate, licked the hominy from it and made a peace offering to the pup.

The bluejay called his "G'night" again, and somewhere afar off a coyote cried.

After a long while he managed to explain. "It's the last race meeting, Rosa. I promised to enter her. I have to leave in the morning."

He went tiredly up the stairs to pack his bag. When this was done, he strapped his deer rifle to it. Next best to chicken and pork Hanley Webb liked deer steak, and there might be time for hunting.

The Claiming Race

Down at Juarez the morning was blowy. Gusts of wind whipped up spirals of dust and sent them swirling around the walls of U-see-it's stall. They made her sneeze, and it was more a filly's sneeze than a full-grown mare's.

Al Hoots smiled as he looked over the half-door. Even U-see-it's sneezes had an endearing quality for him. Then a shadow passed like a cloud across his face. He spoke his thoughts to Hanley Webb, who sat cross-legged in the straw, rubbing the mare's forelegs, putting on the clean bandages, readying her for the afternoon's race.

"Whenever Rosa and I have talked about claiming races," Al Hoots remarked, "it seemed crazy to her that a man who loves his horse would enter her in a race like that." He expected no answer and got none. He was thinking aloud, and Hanley Webb knew it.

"I didn't dare tell her that this was a claiming race. I just couldn't. She'd never understand why I'd put U-see-it in a race where any of the owners could just step up afterwards and buy her for five hundred dollars."

"I know, I know," Hanley Webb agreed as he took a safety pin out of his mouth and fastened the bandage. "It'd take a combination preacher, teacher, liberryan, and lawyer to lay it out clear."

Al Hoots nodded. "I can't explain to Rosa how it is when the racing secretary comes to you and says, 'Al, we don't have enough horses to fill one race, and I want to have a nice program for the day; so I'd like for you to enter U-see-it.' When a good fellow like him is short only one horse, you kind of feel obliged to enter."

Hanley Webb patted the bandage and got to his feet. "Sure, it's a hard thing for wimmenfolk to understand. But with my own ears I heard the secretary pleadin' with you, and I heard him say, 'Al, I know all the owners in the race and everybody's your friend; nobody's going to claim U-see-it; they all know how you feel about her.' So stop your worrying."

"Oh, I'm not really worried. I was only wondering how to make Rosa understand."

"No need to, man! You have my word that I went myself from owner to owner, and every last one agreed not to claim U-see-it."

"Thanks, Webb," Al Hoots smiled, seemingly relieved. He offered U-see-it and Hanley Webb each a peppermint, and ate one himself. "'Tis a fine gentleman's agreement," he said. "Just like with the Indians, a man's word is good."

By afternoon the wind was blowing a gale. It whipped along the track, raising a yellow dust as high as the fence rail. Sprinkling carts went to work, but their thin spattering only seemed to encourage the wind. It boiled up clouds of dust until the sun was nearly hidden. At the barrier all of the entries in the claiming race were nervous, jigging out of position again and again.

"Soon," thought Al Hoots as he watched from the rail, "I can take The Little One back to the Home Place at Skiatook." He carried her there in his mind's eye, thinking: "Around and on her falls the snow she loves. She rolls in it and then stands up to shudder it off, making her own snowstorm."

He laughed inside, going on with his dream. "The racing has made her slim-waisted like a greyhound, but oats and the good hay from our bluestem grass will make her sleek and plump. Next year she'll be ready to run again. She could never loaf her life away, like some horses do."

He beamed now at how lively she was, straining to go, dancing sideways, wanting to challenge the wind. She couldn't wait! With two other entries she ducked under the barrier in a false start. A hundred yards down the track an outrider stopped the runaways, made them turn around and come back.

Then in one tremendous instant the flag was dropped and the horses were off!

Al Hoots' lips stretched tight for a moment as U-see-it broke last, a good half-length behind the others. But almost at once the trip-hammer power of her legs began moving her forward, inch by inch, stride by stride.

He held onto the rail, hearing the caller sound her name and position. "U-see-it in fourth place at the quarter." His grip tightened. U-see-it was a small brown mouse among the bigger horses, taking twice as many strides as they did. Now she scampered her way from fourth position to third, to second. And now the caller was shouting, "U-see-it in second place at the half."

Al's heart pounded and he took off his hat as if the weight of it were more than he could bear. U-see-it was going to do it again, but he wished he hadn't asked it of her, not on a day like this with the wind battering her, blowing dust in her eyes and up her nostrils and down her ears. Now he wished he had scratched her name off. But the pride in him swelled. For at the head of the stretch she was making her bid for the lead. Nothing mouselike about her now! Mane whipping like licks of flame, tail floating on the wind. The Number One horse only a length ahead. Now but a half-length. Now a neck.

She was going to do it again! The finish line just ahead. And U-see-it a gleam of brown light reaching for it, gaining sharply.

But—it's too late! The race is over!

Al Hoots wiped the dust from his lips. He glanced in agony to the heavens and in the voice of the wind he heard Rosa's voice saying, "Now is the time to bring her back to the Home Place. Now, while she is winner."

After the race Al Hoots hovered over U-see-it as if the hairline finish had been a hurt that he himself had inflicted, as if *he* had somehow been to blame for the wind and the dust.

Gently he helped Old Man Webb sponge her face with cool water. Then they washed her whole body with lukewarm water and alcohol. Finally with a long scraper they squeezed the water from her coat and placed the blanket over her for warmth. Then they both walked her slowly, around and around, with no word between them.

When at last they were satisfied that she was cooled out and eating her hay, the two men started off to get their own suppers.

"Don't go just yet, gen'lemen!" a voice mocked. And before them stood a burly stranger, blocking their path. The slanting sun caught him full in the face and lighted the eyes for what they were—glinty and small and shrewd. A hoarse voice said, "Foxy of me to wait until you got her all bathed and cooled out, wasn't it?" The grubby hands now waved a piece of paper. "This here's my receipt. I paid the steward, and now she's mine."

"She's *what?*" the words wrenched themselves from Al Hoots' mouth.

"A claiming race, ain't it?"

There was nothing but silence, a deep, ominous silence, broken only by U-see-it munching her hay and switching about in her stall to look over the half-door. On either side of her, sorrel heads, gray heads, heads with blazes peered out, ears pricked in curiosity.

Grooms with rub rags over their shoulders quickly gathered in a ring around the three men, their mouths gaping, their whole expression saying, "Anybody who tries to claim U-see-it must be part skunk or not very smart."

The cords on either side of Al Hoots' neck bulged big. His mouth opened but no words came. It was Hanley Webb who blurted out, "Who in tunket you think you are?"

The stranger's lips parted, showing long yellow teeth that revealed his age and his tobacco chewing. "I'm the agent for an owner in today's race."

"Wait just a minute!" shouted Hanley Webb, shaking his fist. "We had a gentleman's agreement!"

"Seems my client had a change of heart."

Al Hoots touched Webb's sleeve. "You tell that man," he bit off the words, uttering each one separately, "you tell him to wait right here. I'll be back."

With face tight drawn, he walked around the little knot of men, past the adobe barns, past the row of cottage barns to the very last one. It held Hanley Webb's bunk, and on the bunk lay Al's own traveling bag.

There was just one thing to do.

He unbuckled the straps around the bag and took the rifle out of its case. Pained but resolute, he strode back with firm step. The grooms were roiled to anger now. They gave way to make room for him as he came on. His eyes were on the stranger's and he raised the rifle. "Now!" he commanded. "You get!"

The agent's face went as white as his receipt. He almost toppled over backward.

Webb cried out, "Al! Don't, Al! You can't mean it!"

The stranger, still backing away, gulped in terror. "My mistake, Hoots. My mistake." Then he turned and fled.

Hoots smiled weakly as the grooms came, one by one, to shake his hand. "That rat!" they said. "Doing somebody else's dirty work!"

"But, Al," one shook his head doubtfully, "for your own sake I wish you hadn't of used the rifle."

"Well, it's done now, boys. It's the last time I'll ever enter my little mare in a claiming race." That was all he had to say. His shoulders sagged and he seemed suddenly tired and beaten and old. He went to put his gun away, walking slow and bent, but he had gone only a few paces when a messenger summoned him to the steward's office. He knew what the verdict would be, even before it was said.

The words came slowly, with the steward's kindly hand on his arm, but they were no less final. "Even under circumstances that we all understand, Hoots, you know that a claiming race is a selling race. I have no choice but to bar you and U-see-it from the tracks. *Forever.*" As if this were not punishment enough, the steward added, "And U-see-it's name will be struck from the Thoroughbred Registry. I'm sorry, Hoots. Sorrier than you know." And he reached for the limp hand and wrung it in sympathy.

As Al Hoots walked out of the office, he was tempted to appeal the verdict, but deep in his heart he felt that the track secretary had probably done all he could.

First Lessons

(*Before Al Hoots died he planned that his little mare would be shipped to Lexington, Kentucky, to have a thoroughbred colt.*)

Men remarked that even before he was a month old, the newborn colt was no longer just the son of Black Toney or of U-see-it. He was himself— *Black Gold!* He was little. His mane stood up like a crew cut. His tail was a flat, paddly brush, not much good for anything; yet he flapped it constantly up and down while he nursed, as if it were a pump handle.

But for all his littleness, no one ever gave him a nickname. He had an air of innate dignity about him. Grooms, visitors, horse owners—everyone spoke *of* him and *to* him as Black Gold, and the tone of their voice had something in it amounting almost to respect.

Only one thing bothered the horsemen as they watched U-see-it give Black Gold his first running lessons. He ran upheaded. "A horse that travels with his head in the air may travel fast, but not far," Horace Davis remarked. And Colonel Bradley, to whom he said it, nodded against his will as if his own thought had been spoken.

But Black Gold paid no heed to man-talk. He was furiously busy, trying to keep pace with his mother. He scampered across the pasture, galloping behind her. As he struggled to keep up, the wind came at him, seeming to push him back. He blew and snorted to the wind, and he hollered to his mother to wait for him. "Wait! Wait!" he squealed. But U-see-it went right on pacing him, teaching him to trot, to canter, to gallop. Then she wheeled around the fence corners, staying as close to the rails as if she were at a track.

Onlookers held their sides, laughing. It appeared such fun for U-see-it to school her colt. And her actions spoke more plainly than any words. "Learn to use your tail!" she said, giving a fine example. "See? Let it balance you around the curves; it's really more than a fly switch, you know!"

All these things U-see-it said, and more. "Run low, my son, with your legs and belly close to the ground. Like this! Now try it! Follow me!"

And when they were both tired, Black Gold went to her side to blow until his breathing came quiet and steady again.

One day was like another and they were all good. All frolic and food and sun and wind and starshine and sleep. Besides his mother's milk, he began to enjoy sampling from her oats bin. He liked the way he could grind the kernels with his teeth until they became mush. Then they had a good, sweet flavor.

Each season had its own routine. In summer when the blue bottle flies were pesky beyond endurance, mother and son spent daytimes in the stall and nighttimes grazing out of doors. Being out in the dark was fun—rolling in the dewy wetness, cropping the grass close to the roots, spooking the timid shiny-eyed rabbits that came out in the moonlight.

The days and nights fell away. And the weeks. When fall came and the air grew cool and bracing, the routine was changed back again. Now as in the spring they grazed by day and slept in the stable by night. Always U-see-it was there to protect and mother her colt. Often she arched her neck over his shoulder to keep him warm, or just for nearness' sake.

But one late afternoon when the groom came to lead them to the stable, Black Gold's world suddenly shattered. Instead of letting him follow along behind U-see-it, the groom fastened a shank rope to his halter and led him into a strange stall. And there was no one else in it. No one at all. Only the big empty bed of straw.

As the door closed in on him, he became terrified. Quaking with fear he pointed his nose to the lone high window, whinnying shrilly, then plaintively. No answer came. He began running in circles, around and around his stall until he was breathless. He rushed at the door, striking it with his forefeet, flailing at it. He tried to climb over it. Whinnying, he tried again and again. Once he thought he heard his mother calling. But it was only the high wind blowing. Mouth open, seeking, seeking, he flung his head forward and up, trying somehow to reach his mother's milk bag for comfort. Late into the night he still whimpered, still beat upon the door with his tiny hoofs. There was a morning grayness in the sky when he finally stopped calling her. Then in utter exhaustion he sank to his knees, fell in a little heap, and slept.

Old Hanley Webb came for Black Gold the next day. He looked long into the box stall, long and lovingly, as though he saw things that only he or Al Hoots might see—the sensitive ears, the fineness of bone; but mostly something *inside*. If Al had been alive he would have called it heart. Webb put out his hand and the colt reached over the half-door and suckled all three fingers hungrily. The old man's breath cut short as a great protective instinct welled up in him. He laughed a self-conscious laugh, then tried to hide his joy.

" 'Tain't no good to coddle him," he said gruffly to Mr. Davis. "It's got to be all business atween him and me."

He took the colt away to his new home—a fair-sized paddock behind the blacksmith shop of the old track at Lexington. There Black Gold's career began in earnest.

He never saw his mother again.

Hanley Webb Takes Over

Old Man Webb, they called him. He was squatty-built, like an apple tree, his neck thick and solid with rootlike cords spreading out toward his shoulders. He had only a fringe of hair and no teeth whatever. Of course he owned store teeth, but those he kept in his pocket.

The contrast between the finely made colt and the gnarled old man was so sharp that Webb himself was conscious of it. At first sight he had fallen in love with Black Gold, as if in the colt's beauty his own homeliness were redeemed.

With a fierce joy he began to take care of his charge. So that U-see-it would not be missed too greatly, he bought an old secondhand cot and set up his living quarters in a stall alongside Black Gold's. He even tore out two boards in the partition between them so that he could look in on the colt to see that he was comfortable and happy. Rough, calloused hands, warm with understanding, kept the black coat clean, the manger full, and the bedding fresh and dry.

Each morning before he put Black Gold's halter on, he would run his hands over the young horse's body—not only his neck, barrel, and rump, but legs and tail, too. Then he would place the soft web halter over his nose and head, oftentimes attaching the lead rope to it. Whether or not he led his charge to some choice grazing spot for breakfast, he nearly always laid the rope over the colt's back for a while. "I want fer ye to get the feel of ropes and straps and hands so they'll never make ye jumpy. First things first, I allus say."

Each morning, too, he took Black Gold out on the lunge rein, exercising him in an ever-widening circle. Watching the colt trot and gallop, Hanley Webb wanted to cry and laugh both. The legs, though delicately made, were pinions of great strength and reach. But oh, the head! Must he always go upheaded?

Unconsciously the old man looked to the sky, asking the question. "Al, can he do it? Did y'ever know of a colt to run with his head up, and win over a distance?" Always he thought of Al Hoots as having gone to heaven, living somewhere up there in the clouds. So always he addressed his worries to the sky. Occasionally a cloud would shift, seeming to answer, but this time no answer came.

"I'll make it up to our little horse," he resolved. "I'll see to it he's trained so good that handicap of his won't amount to nothing."

He sent to Skiatook for his old Indian friend, Chief Johnson, still wiry as a cricket, still working with horses. When the Chief arrived, Webb said, "You can sleep right here in the stall with me—you rolled up in your Injun blanket on the floor, and me on my cot. It'll be kinda cozy that way, and cheap, too."

Next morning, when the Chief had admired Black Gold enough to suit even Hanley Webb, he explained his plan of training. "Here's what you do, Chief. Work him long hours, but not fast. We got to leg him up so's he can be a stayer, not just a sprinter. And whatever you do, don't coddle him."

The Chief obeyed to the letter. Rain or shine, he worked Black Gold. And Black Gold responded, developing rapidly into a glossy, hard-muscled, eager yearling.

"What I like about colt," Chief Johnson confided to Hanley Webb one night as the two were bedding down, "is no matter if he feel good or bad, he don't balk. If weather good or bad, he still run good."

For answer there was a satisfied chuckle.

Now once more the days were all alike, days of steady routine, of growth and development. The two old men and the horse were happy, stabled side by side. They even ate at the same time, in their own stalls, one enjoying his warm bran mash, the other two their ham hocks and cabbage cooked in the black pot over their charcoal fire.

"We all of us got to eat good if we're going to make you a champion," the old man explained to Black Gold as he looked through the gap in the partition. "Yep, we got to eat *real* good!"

So highly did Hanley Webb prize his charge that he wrote to Rosa, asking if she could spare the old Skiatook watchdog, Buster. Then when he and the Chief needed to go to town for groceries or a haircut, Buster could stand guard.

From the moment Buster arrived, the two animals became fast friends, playing tag together, lipping and licking each other, and sleeping back-to-back in the quiet intervals between workouts.

Buster on guard duty, however, was a very different character. If any stranger so much as raised a hand to stroke Black Gold, the small red dog became a tiger.

And so Black Gold worked and ate and played and slept, and grew.

Indian Counsel

The night was black and starless. The silence of the long row of stables was broken only now and then by the stomping of a horse or the muted voice of a stableboy crooning the blues.

Jaydee Mooney, an ambitious jockey, had eaten his supper in town and had come back, half walking, half running to the stables. This would be the time to approach Old Man Webb. Now, with everything quiet. The crowd of people gone to their homes. The grooms sleepy. The horses content.

Yes, now was the time. *Now!*

A light showed in the stall next to Black Gold's, and the figure of the old man made a grotesque shadow against the whitewashed wall. Jaydee hesitated a moment, took a deep breath. So much depended on this night. He slowed his steps, thinking. It's like my whole world is at stake. What will happen to Black Gold if I don't get a *yes* answer? If only I can make the old man understand how it has to be!

From Black Gold's stall came a low growl. It deepened, then rose shrilly into the night. "You!" it warned. "Whoever you are, stay away from here!"

A bald head poked out of the stall. "Who's thar?"

"It's me, Jaydee Mooney, the jockey. Can I see you, Mister Webb?"

"Buster, stop yer barkin'! The boy means no harm."

The hand with the three fingers waved to Jaydee to come on in, and motioned him to sit down on the bunk. Then the old man picked up the small leather collar he was saddle soaping and went on working. There was no smile on his face, not even a lifted eyebrow asking, "What's on your mind, boy?" There was more welcome in Chief Johnson's quiet grin as he sat on the floor drowsing and smoking his long-stemmed pipe.

The small sounds of night loomed big. Frogs making *glug-glug* noises. A mockingbird trying out a medley of songs. As his eyes became accustomed to the light, Jaydee could see between the planks into Black Gold's stall. The colt was lying asleep, his head nodding in the straw. His pose seemed more like that of a kitten than a race horse. And curled up beside him was the whiskery red dog, his eyes blinking at the unfamiliar caller.

Jaydee's fingers fumbled at the collar of his shirt. It was hard to breathe. Quite suddenly he remembered the time he had been caught under a raft and nearly drowned. This was like that. He cast about in his mind for a topic of conversation to break the silence. "That leather collar you're soaping," his voice was tight and strained, "I reckon it belongs to Buster."

"To Buster!" Webb's voice was even less friendly than before. "No, begorry. 'Tis my very own, for special occasions when I want to look duded up. Case we win the Derby, I got to look respectable. So I soaps it now and then to keep the leather soft. Why wouldn't I?" he barked.

Silence again.

"I wish I was in good standing with you, Mister Webb," Jaydee tried once more.

"Humph, 'tain't no matter. We don't mean nothing to each other."

"But from now on, we got to!"

"Oh?" The old man strung out the little word and ended it with a wry laugh.

"Mister Webb, I . . . Mister Webb, I got to ride Black Gold from now on. I've been watching him, and watching him. I know why he has such a hard time winning."

The old man slapped the collar down on the table and the rub rag beside it. The blood rose in his face. "I wouldn't let you ride Black Gold if you was the onliest jockey in the hull dang-blasted world!"

At the quick anger in the man's voice, Buster leaped through the gap in the partition and came snuffing up to Jaydee. Then he turned to the old man, his eyes asking, "This boy giving you any trouble?"

"Down, Buster. I'll handle this." He pointed a bony finger at Jaydee. "Oncet I thought you was a very fine jockey, but when I saw you of-a-purpose lose on Tulsie, you lost your chance with me."

"But I didn't lose a-purpose!"

"Oncet you won on him."

"Yes."

"And the next time you didn't even aim to win. You didn't even try."

"Us Mooneys," Jaydee jumped to his feet and clipped out the words, "us Mooneys *always* try. We do our best."

The old man grunted, and was silent.

"I rode Tulsie the same way in both races, but he didn't respond the same way. And you want to know why?"

Webb made no answer. He took up the rub rag, and began working on Black Gold's bridle reins. In his corner behind Hanley Webb, the Chief winked Jaydee on.

"All right, sir! Even if you don't want to know, I'll tell you. I didn't know myself till the race was over. Then I saw why. Tulsie was calked."

"Calked!" the old man snorted again.

"Yes, sir! It was that Number Four horse that did it. Remember how nervous and jigging he was at the gate?"

No answer. Only the night chorus of the frogs, and the dog, back in the other stall, licking Black Gold's face.

"Yes, sir! That horse calked Tulsie; hurt him bad. It was a real deep cut. He just couldn't respond when I asked him. You've got to believe it. You've *got* to, sir, because that's what happened!"

Chief Johnson cupped his hands together in soundless applause. There was a stirring in the next stall as Black Gold rose to his feet and stomped.

Old Man Webb stood up to see that the colt was all right. Satisfied, he reached into his pocket and took out a plug of tobacco. With his hoof-paring knife he cut off a corner of the plug and slipped it into his cheek.

Impatiently watching this ritual, Jaydee could not help wondering if the man put one in the other cheek now, would he look more chipmunk or squirrel?

"Well, 'tain't no matter anyways," Webb said as he sat down again. "I promised Jack Howard he could ride him in the Latonia Jockey Club Stake next Saturday."

"But after that, sir? What about after that?"

"We'll see. Don't rush me, boy. The light and all our gabbin' is keeping Black Gold awake. The Chief and me has got to bed down, too. Away with you now."

The Halter Rope

When Jaydee left the stable, it was nearly midnight. He walked slowly down the road to the small rented room in Louisville where he was staying. The half-moon, a big orange slice, hung low in the sky. It reminded him of the candy he used to eat when he was little.

Walking along, he felt happy that he had been able to find out what had stood between himself and Webb, and he believed he had made some small progress toward his goal. In spite of everything, he liked the homely old man with his toothless mouth that opened and closed like a pocketbook when he talked.

Lots of folks slur him, Jaydee thought. They say he's mulish. But I like him, gruffness and all. He's a poor man's man—like my father, maybe. And *anyone* who would live in a stable to keep watch over a colt . . . well, anyone who would do that is a man to trust.

He thought enviously of Jack Howard, and after he went to bed he dreamed the jockey rode so well that Black Gold became known as a flying horse. "Pegasus the Second" he was called, because he actually flew over the heads of the other horses and always finished going away in a cloud.

Jaydee awakened, drenched in a sweat. How could one little horse take over all of his thoughts, awake *and* asleep?

The day of the Jockey Club Stake was hazy and warm with low-hanging clouds obscuring the sun and reminding Jaydee of his dream. He rode in the third race and won. In the fifth race twelve horses were entered, but to him, on the sidelines, only one horse mattered. His post position was tenth. He carried 122 pounds. His jockey was Jack Howard, wearing the bright rose silks. And his name was Black Gold!

In one minute thirty-nine and three-fifths seconds the race was over, but it seemed to Jaydee as if he had lived a whole lifetime in those few moments, as if he had been changed into an old, old man. A big-going colt by the name of Wise Counselor raced into the lead with a rush, set the pace lightning fast and won all the way. Battle Creek, Bob Tail, King Goren II, Cloister, Chilhowee, Bracadale, all ran gamely, trying to close the gap that Wise Counselor had made. But as for Black Gold, he was always in the ruck.

A boy with a streak of meanness in him might have been secretly glad that Black Gold had lost with another jockey aboard. But Jaydee was stunned. He felt like a parent whose child had a big role in a play—a head angel, perhaps, at Christmastime—and the child not only forgot his lines but stumbled and fell on the stage and never recovered himself. Deeply hurt and disappointed, Jaydee ran from the track, ran belligerently for the jockey rooms. He wanted to hit something, to punch somebody. "I've got to ride that horse before he's hurt. I've got to!" Swiftly, resolutely, he peeled off his silks, pulled on his shirt, and went out to find Old Man Webb.

Webb himself was walking Black Gold around and around in the peaceful shade under the trees. He and his horse seemed so apart from the life about them that Jaydee stopped, waiting.

A small wind played with Black Gold's forelock, revealing the heart on his forehead. The symbol gave Jaydee courage.

"Mister Webb . . ." he began.

The old man sighed. "Oh, it's you again! Your middle name oughta be Nuisance, or mebbe Nettle." But this time he tempered his gruffness with a smile.

Jaydee fell into stride alongside him. "Isn't it true, Mister Webb, that too many defeats can take the heart out of a horse? And then sometimes he won't even try any more?"

"What in tarnation you aiming to say, boy?"

"Don't you see, Mister Webb, if you want Black Gold to be a champion, I got to ride him? I understand him. I could help him."

The old man walked without changing pace—once around the cooling-out ring, and once again. His mind seemed far away and preoccupied as if he had forgotten the boy's presence, almost as if he were talking the matter over with Al Hoots.

Jaydee held his breath. His legs felt leaden. Just when they refused to go another step, the old man placed Black Gold's halter rope in his hands.

"If you expect to ride a champion," he said abruptly, "it's high time you learned to do for him. Now *you* walk him cool."

*   *   *

Two minutes, five and one-fifth seconds—that is all it took. Now it's all over. Lifetimes of effort . . . thousands of miles traveled . . . millions of dollars spent. Work, sweat, grief, joy. Dreams dreamed.

And now it is done.

Horse and jockey can breathe again. They both suck in great lungfuls of air as they come slowly back. Black Gold knows there is no need to hurry any more. His pace has a majestic slowness; he senses the greatness of the moment and is savoring it to the full.

Old Man Webb is limping out on the track to meet them, his ancient topcoat billowing out behind. Jaydee stares, pulls up in midstride. The old man has put on his "respectable" leather collar, but it is dark with sweat, as if he had run the race himself. Jaydee looks down at the exuberant face.

"Well, by gum, the two of ye did it!" the old man grins—a wide, pearly grin.

Even in this moment of triumph, Jaydee cannot help blinking. "Holy mackerel," he gasps, "you're wearing your teeth, too!"

With a nod, half proud, half embarrassed, Webb turns and in great dignity leads Black Gold to the winner's circle out in the centerfield. As Black Gold plants his feet in the turf, the crowd eddies around him, watching with eyes and heart both. Together the old man and Jaydee accept the magnificent horseshoe of roses, the award of the fiftieth anniversary of the Run for the Roses. Gently, they settle the great floral piece about Black Gold's neck.

And now more roses, a great sheaf of them, are held up to Jaydee. One-handed, he takes and holds them awkwardly. "Roses are right for Black Gold," he laughs, "not for me!" His eyes sweep the crowd, searching for Mrs. Hoots. Quickly he dismounts, hands the reins to Webb, and pushes his way to her through the noisy, affectionate mob.

"For you," his words breathless, his eyes shining.

Afterward, Jaydee could never remember how he found his way through the surge of people and climbed the steps to the judges' stand. He did remember the famous Matt Winn standing beside the Governor. But he could never recall more than one sentence in all of the Governor's speech:

"We congratulate a little stallion who raced big."

Words flowed over him, around him, through him. Then Colonel Winn stepped forward, smiling, and placed the grand gleaming golden cup in the calm hands of Rosa Hoots. He turned next to Old Man Webb and gave a gold stop watch into his calloused hands. Then it was Jaydee's turn. With shy pride his hot sweaty hands grasped the Golden Jubilee spurs. His own! His, to put with the lucky horseshoe.

The people went wild. The air crackled with their applause and cheering. Over and over Colonel Winn and the Governor pleaded for silence. At last, into the trough between waves of clamor, came the slow, deep voice of Rosa Hoots over the loudspeaker. "My husband," she said, "he dreamed that U-see-it's colt would win this race and make right the evil that came to her. Black Gold and Mooney, they both did their best. I owe it to them," she finished.

The microphone went next to Hanley Webb. He cleared his throat nervously, but no sound came. Desperately he thrust the mouthpiece at Jaydee.

The boy wanted the chance. "Black Gold ran his own race!" he nearly shouted. "Any other horse would've lost. *The right horse won.*"

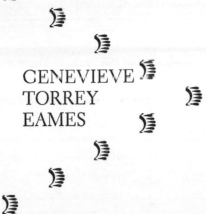

GENEVIEVE
TORREY
EAMES

The Good Luck Colt

The Ringer

(Martin Dennis just knew that his colt, Good Luck, would make a trotter. Now he and his younger brother Cal were excitedly entering him in the trotting races at the County Fair. Their father, an experienced driver in the bigger sulky races, was deferring judgment on Good Luck. But the real problem was that the colt could not be registered, because the pedigree of Lady Luck, his mother, was not established. Her onetime owner, Mr. Jackson, and neighbor Harper came to Martin's aid. They were aware that an unsavory character called Gus had shown a particular interest in Good Luck.)

MARTIN COULD HARDLY WAIT TO GET HOME. ONCE THERE, HE JUMPED out of the car; kissed his mother hastily; and hurried out to the pasture.

"What about lunch?" his mother called after him. "You must be starved."

"I'll be right back. Got to have a look at my horse!"

At the gate Martin stopped. He could see the yearlings at the far end of the pasture near the woods, but the bay colt was not in sight. He gave the shrill whistle that Good Luck had learned to know; but if the colt heard him, he didn't obey the signal.

Martin went back to the house. "Mom," he asked, "have you seen Good Luck today?"

"Why, no; I haven't been out there. What's the trouble?"

"Well, he wasn't in sight and he didn't come when I whistled."

"Did you see the yearlings?" Mr. Dennis asked.

"Yes, they were down near the woods."

"You can be pretty sure he isn't far away, then. If he got out of the pasture, they'd be with him."

"He must be in the woods," Martin said. "I'll go look for him after I've had something to eat."

"Maybe he's dead," Cal remarked cheerfully.

"That will do, Cal," Mrs. Dennis said. "Here, take another sandwich and don't say a word for fifteen minutes. Now that I think of it, Martin, I haven't seen any of the colts since Wednesday afternoon. It rained so hard all day they stayed in among the trees. John may have seen Good Luck, though."

"I'll go look, Mom. Excuse me, please." Martin finished his glass of milk, picked up a piece of cold chicken, and went back to the pasture. By the time he reached the gate he heard Cal's footsteps behind him.

"What do you want?" he asked, turning around.

Cal put one hand over his mouth and gestured elaborately with the other to show that the fifteen-minute period was not up.

"All right, come along if you want to," Martin said, leading the way through the gate.

The two yearlings looked up as the boys passed, but there was no sign of Good Luck. Martin stopped and listened when he reached the woods, but he could hear nothing except the gentle sighing of the wind in the treetops. He whistled shrilly several times but with no result.

"You go that way," he said to Cal. "When you reach the end of the pasture, turn to the right until you come to the wall along the lane. Then follow the wall to the barway. And if you find him, holler! Never mind the fifteen minutes; I'm sure it'll be over by that time, anyway."

He struck off in the opposite direction, listening for sounds, peering through the underbrush, half afraid that he might find the colt down somewhere with a broken leg—or maybe with the same sort of accident that had happened to Peter. When he came to the wall a new worry struck him. Maybe Good Luck had tried to get over the wall and got himself entangled in the barbwire that ran along the top. Martin knew how murderous loose wire could be.

But there was no colt and no loose wire anywhere along the wall, and he came to the barway just ahead of Cal. One end of the top bar that he had fixed so carefully a few days ago had been knocked down. Any ambitious horse could easily step over the low place.

"Well, I guess that's the answer," Martin said.

"Pretty stupid, if you ask me," Cal remarked.

"Who's stupid? I fixed that bar when I turned him in here."

"I mean it takes a pretty stupid horse to knock down a bar and go charging around the country by himself. Doesn't he know when he's well off?"

"If you know when you're well off . . ." Martin began. "Oh, well, skip it. Let's see if he left any tracks. Maybe we can tell which way he went."

There was no mistaking the tracks on the other side of the barway. They had been partly washed out by showers, but they led plainly down the middle of the lane.

"It looks as if he knew just where he was going," Martin said.

"Well, no wonder!" Cal exclaimed. "Look here." He pointed to the partial outline of a man's shoe at the side of the lane. A close examination showed more of the tracks, always at the left of the hoofprints.

"You're right," Martin said. "Somebody was leading him."

It was easy now to follow the trail to the end of the lane. There, hidden from the main road by a bend in the lane, were the telltale marks of a set of truck tires.

"Look," Martin said. "They just backed in here and parked the truck, and led Good Luck up the ramp as nice as you please."

"Horse thieves!" Cal almost shouted. "They can't get away with this; let's go get the sheriff."

"Pipe down a minute and let me think."

"But doesn't the sheriff always catch horse thieves? What are we waiting for?"

"Never mind that movie stuff. I've got to figure this out. We're going back to the house and you're not to say a word to anybody. Understand?"

"But, gee! How about the sheriff?"

"Can you keep a secret?"

"Sure; I've kept lots of secrets."

"Name one! Never mind; if you breathe a word until I tell you, I'll—I'll choke you with one of your own rabbits."

Cal looked properly impressed. "I promise," he said.

"All right. If you do what I say, maybe I'll let you do some detecting with me. You see, I think I know who stole Good Luck."

"Honest? Who is it?"

"Never mind; just come along with me."

By the time they reached the house Martin had decided there was no way of solving the problem without telling his parents. They were sure to ask if he had found the colt, and that would lead to explanations. Fortunately, however, Mr. Dennis had gone to the feed store to consult with John about business. They could do a lot before he came back. But how much should he tell his mother?

"Mom," he said before she had time to ask any questions, "Good Luck got out of the pasture. I'm going over to see Mr. Jackson about him. Come on, Cal."

He grabbed Cal by the hand and hurried him beyond the possibility of further questioning. He didn't trust his brother's ability to keep a secret, no matter what promises he might have made. They took a short cut to the farm next door and found Mr. Jackson sitting on the porch, smoking a pipe.

As briefly as possible Martin told Mr. Jackson the story of Good Luck's disappearance and the clues left in the lane. "What do you think, Mr. Jackson?" he ended.

"Same as you, I reckon. Can't think of only one person would be interested in stealing that particular colt. I thought the other day your gypsy friend was askin' more questions than was natural."

"And the other night, before we went to Goshen, there was somebody in the barn—somebody with a flashlight. I bet he was looking around the place to find out where we kept Good Luck."

"Yep. Worked out pretty good for him, too—you and your Dad goin' away for a couple of days and leaving the colt in the pasture, right handy to the lane. Well, what do you aim to do?"

"I say tell the sheriff," Cal offered. "He'll know what to do with horse thieves. Hang 'em, most likely."

"I thought maybe we could—you could— Would you drive us up there, Mr. Jackson? If G. Jones has Good Luck at his place, it won't take us long to find out; I'd know him anywhere."

"What does your Dad say about it?"

"That's it; he doesn't know—yet. He's at the store and I thought we'd have time to go see Mr. Jones before he gets back. I haven't told Dad anything about Mrs. Adams or Gypsy Gus or Lady Luck. I'd give a lot to get him as much interested in Good Luck as he was in Master Peter; but if there isn't any chance of tracing Lady Luck's pedigree, I'd rather not get his hopes up."

"I don't know as we ought to do anything without asking him."

"Oh, please! Can't we just go see if Good Luck is there? We can talk to Dad about it after we find out."

"Well, I guess it couldn't do any harm. But—well, say! How about picking up Clyde Harper on the way? He knows Gus; he'd be a big help to us. Hop into the bus, there, while I tell Mother where we're off to."

Clyde Harper had just arrived back from Goshen, but he grabbed his hat and climbed into the car when he heard Martin's story. When at last the ancient vehicle chugged to a stop at the end of the rough lane, they were disappointed to find the gypsy's place apparently deserted. The big red truck was gone, and with it Mr. G. Jones. The trailer house was shut tight.

Then a horse's head appeared over a stall door, and Martin was out of the car in a bound. "There he is; there he is!" he cried, running over the stony ground. "Hey, Lucky, old fellow, don't you know me?"

The colt pulled back, snorting, and he looked at Martin with suspicious eyes.

Martin stared back. It wasn't Good Luck, after all. It looked like him; but now that Martin could study him, he saw that it was not the same horse at all. On closer examination the white stripe that wandered crookedly down his face was wider; his ears were larger; and he had only one white foot, whereas Good Luck had two. Besides, Martin knew that Good Luck would never have acted like that.

"He must be his twin brother," Cal said.

"Silly! Good Luck didn't have a twin brother. He's the only colt Lady Luck ever had."

"Well, it sure is strange. Are you *sure* that isn't Good Luck? You haven't seen him for several days; maybe you've forgotten what he looks like."

Martin didn't bother to answer. He looked at Mr. Harper, who had climbed out more slowly and had picked his way across to the stable followed by Mr. Jackson. "What's the answer, Mr. Harper? I can't figure it out. I never saw this horse before, but he does look an awful lot like Good Luck."

Mr. Harper slowly filled his pipe, leaning against the side of the stable and studying the strange colt.

"Shenanigans!" he exclaimed briefly after a couple of puffs.

Martin waited.

"Ever hear of a ringer?"

"Not that I know of."

"Well, it looks to me like our friend Gus had a horse here that didn't have much speed. Then didn't you tell me he tried out your colt on this track of his?"

"Yes, and after that he wanted to buy him."

"I thought so. He's probably raced his colt a few times—enough so everybody knows he's not much good. Who'd want to bet on a horse like that?"

"Nobody." Suddenly Martin remembered the race program he had found, and the horse, Fighting Fury, that had done so poorly.

"Exactly. That'd make him a long shot in the betting—say, twenty to one."

"What does that mean?" Cal wanted to know.

"It means the chances of his winning are so poor that, if he did happen to come in first, anybody who had bet on him would get twenty dollars for each dollar he bet."

"Boy! That's a good way to get rich," Cal said.

"Not much!" Martin replied. "It's a good way to lose your shirt. Dad's told me about lots of people who went broke betting on horse races—especially long shots."

"Well," Mr. Harper continued, "suppose someday our friend shows up with this horse that everybody knows can't win against a field of crippled turtles. He quietly bets all the money he can dig up, and then, for once, the horse wins."

"But how—oh, I get it! You mean it's not really that horse, but one that looks like him but is really much faster."

"Exactly. A ringer."

"But that's cheating!"

"Sure, it's cheating. But haven't we heard some pretty shady things about this Brown-Jones character in the past? Seems like he might be just the fellow to try to get away with something like that."

"But Dad always said—I mean I didn't think things like that could happen any more. Hasn't the Trotting Association made it almost impossible to put over any tricks?"

"Yes, they've done a good job of cleaning things up. But you'll find Gypsy Gus only shows up at some of the small-town places, and he skips around so he's hard to pin down. He's already changed his name a couple of times, as you know."

"It'll be tough for him if he's found out," Martin said. "I'm surprised he'd take the risk. Even if he cleans up on the race, he's almost sure to be caught with a stolen horse."

"Well, he did try pretty hard to buy him. And I suppose he had a chance that looked so good to him he couldn't resist the temptation. He probably counted on your staying at Goshen another day. Anyway, it wouldn't surprise me if you found your colt back in the pasture by tomorrow night," said Mr. Harper.

"Hey!" Martin cried suddenly. "Here we stand and talk; and Good Luck's off somewhere with this crook, getting involved in all his crookedness! Let's get going— That is, will you take us, Mr. Jackson?"

"It's all right with me," Mr. Jackson said. "But where do we go?"

Martin looked hopefully at Clyde Harper. "What about it?" he asked.

Mr. Harper looked thoughtful. "I believe there's some racing over to Ezra-ville this week. It's the only place around these parts where they'd be holding races the week of the Hambletonian. It's a small place; there used to be a fair held there every year, but that was given up long ago. There's a bunch of small-time trotting men have taken over the track and they run off races all through the summer."

"Is it far?" Martin asked.

"About twenty-five miles from here, I'd say, over the back roads."

"Will you take us, Mr. Jackson, *please?* I know it's a lot to ask, but think of Lady Luck's son trotting in crooked races!"

The old man smiled. "It wouldn't do at all, would it? Come on, then. Where's Cal?"

They found Cal snooping among the odds and ends in the shed where Gus kept his feed and his sulky. "Lookit!" he said, holding up two small pails. "Look what he had hidden behind some baled hay." The pails contained paint, black and white.

"That's how he fixed up your colt to look like his," Clyde Harper said. He examined the paint carefully. "He must be an expert. You'll notice the black isn't jet black, like stove polish. It has a tinge of brown in it—just enough to match the black on the legs of a bay horse. And the white isn't dead white. We'll just take this stuff along for evidence."

"Hadn't we ought to get the sheriff?" Cal asked.

"We won't need him," Mr. Harper said. "If we find the man we're looking for, and if he has your colt, any of the track officials can take charge of him."

"Climb in, everybody," said Mr. Jackson, starting the motor.

"Wahoo!" cried Cal. "Watch out, horse thieves; here comes the posse!"

Race with Disgrace

Martin thought the ride would never end. He felt sure they would be too late. His grand, beautiful, honest colt would have run his first race and helped to win a lot of dishonest money for a tricky, cheating horse thief. It was already mid-afternoon and, by the time Mr. Jackson's old car struggled over the hills to Ezraville, most of the day's racing would be over—supposing, of course, that Gus had taken Good Luck to Ezraville. And if not, where was he?

The sun had dropped considerably toward the horizon by the time they caught sight of the paintless grandstand and buildings of Ezraville's trotting park. In spite of the smallness of the place a lot of people had been drawn to the racing, and cars were parked along the road and in the parking field.

Mr. Jackson drove straight to the stables, and the boys hopped out almost before the car braked to a stop. There seemed to be a lot of excitement among the groups of people standing about, and quite a crowd had gathered in front of one of the stables. Martin caught phrases that would have meant little to him at any other time—"that Fury horse," "long shot," "just a fluke; he'll never do it again."

The men turned toward the track officials' office; but Martin pushed his way through the people, heading for the spot where the crowd was thickest. A man stood with his back to Martin, hitching a horse into a sulky. One glimpse of those shoulders and the straight black hair under the racing cap told him the man was Gus Brown, or G. Jones, or Gypsy Gus—the name didn't matter.

The colt tossed his head and Martin saw the crooked blaze, slightly wider than Good Luck's—widened, he was sure, by the clever use of a little white paint. Martin knew, too, that one hind foot would have been disguised with black paint. No doubt of it, his Good Luck had been changed into a "dead ringer" for the horse that had been left behind in the gypsy's stable. But the ears were Good Luck's, and the rump that was unmistakably higher than his withers.

Martin had not waited for the men to come with him and now, blazing with indignation, he forced his way between staring faces and bodies that seemed to melt away as he approached. The way he felt, he was sure he would have bowled over anyone who got in his way. Unnoticed, Cal followed in his wake like a rowboat towed behind a launch. This was the biggest excitement since Christmas and he wasn't going to miss any of it.

Martin put his hand on the colt's neck and Good Luck sniffed his arm and then gave his sleeve a playful nip. "Hey, you!" Martin said, not stopping to choose his words. "What do you think you're doing with my colt?"

The man looked up. His face was paler than Martin remembered it, and there was a momentary expression of panic in his eyes. Then, seeing only a couple of boys, he appeared to do some quick thinking; and his first words were friendly, low-toned, and confidential. "Just a minute," he said. "Don't get excited. I've got some good news for you. Come over here where we can talk." He handed the reins to a boy who had been helping him, and led the way into an empty stall. Martin had expected anger, denials, a fight—anything but this attitude of conciliation.

"Listen," said Gus. "This is for your own good. That colt's got speed. You know it and I know it, but these suckers around here haven't found it out. He's already won the first heat of the race and I was holding him back most of the way. In the second heat I let another horse win, just to make it look good. Now he can take the third heat on three legs and we stand to make three thousand bucks. Just keep your trap shut and in five minutes you'll pick up fifteen hundred dollars like taking candy from a baby."

Martin gasped. He was too astounded to speak and the gypsy misunderstood his silence. "Not only that," he went on. "You'll get your colt back tonight and nobody the wiser. I'll clean him up good and put him back in the pasture." Then, as Martin still seemed to hesitate, he added the final piece of bait. "Another thing; I can fix you up with papers for the colt's dam. I owned her sire and I owned her. I sold her to old man Blake as a filly. Once you get her registered, you can get papers on your colt and you've got a horse that'll be worth real money."

For a fleeting second Martin had visions of Good Luck, with a properly certified pedigree, taking his place as a great track winner and sire of winners; racing next season on the Grand Circuit; making up to Martin's Dad for the loss of Master Peter. All the things he'd longed for—just for keeping his "trap shut." Then the vision faded.

"Boy, that's a lot of money!" Cal was saying at his elbow, but Martin hardly heard him.

"Why, you—you—" he stammered. "I wouldn't let my colt get mixed up in anything crooked like that!"

"He'd never be connected with it. You'd bring him out later under his own name. Who's ever going to know?"

"I'd know. I'd like to—to—" Martin's voice failed him as he thought what he'd like to do to the man who had planned to use Good Luck for such a dishonest purpose.

"I told you we should have got the sheriff," Cal said.

"Look," said Gus, trying to conceal his impatience. "You got a good offer and you don't have to do a thing. Like finding money in the street—and a pedigree for your colt, to boot. Come on—what do you say? It's almost time for the third heat."

"How do I know the pedigree wouldn't be faked?" Martin asked.

"I can prove it. Charlie Blake's daughter will back me up. For one thing, the mare's sire had that same crooked blaze. Some of his colts had it—not many, but once in a while it came out in the next generation. Like your colt, here, and my Fury horse."

A light dawned in Martin's mind. The crooked stripe on Good Luck's face was the clue to a lot of the gypsy's strange behavior.

"No," he said firmly. "Nothing doing. I'm going to take my colt right home with me—just as soon as I can find a man with a truck to haul him for me."

Quick as a panther, the gypsy lunged at Martin. He grasped one wrist with a grip like steel, clamped the other hand over the boy's mouth, and pushed him back against the wall. Martin struck out desperately with his free hand, but the man twisted the other arm behind his back and the pain left him helpless. He let himself go limp, hoping to slip out of the man's clutches long enough to call for help. Why—oh, why—hadn't he had sense enough to wait for the two men to come with him, before tackling Gypsy Gus?

Then half a dozen dark forms loomed in the doorway and Martin heard a strange voice say, "That's enough, Jones. We want to see you."

Even the most pestiferous younger brother can have his good moments, Martin realized, wiping the taste of G. Jones' dirty hand from his lips. Cal had darted for help the moment Gus attacked Martin, and he had met Mr. Jackson and Mr. Harper, with several of the track officials, looking for Martin in the crowd.

Martin was glad to leave Mr. Brown-Jones to the track management and to ride home with Clyde Harper in the truck that was soon hired to take Good Luck back to the Dennis stable. Cal would go with Mr. Jackson in his car.

"It's too bad about Gus," Mr. Harper said. "He's a born horseman and there isn't a better driver anywhere. He could have had as good a reputation and as much respect as Ben White or Sep Palin or any driver in the business, but he was always just a little too smart to play it straight."

"What will they do to him?"

"This will put him off the track for good. He's been in trouble before; he's been warned and he's been suspended, but now he's finished."

"What will they do about the race Good Luck was in?"

"I didn't wait to find out. They'll probably disqualify the Jones entry and declare the second-place horse the winner. Or they could run the race over tomorrow."

"Will Gypsy Gus go to jail?"

"I don't know what the Racing Commission will do about him; but he'll certainly go to jail for horse stealing, if your Dad brings charges against him."

Martin thought this over. He was still indignant at the way he had been treated, and most of all at Good Luck's being involved in a crooked, messy scheme to cheat the public. And yet he couldn't help feeling a little sorry for a man who cared as much about horses as Gypsy Gus did. It seemed a shame that men who made their living around horses couldn't always be as honest as their animals.

For the present, Martin could hardly feel glad about discovering proof of Good Luck's pedigree. It depended on the word of a dishonest man; maybe the Trotting Register Association wouldn't accept it; maybe Good Luck himself would be barred from racing because of the incident at Ezraville this afternoon.

It was long past suppertime when the truck rolled in the Dennis drive and stopped by the barn. Martin almost fell out of the cab in his eagerness to tell his parents all about the afternoon's adventure. They had heard the truck approaching and were waiting at the barn by the time it drove in. Mr. Jackson's car pulled up behind the truck a few seconds later, and Cal was almost bursting with his excited version of the story.

"Let's get the colt unloaded first," Mr. Harper said. "The man wants to get his truck back to Ezraville tonight."

They let down the tailgate and Martin led Good Luck down the ramp and into his stall. The colt sniffed the straw as if he were glad to get home. While Martin was getting hay and oats and a pail of water, his father paid the driver and the truck rumbled away.

"Now," Mr. Dennis said, "let's hear all about it."

"Wait a minute before you begin," Mrs. Dennis interrupted. "I'm sure everybody's hungry, and I have supper keeping hot on the stove. Come on in, and you can eat and talk at the same time."

"You won't need me," Mr. Jackson said. "I'll go along home before Mother gets to worrying. Besides, I'm not so young as I was; this tearing around the country is almost too much for me."

"Thanks for everything, Mr. Jackson," Martin said. "If it hadn't been for you, there's no telling what might have happened. One thing sure, Good Luck wouldn't be in his stall right this minute."

"That's all right, Martin; I've got a sort of family interest in that colt, you know."

Soon they were all seated around the table, heartily eating Mrs. Dennis' famous beef stew and a big bowl of salad, with plenty of bread and butter and milk to fill in the crevices. Martin thought he had never been so hungry and food had never tasted so good.

"All right," Mr. Dennis said, "let's have it. All I know is that Mrs. Jackson told us her husband had taken the boys to go look for the colt. What's all this about horse thieves and gypsies and ringers and what not? I must admit I'm a bit confused."

"I told them in the very beginning we should have got the sheriff," Cal said.

"Cal," his mother said, "don't talk with your mouth full. Better yet, you eat—and let the others tell the story. I think we'll understand it better that way."

Martin hardly knew where to begin. "You remember my asking you about Gus Brown. Well, I wanted to see if I could trace Good Luck's pedigree so he could be registered; and I found that Gus Brown had owned Lady Luck and sold her when she was a filly. So I went to his place to find out if she was standard bred." He went on to tell about the man's changed name and his mysterious interest in Good Luck, then of the inquisitive stranger's visit to Mr. Jackson.

"It seemed to add up to something, but I didn't know what. And when Good Luck's trail led to tire tracks in the lane this afternoon, I was sure Gus was at the bottom of it."

He told about enlisting the aid of Mr. Jackson and picking up Clyde Harper on the way. "And it was a good thing, too, because we sure needed all the help we could get before the day was over."

Cal opened his mouth to say something about the sheriff, but thought better of it and closed it on a large bite of bread and butter.

"Why didn't you call me?" Mr. Dennis asked.

Martin hesitated uncomfortably. "Well, you see, we didn't have any time to lose, for one thing. Besides, I wanted to be sure about Good Luck before I told you anything. Well, when we got to the gypsy's place, he wasn't there —only this horse in a stall, looking so much like Good Luck I thought at first that's who it was. Then we saw he wasn't exactly like Good Luck. His blaze was different and he had only one white foot. And, of course, he didn't act like Good Luck. So then Mr. Jackson and Mr. Harper guessed that Gus was using my colt as a ringer, and we took a chance on going to Ezraville because that's the only place around here where there's any racing this week. And—and there he was!"

"Boy! Some fight!" Cal exclaimed.

When Mr. Dennis had heard the rest of the tale, he shook his head in amazement. "It's fantastic," he said. "Like something out of a book or a movie. I wouldn't have believed things like that could happen today. I know lots of shady tricks went on in the old days; that's probably how Gus got started in his career, but for years now the Trotting Association and the State Racing Commission have kept such a strict watch that harness racing is one of the straightest sports there is."

"Dad," Martin asked, "what will this do to Good Luck? I mean will he be disqualified from racing, or—or anything? Will I be allowed to register him?"

Mr. Dennis looked at Clyde Harper. "What do you think?"

"I don't know," Mr. Harper answered. "It shouldn't make any difference. Of course there will be a big investigation into Gus Brown's entire history and everything he was connected with; but I can't see that anything can be held against Martin and you, or the colt either—especially since we got there in time to stop the colt from running in the last heat of the race. Gus didn't actually collect any of that crooked money."

"I hope so," Mr. Dennis said. "I'd hate to be mixed up in that sort of thing, or have it affect any of my family."

"I think it will work out all right," Mr. Harper answered. "Nobody can question your reputation, and Jim Jackson and I can testify that the horse was stolen and that Martin didn't know anything about it."

"Well, I certainly appreciate all that you and Jim did today. I'd hate to think of Martin tangling with that tough customer by himself."

"I was with him," Cal informed his father. "He was safe enough." He looked surprised when everybody laughed.

"You certainly were," Mr. Dennis said, "and you did exactly right when you went for help. I'm proud of you both."

Martin drew a deep breath. "If it's all right—I mean with the Trotting Association—you will let me race him, won't you, Dad? At the County Fair, like you said? I want to show you what he can do."

"One thing at a time, Martin. Let's get this mess straightened out. Then— well, a promise is a promise, isn't it?"

Martin flashed a smile at his father and slipped out for a little private talk with Good Luck.

The Good Luck Colt

One week more before the County Fair. One week to complete Good Luck's training for his first race under his own name; the race that was going to bring him out as the honest horse he was, trotting to win if he could—doing his best in every heat. The colt was coming along well, and Mr. Dennis was giving Martin all the help and advice he could. Martin felt he was really interested, and he took it as a hopeful sign that for the present, at least, nothing more was said about the sale of the mares and yearlings. His father had not begun training the colts, but neither had he done anything about advertising or preparing them for sale.

Martin was still bothered by one big uncertainty. No word had been received from the Trotting Register Association with regard to papers for Lady Luck. He and his father had been cleared of all complicity in the Ezraville affair, and Martin was free to race his colt if he wished; but as long as Lady Luck's breeding was not established, Good Luck would have to be entered as "nonstandard." He tried not to worry about it, and to convince himself it was enough to have this one opportunity to show what the colt could do.

Now Martin and his father were watching the blacksmith putting a new set of shoes on Good Luck. After consultation between Mr. Dennis and Clyde Harper, it had been decided to use a slightly heavier shoe in front.

"I believe it will clip a second or two off his time," Mr. Dennis said. "With such long hind legs, he needs a good stride in front to keep out of his own way."

The smith clinched the nails and rasped down the rough ends. "There," he said, putting down the last foot and studying it critically, "if he doesn't go right, let me know. If he needs anything more, a couple of small toe weights ought to do it."

"When Dad superintends his shoeing, he really rates," Martin thought, glad that at last Good Luck was getting the recognition he deserved as a trotter.

He tried the colt again on the track, while his father held the watch. The expression on his father's face after a trial half mile was enough to tell him they had done well. "He's coming on, son. How would you like to take him up to the fair grounds a few days before opening day, so you can get him used to the half-mile track?"

"Dad! Do you mean stay there with him—could I, really?"

"I don't know why not. You can take a cot along and sleep right there in a stall, if you want to. Clyde Harper will be there with Florita, and some of the other trainers are already there with their horses."

This was better than Martin could have hoped. "Are you going to drive Florita?"

"If Clyde wants me to, but I'm trying to persuade him to drive her himself. He can do it perfectly well, and he'd get a lot more fun out of it."

When his father's truck rolled into the fair grounds a few days later, the place was dead and deserted—not much like the gay, noisy scene it became during Fair Week. The only sign of activity was around the stables, where several trotters had been in training for some weeks and where others, like Good Luck, had just arrived to work out on the track in advance of the races.

Clyde Harper's Florita had the stall next to Good Luck's, and Clyde came to meet the truck and help them unload.

"Well," Clyde said as Martin led Good Luck into his stall, "now you're an owner and driver, I guess I'll have to look somewhere else for a stable boy."

"Oh, I can help you part of the time, Mr. Harper. But I'll be pretty busy, myself. You see, I've got to be my own stable boy."

Mr. Dennis helped Martin hang up the harness, blankets, and other equipment on the wall outside Good Luck's stall, while Clyde Harper wheeled the sulky under the overhanging roof. Then they set up Martin's cot in the empty stall next to Florita's which he was to share with Mr. Harper as a bedroom.

"This is swell," Martin said, looking around at the improvised washstand made out of orange crates and at the clothes hooks on the wall. "I've always wanted to sleep in a stable, but at home Mom won't let me."

"No," his father answered, "but I remember when you and your horse slept in the kitchen."

Martin laughed. "That was a long time ago, wasn't it? What a night! About three o'clock in the morning I was sure he was going to die before daylight."

"And here he is."

"Here he is, for sure. Dad, will you see that Mr. Jackson gets here for the race? I meant to speak to him about it, but I forgot. In a way, Good Luck belongs to him too."

"Don't worry; he wouldn't miss it for a Sunday suit."

Mr. Dennis watched Martin jog the colt a couple of times around the track, and then timed him in a fast half mile. He was smiling when Martin came back to the gate.

"He'll do all right," he said. "After training on our little track this will seem like the wide-open spaces to him, and he can really let himself out. Well, if you don't need me any more, I'll go on back. See you in the morning."

"What about Florita, Dad?"

"Don't say a word. That's why I'm not hanging around. After Clyde works her for a few days on this track, I'm hoping he'll decide to drive her himself. If he doesn't, I'll be around."

That evening Martin ate supper with Mr. Harper and some of the other drivers at a little hamburger stand that had been opened on the grounds. Later a few of the men went to see a movie; but the others sat around on folding camp chairs, swapping horse stories and talking about prospects for the coming races. Now that he was an owner and driver, Martin felt that he "belonged." He didn't have much to add to the conversation, but he listened to the talk with eager ears. At last his head began to nod and he got up to take a last look at Good Luck before going to bed.

"I'll turn in, too," Mr. Harper said, and went to draw a pail of water for Florita.

Lying on his cot a little later, with his army blankets pulled up under his chin, Martin thought back over all the events of the past few weeks. So much had happened in such a short time that it was hard to sort them out.

"Are you asleep, Mr. Harper?" he asked softly.

"Not yet."

"It's pretty nice, being here. I still can't believe it, though."

"We had a pretty close call, there at Ezraville, didn't we?"

"Yes. Do you know, I almost hope they won't send Gus to jail. I'm not mad at him now and I can't help wondering what will become of him if he has to give up horses."

"A few months in jail might do him a lot of good. After that I think you'll still find him around trotting stables somewhere. Even if he can't race, he's such a good horseman he'll be able to get a job breaking colts or caring for brood mares."

"I hope so. Then he wouldn't be tempted to pull any more dishonest tricks. You do think Mr. Jackson can get Lady Luck's papers, don't you?"

"I wish I knew. Better go to sleep now and stop worrying about it."

All the horsemen turned out early in the morning, and the sun was just coming up when Mr. Harper and Martin watered and fed their horses. After the horses were taken care of, the men had bacon and eggs at the lunch stand and went back to the routine of cleaning stables, grooming horses, and hitching up for the morning workout.

Martin was brushing Good Luck when a shadow fell across the straw underfoot, and he looked up to see his father in the doorway.

"Your mother was afraid you wouldn't be eating properly," Mr. Dennis said, "so she sent you up a little snack. Don't open it now, but I peeked in the basket and her idea of a snack appears to be some cold fried chicken, about a dozen sandwiches, and an apple pie. There's plenty to share with your roommate."

"That's great. I'm hungry already."

"I'll put it in your living room. And when you get around to it, there's another little package from your Mom and me. Sort of an advance birthday present, as it were."

Martin dropped the brush and was out of the stall in a flash. "A birthday present! Gee! Let's see it. But why— My birthday's over a week off."

"I know, but we thought this would be useful now."

Martin tore off the string and opened the box. "Racing silks!" he exclaimed, taking out the gleaming crimson jacket with white sleeves. "But—but your colors are red and black."

"We thought you'd like your own colors for your own horse. We couldn't ask you about it because we wanted it to be a surprise, so we took a chance on red and white. Similar, in a way, but different. I hope they're the right size."

"Boy, that's really something! The best present I ever had. Thanks a lot, Dad. Say, how do I look?" He put on the matching cap and held the silks up against his chest; then, because his throat felt a little queer, he ducked into the stall he had slept in and took a look at himself in the little shaving mirror Mr. Harper had hung on the wall. His own horse and his own colors—it was almost too much. He hung the silks carefully on a hook and went back to brushing Good Luck so vigorously that the colt gave him a warning nip on the shoulder.

The night before the race Martin found it hard to go to sleep. His hands and feet felt cold and he had a nervous tension in the pit of his stomach. Suppose something went wrong; suppose he failed miserably as a driver; suppose he got his wheels tangled with another sulky. He was so *green*. How could he remember all the good advice his father and other drivers had given him? "Don't try to set the pace; don't go all out at first; save something for the stretch; don't let yourself get pocketed." And on and on and on.

Good Luck had been doing well in the workouts—almost too well. The sense of competition with other horses that he had acquired here at the track had made him almost too ambitious. Martin wondered if he would be able to keep him in hand; rate him as he had been taught to do.

Out of the darkness came Clyde Harper's voice from the other cot. "I was just thinking, Martin. I've been trying to get your Dad to drive Florita for me, but I've changed my mind. I'll tell you why. I just said to myself, 'Clyde Harper, you old fool, if that Martin Dennis can drive his own horse—and him not yet fifteen—you can do it, too.' So that's that."

"Thanks, Mr. Harper. That means a lot—a lot more than you know." And in five minutes Martin was sound asleep.

Martin felt fairly calm in the morning and went about his work as usual. By acting as if it were like any other morning he was able to eat a good breakfast and groom and harness Good Luck without trembling all over. The colt did his three miles of exercise and one fairly fast mile, with a real burst of speed in the last quarter. As Martin brought him back to the stable he heard one of the rail birds remark, "That Good Luck colt is one to watch. I like the way he goes. In another year it'll take a good one to beat him."

Everything was perfect—too perfect, perhaps. Martin's jitters returned and by lunchtime he was unable to eat. His mother and father came to wish him luck and to tell him they would be in the grandstand. "Unless you want me to help you?" his father asked.

"No thanks, Dad. Mr. Harper's going to help me. He doesn't race until tomorrow. I guess I'd feel a little better if you didn't stick around—at least, until after the first heat. Maybe I'm superstitious, or something. You don't mind, do you?"

"Of course not; I'd feel the same way myself."

Cal had just come down along the row of stalls. "I've looked at every colt in your race," he stated, "and Good Luck can beat 'em all. But you look terrible. You aren't going to die, are you?"

"Come on, Cal," said his mother. "You haven't the sense of a dim-witted duck. Good luck, Martin; happy racing! We'll be rooting for you."

"Oh, Dad!" Martin called as they started away. "Any word from the Registration Association?"

"No; not a thing."

Good Luck's race, a local two-year-old trot, was the first on the program. Martin would have felt better if he could have seen one or two other races run off ahead of him. "But maybe it's a good thing, after all," he thought. "I won't have so much time to get scared."

"Run along, boy, and get into your silks," Clyde Harper said as he helped with the final hitching-up. "Make yourself look as good as your horse; I'll hold him until you get back."

Martin sloshed cold water over his hot face and washed his grimy hands at the crude washstand. He slicked down his hair and put on the jacket and cap. A glance in the mirror showed an anxious-looking face, a little pale; but he was sure he did not, as Cal said, "look terrible."

The parade to the post began badly. Martin had drawn the number-three position, but when they went out on the track Good Luck didn't want to wait for his turn and dashed ahead into the second place behind the lead pony and had to be called back. It was a small thing, but embarrassing to his driver.

Then one of the colts caused trouble in the scoring, and they had to be called back half a dozen times before they got off to a good start. By that time Good Luck's usually good temperament was upset. He was wild with impatience, and when they finally heard the word "Go!" he was fighting to get the lead from the horse next to him. Martin tried to hold him back; but when the big black colt edged alongside, Good Luck, who had almost never been known to break, did so now. He was galloping wildly and, because he was not used to being pulled back into stride, Martin had to strive desperately to keep him from running away. "Steady there, Lucky. Steady, old fellow," he repeated, and Good Luck, heeding the familiar voice rather than the reins, at last swung back into a trot.

He was hopelessly distanced by this time. "There goes the race," Martin thought; but he held the colt steady and urged him on, determined to close as much of the gap as possible. At the end of the first lap he had passed the fourth horse. The leaders, the big black and a chestnut, were battling it out for first. There was no chance of overtaking them; but Good Luck nosed up toward the filly that was running third, and passed her on the outside at the finish line.

Martin hoped he wouldn't see any of his family between heats. He had done everything wrong, he knew, and now the black had only to take the next heat and the race would be over. "But we aren't licked yet," he said aloud to Good Luck as he drove back to the gate. "Remember Bi Shively. But you weren't at the Hambletonian, so how can you remember? And you aren't Sharp Note, either," he added, smiling to himself.

Jim Jackson met them at the gate and walked with him to the stable. "A tough break," he said, "and you'd better laugh because that's a joke. I've got a message from your Dad. He said you handled the situation just right, and he's not coming down to talk to you because you'll know exactly what to do in the next heat without any advice from him."

Martin's spirits rose several notches.

"And I've got some more news for you. Came in the morning's mail. Look! Lady Luck's pedigree, all signed, sealed, and delivered."

Martin took a long look. He had never seen a document that had meant so much to him. It was undoubtedly the most beautiful and impressive piece of paper in the world. "There, now," he said, patting Good Luck's sweaty neck. "I always said you had the right ancestors. You're bound to win this race—honor bound, for home and country and mother."

The second heat started better. Good Luck was easier to handle and he matched the big black, stride for stride, around the track. Martin held the colt's nose close to the other's sulky wheel, not attempting to pull ahead. Over his shoulder he caught a glimpse of the chestnut crowding him at the turn, but after the first half mile the chestnut dropped back and he knew he had only the black to beat. Martin's heart was singing in time with Good Luck's flying feet. Win or lose, this was a real horse he was handling!

They came to the stretch—the critical moment when Good Luck must show what was in him. "Come on, Lucky—now!" Martin yelled. Could he do it? Did he have that extra spurt he would need to pass the black? The little bay's nose inched past the other's flank, reached his shoulder, hung there a moment—crept a little farther, and then—the black broke badly and Good Luck flashed across the finish line, an easy winner.

When it was over, Martin felt almost too weak and shaky to drive back to the stable. At the gate Clyde Harper, grinning, took the colt by the bridle and Martin slumped down in the seat. He was afraid to dismount from the sulky for fear his legs wouldn't hold him. It would look pretty silly to have his knees collapse right there in front of everybody.

Then he was at the stable and Clyde was helping him unhitch and his father was patting him on the shoulder and Cal was begging for the privilege of leading Good Luck around the tow ring.

"Good work, Martin," his father said. "You drove that heat like a veteran. Did you see the time for the mile?"

"No," Martin said in a weak voice. "I didn't see anything; I didn't look."

"Two eleven and two-fifths. A mighty good mark for this track, especially with a green colt."

"Honest, Dad? Do you think he can do it again? I'm not sure he would have won if it hadn't been for the black breaking at the end. Gee, I almost wish he hadn't made it; then it would be all over and I wouldn't have to worry about the next heat."

"Nonsense. Of course you can do it again. The black may beat you, but he'll know he's been in a race. The main thing is that Good Luck has it in him to develop into a fast trotter. All he needs is experience and training."

Martin stared. "I must be dreaming," he thought. "This was to be Good Luck's one and only race, and Dad talks as if he had a long career ahead of him." He finished sponging Good Luck's legs and turned him over to Cal. "Dad," he said as a sudden thought struck him, "will you drive this next heat for me? It's going to be close, and I don't feel sure of myself."

Mr. Dennis laughed. "Not a chance," he said. "He's your horse and you're stuck with him. I'm going to be right up there in the grandstand having the time of my life."

Martin walked about restlessly until it was time for the third and deciding heat of his race. He was glad, in a way, that his father had refused to drive for him. Still it would have been a load off his mind if he could have put the reins and the responsibility into his father's capable hands. He wondered if Bion Shively had felt this way between heats of the Hambletonian. Probably not, after all his years of driving.

Out on the track, at last, he felt a little steadier. Good Luck, having won the preceding heat, was now the pole horse. This meant that he had the favored spot next to the rail; but it involved the problem of keeping the lead, or letting the black get ahead and possibly cutting in ahead of him. He wished he had asked his father what to do.

He hadn't much time to think about it before they were off, with the black striking out at once for the lead. Martin urged Good Luck just enough so the black couldn't cut in front of him. The other horse's driver was trying hard for the rail; but Martin knew he was afraid of pushing the colt so far that he would break, as he had done in the second heat. Martin felt pretty sure Good Luck would keep steady, so long as he didn't get too excited.

They passed the quarter pole, the three-eighth, the half, without any change in their positions—the black straining to get out in front, and the bay's head nodding at his flank. "If he can just keep it up!" Martin thought. "If he can just put on a little more when I ask for it!"

On the back stretch the black colt's driver decided to go all out to get the rail before the last turn. Martin let him go by and groaned to see him take the inside a length ahead of him. He held Good Luck close to the rail as they rounded the turn and then steered him a little wide to the outside of the leading sulky. "Now—now—now!" he said as they came into the stretch. "Yeah, Lucky!"

A sudden electric message seemed to flash along the lines to the colt. He laid back his ears and appeared to flatten against the ground, as if now for the first time he was trotting in earnest. The black colt's driver was using his whip, but his horse had no more speed to give. Good Luck crept up on him, held even, and pulled ahead—to win by a neck as they crossed the line.

At the gate some of the other horsemen were waiting to congratulate Martin on his win. There were friendly smiles and handshakes, and welcoming pats for Good Luck. "Gangway for the Good Luck colt," somebody called. Then, "Hey, Martin, don't spend all that money in one place."

At the stable Cal was turning cartwheels to show his feelings, but it was his father's pleased smile that meant the most to Martin.

"How does it feel to drive a winner?" his father asked.

"Oh, Dad!" was all Martin could say as he swung down from the sulky.

Then his mother came through the crowd and hugged him, and Mr. Jackson patted him and the colt, and everybody talked and laughed at once. Clyde Harper had the colt unharnessed before Martin came to himself and started to help.

"Go get yourself out of that fancy rigging, boy," Clyde said. "You've got to save those silks for your next race."

Martin hung up the jacket and cap and came back in his working clothes. "Dad," he said, "it wasn't the Hambletonian, but I did win two hundred dollars. Now I can pay for the sulky."

"It won't take that much. You'd better keep some of it for entry fees on the Grand Circuit next year."

"The Grand Circuit! Honest, Dad?"

"You've got a real trotter there, Martin."

"I knew that, but—the Grand Circuit! Will you drive him for me, Dad? A colt like that deserves the best."

"Well, I don't know. I've got a couple of likely prospects of my own I've got to start training tomorrow. What do you say we go together?"

Martin picked up a sponge and went to work, whistling.

VI

HORSES TO KNOW

Famous breeds and careers

IRENE
SMITH

Ancestors and Modern Relatives
in the Family of Horses

MEN AND THEIR HORSES HAVE COME ALONG TOGETHER THROUGH CENTURIES of slow change, since that dimly distant day when a primitive human discovered that the fleet-flooted animal could be useful to him. The tamed horse has remained man's strong and faithful partner and, until the early years of this century, his necessity for travel and for everyday work. Times changed in the western world when modern engines were invented. These enabled machines to take over most of what had been the horses' work. Horses themselves have not changed, and are still ready to serve when called upon, but most of the demands made upon them nowadays come from the realm of sports. People own these beautiful animals for pleasure, and horsemanship with all its lively attraction, from trail riding to the racetrack, grows more and more popular. Millions attend horse shows, horse races, rodeos, and whenever possible, ride for sheer enjoyment. The age-old bonds of love and loyalty between horses and masters, or mistresses, remain steadfast, deeply rooted in generations of history.

Longer ago than any date can reveal, horses learned their first duty, to go with their owners to war. The ancient Assyrians and Egyptians rode their war chariots, and in later times warriors fought on horseback, a custom established with notable success by Alexander the Great. Mankind's endless quarrels have caused armies of horses, obedient as soldiers to the command, to be strewn on countless battlefields. The helpless animals faced spears and arrows, and

141

in later periods cannon, shrapnel, and machine guns. All these weapons meant terror and pitiless death.

The ancient Greeks' chariot races were among the first sports in which horses had to perform. Even the Greek gods were pictured riding horses and driving swift chariots across the heavens. Four and six abreast the Roman horses galloped wildly around the Circus Maximus, in chariot races that thrilled the crowds with their danger and fury.

When the Huns invaded Europe they came on horseback, bringing the small eastern horses into western civilization. During the Middle Ages Moslems on their fine Arabian steeds reached Spain, and Spanish horses acquired new traits. Through breeding, the strength and character of Arabian horses improved the European strains. Knights in the age of chivalry decked their chargers with rich trappings, as became their rank. These horses were powerfully built, to carry the armor which they and their riders wore in combat. They became the ancestors of our draft horses. Crusaders returning from the Holy Land brought back lighter, swifter horses than their own, and these too added good traits to the European bloodstream.

A prehistoric animal the anthropologists call the Dawn Horse roamed North America a million years ago. He was no larger than a medium-sized dog, and did not survive the ordeal of polar icecaps when they moved down across the continent. No more horses lived in all America until the Spanish explorers came to the New World. Cortes, de Soto, and others brought troops of horses to carry soldiers and supplies, and left many behind. Animals without masters drifted off into the wilderness and survived by their own effort. All horses called wild in this country descended from these early Spanish steeds that escaped from their duties.

The Indians were terrified when they began seeing mounted invaders in their land. They thought the Spaniard on horseback was a giant with four legs and a humped back. After they learned about horses, they of course desired them, and learned to steal them from settlers' corrals. Indian ponies, or cayuses, were also captured from wild bands of horses, giving the red men new power on the warpath.

As the years went by thousands of horses thundered on the Great Plains. Sparse vegetation and the rugged terrain shaped a tough breed, usually small in size. Each herd had its stallion leader to protect the mares and colts from all enemies and fight off other stallions. Settlers called these roving bands of horses *mustangs*, their version of the Spanish word for *wild*. The mustang traits live on in western cow ponies, which of course are not ponies at all, but regular horses. Some mustangs are marked with patches of color, as if their coats had been put on with a paint brush. They go by a variety of names, pinto, paint pony, calico, piebald. The half-wild, half-tamed mustangs used in rodeos are called broncos.

Colonists on the eastern seaboard brought in English Thoroughbreds, and horse breeding and horse racing attracted the popular fancy even before the Revolution. In colonial Rhode Island a small sturdy new horse strain was developed and became the Narragansett Pacer, much admired for a while.

In this country at present some of the lighter breeds are the Arabian, the American Quarter Horse, the Hackney, Tennessee Walking Horse, Standardbred, Morgan, and Thoroughbred. Registered horses are said to be *purebred*, whereas Thoroughbred is the name for a breed of racehorses, the fastest ones on the track. Many of the great Thoroughbreds are born and trained in the bluegrass country around Lexington, Kentucky, and the few that show unusual mettle may be destined for the Kentucky Derby. Man o' War and Citation are two famous names from this aristocracy of the vast horse family.

In harness racing the horse is driven from a two-wheeled sulky, and here the Standardbred is the best trotter. On a quarter-mile track the Quarter Horse is the winning sprinter. A good show horse is the Hackney, with his natural ability to learn and his smart looks. Palominos are not considered purebred because the colts do not always inherit the fancy golden color of their parents. Breeders are trying to perfect the strain.

The huge, gentle draft horse, a handsome animal, came to America after the lighter breeds and has been improved here. He is found wherever there is work for a horse to do. His strong muscles and deep chest enable him to pull tremendous loads. He himself may weigh two thousand pounds, and is likely to be of Clydesdale, Shire, Belgian, or Percheron stock. A thatch of hair on the back of his legs, called feathers, kept his legs warm and dry in the damp cold of the British Isles and Low Countries, where these animals lived. The Percheron, an exception, originated in France. The Morgans also work hard, but are smaller than draft horses. They are stocky and sturdy and make fast trotters. Justin Morgan, a Vermont schoolmaster, owned the first Morgan-type horse. This finest of the native American breeds dates from about 1789.

The Shetland pony is a true member of the horse family, but a small one, with a strong body and shaggy mane. These little favorites were born on the Shetland Islands, off the Scottish coast. They can carry or pull a heavy load, and make perfect pets for children.

The domesticated horse is the familiar figure in nearly all parts of the world, but two varieties of wild horses still exist, the tarpans and zebras. Striped zebras are the wild horses of Africa. Herds of tarpans, which are the size of ponies, roam in parts of Asia. When prehistoric men painted horses on the walls of their caves, they were painting tarpans, and the fleet, tough little animals still at large are direct descendants of this ancient breed. Many mustangs and Chincoteagues continue to run wild, but their ancestors were tame before they escaped to a life of freedom.

Most of the horses of the world have been molded to men's needs and know nothing of life without halters and bits. There are fewer of them around today, but they still have a warm place in human affairs and human regard, a place they earned and deserve to keep forever.

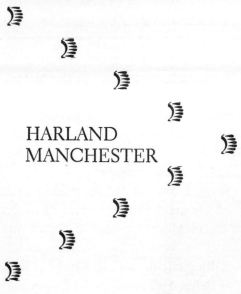

HARLAND
MANCHESTER

Justin Morgan

Vermont Horse Hero

THERE ARE IN AMERICA SOME TWENTY BREEDS OF HORSES, BUT IN THE GREEN Mountain country only two breeds are recognized: Morgans and "other horses." The Morgan, as all Vermonters know, can outpull, outwalk, outlast and out-think any hunk of horseflesh on earth. He is gentle as a kitten, sure-footed as a mountain goat, hardy as a bronco. And as for looks, the most magnificent spectacle on the terrestrial ball is a proud young Morgan, head high, eyes flashing, sleek coat shining, trotting down a Vermont dirt road.

There is every reason why the Morgan should be a great horse. The only breed on earth descended from a single sire, all Morgans carry the powerful genes of Justin Morgan, the equine Paul Bunyan of Randolph, Vermont. Every Morgan alive is a reincarnation of that game little stallion who stands with Ethan Allen and Mount Mansfield as one of Vermont's proudest monuments. The tireless tribe which sprang from his loins pitched in to build America, clearing land, hauling covered wagons, fighting battles and coralling cattle. Now that gasoline has taken over, they have become America's best-loved recreation horses.

Justin Morgan was a bold, chunky little horse about 14 hands high, weight about 950 pounds, who plowed fields, hauled logs, took the ladies to meeting and raced the shoes off any horse in the countryside on Saturday nights.

His story begins with a man named Justin Morgan, a frail, itinerant teacher of penmanship and singing who was town clerk of Randolph. In 1791 his wife died, leaving him deeply in debt, with five children to care for. A farmer of West Springfield, Massachusetts, owed him money, and he made the tedious trip to collect it. To Morgan's great disappointment, the man had no money, but offered him a serviceable three-year-old gelding in lieu of payment. In the pasture with the gelding was his inseparable companion, a two-year-old bay stud colt, origin unknown, with black mane and tail, a deep chest and a strong, short back. The farmer threw him in for good measure.

Making the best of what seemed a bad bargain, Morgan led the gelding back home, while the colt tagged along toward his great destiny. Later when he became famous, people called him "the Justin Morgan horse," and this was shortened in time to Justin Morgan.

Mr. Morgan rode the gelding on his teaching circuit, and broke the colt to harness, planning to sell him to reduce his debts. Fall came and Morgan had no hay to winter him, so he rented him for a year for $15 to a neighbor, Robert Evans, who had a contract to clear some timbered land. With only the half-grown colt for a "team," Evans' outlook was dubious, but when he hooked the chain around the first log and spoke to Justin, the colt threw his shoulders into the collar, dug in his feet and snaked the log to the skidway like a veteran. Soon Evans was boasting at the village tavern that the Justin Morgan colt could outdraw any horse he ever saw.

One night Evans rode Justin to the tavern hitching rail after a day's work in the woods and found that a match had been held in which even 1200-pound horses had been unable to pull a big pine log ten rods to the sawmill. Evans bet a gallon of rum that his colt could do it in three pulls. Then he said he was ashamed to hitch Justin to such a little log, and asked three spectators to get on and ride. The three "least able to stand," according to the chronicler, mounted the log. Justin made it in two pulls.

A few days later the beaten parties picked a fast horse and tried to retrieve the gallon of rum by challenging Evans to a quarter-mile race from a standing start. After his usual hard day's work, Justin was off the mark before the hat hit the dust, and passed the finish line several lengths ahead. Three other entries came forward that evening, and the eager little stallion beat them all. Soon Justin was hailed as the local champion.

"When brought up to the line," wrote D. C. Linsley, one of Justin's early biographers, "his eyes flash and ears quiver with intense excitement, he grinds the bit with his teeth, his hind legs are drawn under him, every muscle of his frame trembles and swells almost to bursting, and at the given signal he goes off like the springing of a steel-trap."

Morgan the man soon sickened and died of consumption. The colt was sold to pay his creditors, and went on clearing forests and racing all comers. Because of Justin's feats of brawn and speed, farmers brought their mares. The foals were the spit and image of the tough little bay, and outworked, outpulled, outran and out-endured all lesser North Country horseflesh.

Few farmers bothered to record pedigrees, and no one knows how many colts Justin sired during the 25 years when he was presumably eligible for parenthood. But by the middle of the century you could hardly enter a barn or pasture in northern New England without recognizing the unmistakable candid, friendly eye; delicate muzzle; short, fine ears; deep, wide chest; short, strong back; and barrel trunk of the old Justin.

Three famous sons stand out from the Justin brood—Sherman, Bulrush and Woodbury—and the greatest of these was Sherman Morgan, who was foaled in 1808 in Lyndon, Vermont. Like Justin, he was small but tough. Hitched to a freight wagon with another son of Justin, he made regular trips to Portland, Maine, and the "little team" became famous at every overnight inn on the route, where their owner matched them at pulling or running against horses of any size, and usually won.

Among Sherman's many colts was the immortal Black Hawk. Foaled in 1833 out of a peddler's mare in Durham, New Hampshire, Justin's grandson became one of the most celebrated sires of American trotters. Broken to harness and used on the family carriage, he showed an irresistible desire to pass everything on the road. His fame spread to Boston, where he was matched against New England's best in a five-mile, $1000-stake race, which he won easily in 16 minutes. His owners offered to match him against any stallion in America for symmetry, ease and elegance of action and fast trotting. There were no takers. Soon every horseman had to have a colt by the famous black Morgan.

In his long life, about 2000 mares were bred to Black Hawk. Many of his colts went to Kentucky, Tennessee, Illinois, Michigan and the Far West, there to pass on the fabulous genes of his grandfather Justin. In his latter years the horse was revered like an elder statesman, and not so long ago, living Vermonters could recall a stirring spectacle at the 1852 State Fair at Rutland, when the 19-year-old patriarch, head high and snorting, was driven around the track by his owner, followed by a glittering retinue of 100 descendants.

The pampered darling of the entire dynasty was Black Hawk's son, Ethan

Allen, champion trotter of the world at the age of four (2:25½) and winner
of 33 out of 55 races. No log-pulling for Ethan—he was owned by several
wealthy Bostonians, had personal lackeys, and became the great American
pin-up horse. "The handsomest, finest-styled and most perfectly gaited trotter
that has ever been produced," said the *American Cultivator*. Ethan was so
good that New York and New Jersey tracks offered purses as high as $5000 for
horses to compete with him. General Grant rode behind Ethan and promptly
ordered two mares to breed to him. At the ripe age of 21 Ethan was sold for
$7500, and spent an honored dotage on a stock farm at Lawrence, Kansas.

While Morgan stars captured the limelight, their kin by the thousands,
recognized as the finest general utility horses in the country, spent their bound-
less energy doing the world's work. Doctors swore by them—come snowdrift or
high water, the little Morgan always got through. In 1853 it was reported that
four-fifths of all the horses on New York's Sixth Avenue street-car line came
from Vermont and New Hampshire, and nearly all were Morgans. Said the
New York *Herald*: "They are remarkable for their great strength in proportion
to their size and for their power of endurance, bearing up under hard labor
that would break down the strength of the strongest draft horse."

In the Civil War the Morgan covered himself with glory. When Fort Sum-
ter was fired upon, Secretary of War Cameron sent buyers to comb the North
Country for 1100 Morgans to mount the crack First Vermont Cavalry.
Grouped in companies according to color, they won all hearts on parade in
New York, Newark and Washington as they pranced to the front. The regi-
ment fought in 75 battles and skirmishes, and its annals are full of praise for
Morgan speed and stamina.

At Gettysburg the First Vermont, already jaded and half shot to pieces, was
ordered to make an almost hopeless charge over rough ground on a strongly
entrenched enemy force. "The behavior of the horses was admirable," wrote
a chronicler, "running low and swift, as in a race, guiding at the slightest touch
on the neck; never refusing a fence or breaking from the column." The commander, General Farnsworth, was shot from his horse and 75 Vermonters fell,
but the diversion was successful, and eyewitnesses called it one of the most
gallant cavalry charges of the war. On a bas-relief at the base of a statue on
the battlefield, Vermonters still ride their Morgans in bronze. At Appomattox,
the surviving Morgans were in the middle of a charge when the cease-fire
order came through. Two hundred of them outlasted the war; a few got back
to Vermont.

Morgans fell on evil days toward the end of the century. The faster "Ham-
bletonians"—with the aid of good Morgan dams—took over the harness tracks.

Farmers who could afford them bought strapping Percherons for work, and the shadow of Henry Ford fell across the highways. Their days of glamour gone, Morgans retreated to stony back farms, grew shaggy coats against the cold, and lived on grass.

But they still had powerful friends. One of them, Colonel Joseph Battell, gentleman farmer, conservationist and philanthropist of Middlebury, Vermont, spent a small fortune and most of his life collecting fine Morgans and firmly establishing them as a properly registered breed. He traveled throughout the states and Canada looking at Morgans and listening to Morgan lore. and wrote 100,000 letters tracing Morgan pedigrees. Starting with the stallion, General Gates, great-grandson of Ethan the Magnificent, the Colonel rescued the dynasty from the exhaust fumes of progress, and other loyal Morgan men followed in his train.

In 1905, Colonel Battell presented his farm and stock to the U.S. Government. Breeding continued under the direction of the Department of Agriculture, and in 1951 the 940 rolling acres and 40-odd Morgans were acquired by the University of Vermont. In front of the stallion barn, a heroic bronze figure of Justin overlooks the pasture meadow where a dozen of his saucy offspring frisk around their patient dams.

With the great national surge toward the outdoors, the smart, willing, unfussy Morgan has found a new career as a pleasure horse. Women and children love him for his gentle personality and close rapport with his owner. Their sure-footedness and good temper have made them popular on dude ranches. As President Benjamin Harrison once pointed out, in an emergency the Morgan always consults his rider. Yet he has stuff enough in him for a man to ride, and is famous for his "bottom," which in horsey talk means guts. Every year this is demonstrated in the 100-mile trail ride of the Green Mountain Horse Association held at Woodstock, Vermont, open to all breeds. Morgans are always among the leaders, and in the 19th annual ride they swept the field of 66 horses from ten states and Canada, taking first place in all three divisions.

There are approximately 7500 registered Morgans in the country today, and there are probably at least as many perfectly good high-grade Morgans who never made the Register. California now leads in breeding Morgans, with Vermont running second and Illinois third. New England has been exporting Morgans for more than a century, and there is some concern lest this migration deplete the local stock. Recently, J. Cecil Ferguson, a Rhode Island breeder, went to Kansas and brought back 51 fine Morgans to redress the balance.

There are now two politely warring schools of Morgan breeders: the "old

Morgan" or "purist" minority who pride themselves on high percentages of old Justin's blood, and the "new Morgan" group who believe that the breed is improved by discreet admissions of less exalted ancestry. The whole argument would bring a horse laugh from Justin, who never had a pedigree. Many earnest historians have tried to supply him with one, and there are at least six conflicting accounts of his origin. The one most often printed is that he was sired by True Briton, an imported English Thoroughbred stolen from a British colonel during the Revolution.

It would be pleasant to report that Justin Morgan spent his final years in green pastures, suitably honored. Such was not the case. The world did not know him for what he was, and he was batted from pillar to post like most old horses of the day. Again and again he was sold, each time for a lower price and to a lower station. At the age of 22, he was working on a six-horse freight team, with his ribs showing. In 1821, when he was 32, he was seen on a farm in Chelsea, Vermont, still hale and vigorous and without a blemish. He spent that winter in an open yard with other horses. One of them kicked him in the flank. The wound went untended; inflammation set in and he died. But his indomitable genes persist. Wherever a Morgan canters through the morning mist, Justin lives again.

ROBERT
FROST

The Runaway

ONCE WHEN THE SNOW OF THE YEAR WAS BEGINNING TO FALL,
We stopped by a mountain pasture to say "Whose colt?"
A little Morgan had one forefoot on the wall,
The other curled at his breast. He dipped his head
And snorted at us. And then he had to bolt.
We heard the miniature thunder where he fled,
And we saw him, or thought we saw him, dim and gray,
Like a shadow against the curtain of falling flakes.
"I think the little fellow's afraid of the snow.
He isn't winter-broken. It isn't play
With the little fellow at all. He's running away.
I doubt if even his mother could tell him, 'Sakes,
It's only weather.' He'd think she didn't know!
Where is his mother? He can't be out alone."
And now he comes again with a clatter of stone
And mounts the wall again with whited eyes
And all his tail that isn't hair up straight.
He shudders his coat as if to throw off flies.
"Whoever it is that leaves him out so late,
When other creatures have gone to stall and bin,
Ought to be told to come and take him in."

151

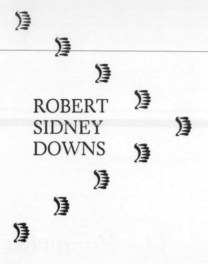

ROBERT
SIDNEY
DOWNS

The Arabian

JEFF ALLEN RODE ALONG THE GRAY SANDY FLOOR OF SILVER CANYON. HERE and there stood tall dead cottonwood trees with their skeletonlike arms reaching upward toward the sky showing clear blue above the high steep sides. Long centuries ago torrents of water had probably rushed down through Silver Canyon, but now it was as dry as a baking oven, and the only hint of water was a small spring halfway along its pencil-shaped length that just barely touched the surface between two boulders. A stranger could ride by a hundred times over and never see it.

As Jeff neared the half-hidden spring, his horse shied slightly. Looking down and ahead he saw a rattlesnake slither toward a hole and disappear. His horse watched it also and not until it was gone from view did the animal move forward. A gray bird perched on one of the spring's boulders, with cocked head and critical eye as though deciding whether friend or foe, and watched them approach. Suddenly it dropped down to the spring, stuck its beak in the water and, throwing back its head, drank. When the rider and horse came close, the little bird took a final drink and flew away.

Jeff rode past the spring until he came to a gap in the canyon wall. He turned into it and rode on up out of the canyon to higher ground. A little while later he stopped his horse on the crest of a pine knoll, dismounted, and let the reins dangle. While the horse searched the bed of pine needles for small tufts of edible grass, Jeff looked back over the way he'd come. Far down in the distance he could make out the buildings of the Diamond T ranch nestled together in a virgin green valley, which fanned out onto flat ground that reached far to the horizon line where it seemed to drop off.

It was a sight that always made his blood dance, particularly so when he thought of the day when it would be all his and he would become owner of the famous Diamond T. . .

As Jeff rode along he thought of his uncle. Jeff had loved horses almost from the day he was born, but it was nothing compared to the love his Uncle Frank Mason held for his pure-blooded Arabians. His horses were his whole life and nothing else in it measured even close in importance.

Frank Mason never tired of talking about his horses, nor of relating the stories and legends of the first and purest breed of livestock ever developed by man. A hundred nights Jeff had listened, enthralled, while his uncle talked about the Arabian horse.

Story after story, legend after legend, and fact upon fact. The legend of how in ancient times Mohammed wanted only the finest mares for his war campaigns. To select the ones that would mother a race he penned up a hundred thirst-crazy Arabian mares within sight and smell of clear cool water. Suddenly he released the lot and they all went plunging madly toward the water. When they were close Mohammed sounded the war bungle. Five of the mares stopped while all the others raced onward. Those five were selected to mother the race of pure-blooded Arabian horses that has come down unsullied through the centuries to modern times.

And another legend—that in the year 2,000 B.C. Ishmael, son of Abraham and Hagar, was believed to have received a present of a mare from heaven. Later the mare had a foal, but the foal was crippled because it was carried in a camel's saddle bag. The foal—whom legend calls *Benat el Ahwaj*, which means Son of the Crooked—became the original sire of the centuries-famous breed of horse.

Stories of how the Arabian warriors rode only mares into their desert battles and thought more of their horses' lives than of their own. Of how the Arab, or the Bedouin, treated his horse like a member of the family, and usually the most important one. How the horse slept in the big tent next to his master, and was always fed before anybody else. And how the Arab might not have a stitch on his back, nor a mouthful of food to eat, but he would not sell his horse for all the money in the land. The Arab might give his horse away, and such was regarded as a princely act of the highest order, but never would he sell his splendid beast even though it meant the price of his own life. And the story of how . . .

Jeff Allen shook his head and brought himself back to the present. Uncle Frank's fact-filled colorful stories could be remembered and mused on some other time. . . . The mount under him was a pure-blooded Arabian mare, and was one of the few all-blacks on the Diamond T. Arabian horses are all solid colors, but the most highly prized are the whites, or the blacks. Possibly more so the blacks.

His uncle had made Jeff a present of the mare the first summer he spent at the Diamond T, and he had named her Mecca. Not because he especially liked the name, nor because it was the birthplace of Mohammed. As a matter of fact he had taken a map of Saudi Arabia, poised a pin above it with his eyes closed, and brought the pin down on the map. The pin had stuck into Mecca, located on the eastern shores of the Red Sea.

From that day on, the mare was Mecca, and he had come to love her dearly. Perhaps just a little like the Arabs and Bedouins of ancient times. She was a beautiful specimen of horseflesh and possessed all the famous characteristics of the pure Arabian. She stood fifteen hands high and weighed close to a thousand pounds. Her head was short, the delicately shaped wedge style making the muzzle small. Her profile was "dished," and her eyes were large and protruding. They were set lower than on any other breed of horse, and wide enough apart to enable her to see objects to the rear. Her ears were curved and pointed, and so set that they almost touched at the tips. Her back was short, as in all Arabians, her tail set high, and her legs were unusually strong-boned. Last but not least she was gentle and intelligent, just as her ancestors had been long centuries ago. She was Mecca, she was his horse, and she would always remain his most prized and most beloved possession.

Jeff now turned Mecca toward the north and rode higher and higher into the foothills until he came to the rim of the Upper Forty. And a rim it actually was, too. The Upper Forty was like a bowl of green grazing land set down among the hills. It was almost a perfect circle in shape. It looked as though the gods had at one time dropped a gigantic ball down among the rock-studded hills, lifted the ball away, and planted the circular depression with some of the sweetest, most luscious grass to be found anywhere in the west. And at the very center put a spring that never went dry any season of the year.

No fences were needed in the Upper Forty because, save at one point that led down toward Silver Canyon, the area was ringed with rocks and heavy growth that would discourage any horse who might be foolish enough to want to wander from that perfect grazing land. Jeff turned Mecca away from the Upper Forty and toward the even higher foothills to the north. At the end of an hour he stopped by a small stream, dismounted, and ate some of the grub he carried in his saddlebag. And in the manner of the ancient Arabs, he shared his meal with his horse.

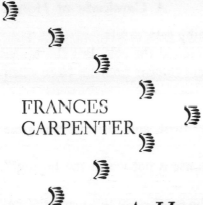

FRANCES
CARPENTER

A Horse Afraid of His Shadow

ONE DAY, LONG, LONG AGO, IN THE ANCIENT EASTERN LAND OF MACEDONIA, the horse market in its capital, Pella, was crowded with buyers. King Philip II, himself, was there. With him were the keepers of his royal stables. A fine lot of horses had been gathered for selling. First choice would go to the King and his warriors.

At the side of King Philip stood his young son, Alexander, a boy then twelve years of age. None in that throng of buyers had a better eye for a good horse than this lad. No boys of his own age in all Macedonia could compare with the young Alexander in horsemanship.

"Look well at all the animals, my son," King Philip said. "Then tell me which ones you would choose from among them."

"Many of these colts are well formed, my father." The boy spoke with sure tones. "Many have spirit. They would ride bravely to battle. But none is so noble as that young black stallion yonder, that one with the white mark shaped like an ox's head on his face."

"The young Prince chooses well," the black stallion's owner cried. "That is indeed the finest colt in all the market today. My price for him is high, thirteen talents, in fact. But I will be honest with you, Your Majesty. That young black stallion will wear a saddle and bridle, but he will not be ridden. He is wild as the North Wind. None can stay long upon his back." The black colt even then was prancing and snorting as the noisy crowd gathered round him.

"No other horse here can compare with that one," the boy, Alexander, insisted. "Surely skilled horsemen from the palace stables can tame him."

155

"Let the black stallion be ridden!" King Philip gave orders.

The most daring horsemen of his court mounted the colt. But the trader had spoken truly. One after another, they were thrown from his back when they attempted to ride him over the plain.

The colt started at every sound. As soon as one tried to ride him away, he whirled and reared high. He gave one mighty twist, and his rider was gone from his back.

"Are you satisfied now, my son, that this horse is not worth the buying?" the King asked Alexander.

"No, Father, I still say the black stallion is the very best in this market place. His riders do not understand him. Let me try my hand on his bridle."

The King was pleased with his son's courage. He had no fear for his safety. The boy knew how to fall off a horse quite as well as how to ride one.

"Ride him, then, Alexander!" the King said. "And if you can succeed where these others have failed, I will buy the horse for you."

The men in the horse market marveled to see the fearless lad leap into the saddle. The trembling black horse stood still. The boy stroked his glossy neck, which shone like ebony. Alexander talked to the horse softly. Then he turned his head straight toward the afternoon sun and galloped away over the plain.

It grew late. The sun was dropping below the horizon when the anxious crowd in that market place saw the boy coming back. Like lightning, the black stallion was galloping, galloping, but the boy was still on his back. Easily Alexander pulled the spirited steed to a halt. He patted the sides of the stallion, which now seemed tame as a kitten.

"Well ridden, my son! The black stallion is yours," King Philip cried.

"Tell us your secret, young Prince," the palace horsemen asked. "How did you tame that wild spitfire so easily?"

"It was as I said," Alexander replied. "You did not understand him. This stallion is a horse of high and noble spirit. He starts at the sight of each moving thing that is strange to him. While the others were trying to ride him, I saw that what frightened him the most was his own moving shadow. When he ran from the sun, the black shadow leaped along, just under his nose. I took care to turn his face toward the sun, so that his shadow could not be seen. The horse forgot his fear. I let him gallop to his heart's content, and now he trusts me as his master."

The King wept for pride and joy in his son's wisdom and bravery. "One day you will make a great king, Alexander," he said to the Prince. "But you must seek larger kingdoms. The one I shall leave for you will be too small for your powers."

Bucephalus, the ancient Macedonian word for "ox-head," was the name Alexander gave this favorite horse. The shining black stallion with the ox-head blaze on his face carried the Prince through many a battle. So tame was Bucephalus that he would kneel down, like a camel, for his young master to mount. Yet, throughout his life, this spirited horse would carry no other rider.

When he was twenty years old, the young Prince succeeded his father on the Macedonian throne. Many were the countries conquered by this Alexander, whom men called the Great. To Greece and to Egypt, to Persia, even to India, he led his Macedonian warriors. As his father foretold, he did indeed seek and conquer broader kingdoms. So great were his deeds that people began to believe Alexander must be descended from the gods themselves.

Now, in that part of the Eastern world, there was also a kingdom known as Phrygia. When the Phrygian King died, the people had begged the gods to guide them in choosing their new ruler.

"Who shall next be our King?" they asked the gods. The answer, which they called an oracle, came through the priests in the temple. "Your King shall come riding to you in a wagon," the oracle said.

Hardly had the priest given the message of the gods, when Gordius, a wise but poor country fellow, rode into the public square in his farm wagon. At once the people cried out, "The oracle is fulfilled! Gordius shall be our King!"

In thanks to the gods, Gordius set his farm wagon up in their temple. He tied it in place with thick leather thongs. And he made the knot so skillfully that none could untie it.

People called this the Gordian knot. A legend grew up about it. This foretold that the man who could part its tight thongs would one day become ruler of all the world.

Princes of many lands, and other young heroes tried to undo the Gordian knot. But it was not until Alexander the Great came on his black stallion, Bucephalus, that the deed was done.

At first Alexander also tried to untie the Gordian knot. His fingers, too, failed to pull its thongs apart. Then, losing patience, but determined to succeed, the King drew his sword. With one swift thrust he cut the knot and the leather thongs fell apart.

Cutting the Gordian knot was an example of Alexander's way of taking a short cut to success. That is why, when someone solves a difficult problem with daring and skill, we still say today, "He cut the Gordian knot."

Bucephalus was Alexander's faithful companion in battle throughout his life. The noble stallion lived to be thirty years old, a good age for a horse.

One story tells how, at last, in a battle in India, the brave horse, Bucephalus, was sorely wounded. Straightway he galloped out of the fray. He carried his master to a safe place before he fell to the ground. On that spot by the Indian river, Hydaspes, Alexander the Great founded a city. In loving remembrance of his favorite horse, the Emperor of the Eastern World gave the city the name of Bucephala.

ELEANOR
and
HERBERT
FARJEON

Alexander the Great
B. C. 356–323

Alexander the Great
  Looked very ornate
In his beautiful plumes and his gold armour-plate,
  And he rode on a steed
  Of the very best breed
With an elegant tail and a delicate gait,
  But he sighed as he cried,
  "I shall now have to ride
Home to Macedon since, I regret to relate,
  With the map at my feet,
  There is no one to beat,
I have conquered the world at too early a date!"

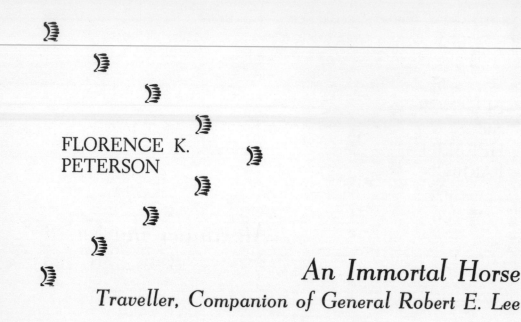

FLORENCE K.
PETERSON

An Immortal Horse
Traveller, Companion of General Robert E. Lee

*"There is many a war horse who is more entitled
to immortality than the man who rides him."*

THIS WAS A HUMBLE YET SINCERE STATEMENT FROM THE GREAT GENERAL Robert E. Lee. The sight of the gray bearded, vital General astride his magnificent gray mount was sufficient to rouse the cheers of the troops . . . to give them spirit to go anew into battle in their tattered uniforms . . . to act as a symbol to the Army of the Confederacy of the dignity with which they fought the battle for their beliefs.

Traveller was a four-year-old colt when Lee acquired him. Beautifully proportioned with a muscular figure, fine head, superb carriage, he truly was a General's horse. And Lee loved him! Never were man and horse more attuned! Here was not a case of master and servant. Horse and General shared alike and *gave* alike in the hard, bitter heat and cold of battle.

Traveller's firm, bold tread carried his beloved partner and General from Georgia to the Carolinas . . . Manassas, Sharpsburg, Fredericksburg . . . to Chancellorsville, Gettysburg, the Rappahannock. This horse made history and never faltered in duty nor in his loyalty to his master.

Alert in the fray, Traveller gloried in battle. He reveled in the fierce advance of foe on foe. His keen eye, his oneness with his General, led him dauntless into onsets that earned him the title of one of the most fearless of war horses ever to be honored in history.

War over, Traveller had a very different but equally difficult row to hoe. He was a hero!—and subject to the trials and difficulties thrust upon him by an adoring public.

Nineteenth Century autograph collectors wanted hairs plucked from poor weary Traveller! Lee and his grooms protected him as best they could. So frightened did Traveller become of souvenir hunters that Lee is reported to have pleaded with an ardent fan to pull one of his own hairs instead.

In peace, Lee served as President of Washington and Lee University. He and his family maintained a string of beloved horses, but none outshone Traveller in the love and affection of the entire Lee family. A stirring and heart-warming sight for the students on the campus was Lee mounting Traveller for his daily ride. And when Lee and Traveller, in their great affection for children, allowed eager little ones to be led about on the famous war horse, there was jubilation beyond all belief. Many a post-Civil War diary reports the thrilling words: "Today I rode Traveller."

In 1870, the nation mourned the death of the gallant Robert E. Lee. Proudly and solemnly, Traveller led the funeral procession.

Traveller remained the beloved of the Lee family, luxuriating in a fine stable built just for him. Survivor of many a fierce battle, Traveller succumbed, ironically, a year later to a mere rusty nail. He died of tetanus.

Traveller, the trusty, beloved horse of a great General, was buried near Lee.

Many years later, Traveller's skeleton was exhumed and now stands in the Washington and Lee Museum as an eternal memorial to his gallantry.

Immortal, too, is Traveller in sculpture, canvas, prose and poetry. The men of the scalpel, brush and pen find in this black-maned, black-tailed handsome gray a never-ending challenge to ways and means of extolling his virtues and his glories.

FLORENCE K.
PETERSON

Cream White Marengo
Favorite of Napoleon

THERE WERE BEHIND-THE-HAND WHISPERS, YET NO ONE WOULD SAY IT ALOUD, "Napoleon is an extremely poor horseman." There were those who muttered too that the redoubtable little Emperor chose the splendid gleaming cream-white stallion, Marengo, only because the mount added stature and glamour to his own appearance.

But the reasons for Napoleon's choice of Marengo are obscured in the fact that the stallion performed so admirably in battle and in his service to his master. No bullet, no heavy cannonade, no beyond-endurance situation could daunt this gallant creature. He was glorious in battle and withstood his wounds like a man and a soldier.

Marengo was one of many fine horses presented to Napoleon by the Bey of Tunis. The Bey, currying favor of France against England, made available to the apparent world-conqueror fifty of his best studs. They had all weathered a stringent training . . . trial by gunfire, cannon bombardment—even charges of dogs and pigs between their legs to teach them not to shy from immediate dangers.

Marengo was Napoleon's first choice—and became his favorite. Though unflinching and sure-footed in battle, Marengo was docile and amenable to the slightest whim of his careless rider.

Through many a campaign, Marengo's wits saved his Emperor.

Cossacks came within a hair's breadth of capturing Napoleon. Marengo saved him by rearing suddenly in the path of a bullet intended for his master. The Russian campaign with its horrors of bitter cold and privation brought death to scores—but not so to Marengo. He became the barometer, the pulse, the driving force of the morale of Napoleon's Army.

When Napoleon was exiled to Elba, Marengo was one of only eight horses which he was permitted to take with him. Marengo shared his Emperor's dramatic escape from that island—and entered again with his master the great but doomed effort to conquer the world.

Waterloo was the death-knell for Napoleon. He ended his days, imprisoned on the island of St. Helena, deprived even of the loving companionship of his Marengo.

Sadly, the cream-white charger pined away his life on an estate in England, far from the fury and the excitement of attempting to conquer the world with a man whom history shall never forget!

ELEANOR
and
HERBERT
FARJEON

Buffalo Bill
1846–1917

I SAY! WHAT A THRILL!
    Here's Buffalo Bill,
The King of the Cowboys in valour and skill,
With his fringes of leather, his cowpuncher's hat,
His lasso and pistols and boots and all that!
    Stout-hearted and hairy,
    With confidence airy
He slew the wild buffalo roaming the prairie,
And played the chief part in exciting events
Enacted around the Red Indian tents,
    And when the news came,
    As part of the game,
That the Redskins had set his log cabin aflame,
    He rode without pause
    To put down the cause
'Mid the yelling of braves and the squawking of squaws.
    He fought a lot more
    As Scoutmaster for
The troops of the North in the Great Civil War,
And America's mail through the land was conveyed
By his Pony Express ere the railway was made.

And I say! what a thrill
When Buffalo Bill,
Who, agog for adventure, could never keep still,
Got up a fine circus, to show every one
How the Redskin-and-buffalo business was done!
What glee and what glory
To see his life-story
Presented in episodes pleasantly gory,
With whips and with scalps that were cracked with a will
By breakneck, unbeatable Buffalo Bill!

GERTRUDE
HECKER
WINDERS

Jeb Stuart, Boy in the Saddle

(*At 28, James Ewell Brown Stuart was appointed Colonel in the Confederate Army and Commander of General Lee's Cavalry. Considered the "eyes" of the Army, Stuart's exploits in the war of the States are legendary. What was he like as a youth?*)

IT WAS A CHILLY NIGHT EARLY IN JANUARY. JEMMY WAS STUDYING HIS LATIN lesson by the open fire in the living room. He had missed his lessons that day because he had gone hunting. His brothers were away at a private school.

He looked up from his book. "Mother, when am I going to have a horse of my own?" he asked.

His mother sat at her desk writing in a big account book. She frowned. "I don't know, Jemmy. We can't afford it now."

"But I need a horse, Mother. Father is away on Firebrand most of the time. The boys took their horses back to school with them. All I have to ride is a plowhorse or a mule. I can't ride in a fox hunt with either of those! Last week I had to ride a mule down to the west field to hunt. I'd have been ashamed if anybody had seen me."

"Never be ashamed of being poor, Jemmy. Our family is rich in honors." She nodded toward the picture over the mantel. It was a portrait of Jemmy's great-grandfather, Major Alexander Stuart. He was wearing an officer's blue coat trimmed with gold braid. A small sword hanging under the picture flashed in the firelight.

"Your great-grandfather fought in our War for Independence," Mrs. Stuart said. "He was a very brave man. Even the enemy admired his bravery."

"I know, Mother," said Jemmy. He had been told a great deal about the Stuarts and the Letchers. The Letchers were his mother's relatives. "I know your Grandfather Letcher was a famous judge. I know Father was an officer in the War of 1812. But what has that to do with my not having a horse?"

"Just this. Our families served their state instead of making money. They helped to make our country what it is, but they didn't grow rich. We just don't have the money to buy another horse now, Jemmy. You mustn't feel ashamed to ride a mule if you have to."

The Stuarts were not really poor. They lived in a big house set among great oak trees on a hill. The gardens were filled with beautiful flowers. The paths were lined with hedges.

Jemmy's brothers went to a private school. Later Jemmy would go away to school, too. There were no public schools nearby. The Stuarts agreed that their boys must be educated as gentlemen should be.

However, the farm was not large. Mrs. Stuart ran it with only a few field hands. They raise small crops of corn, tobacco and sweet potatoes. All sorts of vegetables grew in the kitchen garden. There were chickens and pigs as well as cattle.

Furthermore, the woods were full of game and the streams of fish. The long dining room table at Laurel Hill was always filled with good things to eat. Company was always welcome, but the Stuarts didn't have much money.

Tobacco was the only crop they sold. They could have raised larger crops if they had wanted to. Mr. Stuart and the boys could have worked in the fields. But gentlemen didn't work like that in Virginia in the year 1842.

Jemmy turned back to his book. "I'd rather have a horse than anything in the world," he sighed to himself.

He was nodding over his Latin book when his father appeared in the door. Mr. Stuart was splashed with mud from his riding boots to his hair. His face was pale.

"Archibald!" exclaimed Mrs. Stuart, dropping her pen. "What is the matter?"

Jemmy ran to his father. He put his hand on his father's arm. "Did Firebrand throw you?" he asked anxiously.

"No, Jemmy, but I have bad news. Elizabeth, I did a foolish thing, I'm afraid. I bought a horse, a fine little bay that——"

Jemmy's heart beat fast. "How could that be bad news?" he asked himself.

"Oh, Arch, you didn't!" cried Mrs. Stuart. "You know we can't afford another horse."

"I—I traded tobacco for him."

"That is bad news," said Mrs. Stuart. "We don't need the horse, and tobacco is as good as cash."

"My dear, you haven't heard the bad news yet. The horse was a bargain. I could have traded him for double what I paid, but——" He sank into an arm-chair and dropped his face into his hands.

Jemmy put his arm around his father's neck. He looked from his father to his mother with worried eyes. "Was there an accident, Father?"

"Yes, Jemmy. The horse jumped away from something in the road as I was leading him home. A sharp rock sticks out from a bluff on one side of the road there. The horse fell on the rock and cut his leg. He's ruined, Pete says. There's no hope. We must kill him."

"Oh, no!" Jemmy and his mother cried.

"Can't someone cure him?" asked Jemmy.

"If the leg isn't——" Mrs. Stuart began.

"Pete says there is no use calling anyone. He says nobody can help."

"Why? Is the cut too deep to heal?" Mrs. Stuart wanted to know.

"No, Elizabeth. The cut could heal all right. But the horse is upset and refuses to eat or drink. He will starve to death. I've seen such cases before. I'm afraid we'll have to shoot him."

Tears rose in Mrs. Stuart's eyes. Jemmy blinked back tears himself. "May I see the horse, Father?"

"It will break your heart, Jemmy. He's a beautiful little bay——" Mr. Stuart choked.

"Surely something can be done," said Mrs. Stuart.

"If you'd see the horse, you'd understand. He's trembling and plunging in his stall."

She shivered. "I don't want to see him."

"I do," said Jemmy

With his father he went out to the stable. Pete held a lantern high so that Jemmy could see the horse. The horse was trembling all over. His eyes were rolling wildly.

"Good boy," said Jemmy softly.

The horse tossed back his head and showed his teeth. Jemmy drew back.

"Don't try to touch him," said Mr. Stuart. "He's naturally a nervous animal. The pain has made him almost wild. Be careful."

"I can't stand to have him killed," Jemmy declared. "I just can't! Look at his neck, Father. He's more beautiful than Firebrand!" He went on softly and coaxingly, "Why can't you be good? You're going to be all right."

The animal turned his head toward Jemmy.

"He likes that, I do believe," said Jemmy's father.

Jemmy carefully put out his hand and patted the horse. He didn't tremble quite so hard. Jemmy kept on talking and petting.

"Pete, bring a bucket of water," ordered Mr. Stuart. His voice shook. "Maybe Jemmy can coax him to drink some water."

Pete brought the water. As soon as Jemmy held up the bucket, the horse jerked back his head. He kicked with his sore leg.

"No use," said Mr. Stuart sadly.

Pete nodded. "I've seen horses like this before. They won't let you do a thing for them."

"We'll wait until morning," said Mr. Stuart, with a thoughtful frown.

Jemmy hung his head as he followed his father into the house. If he hadn't been nearly ten years old, he would have cried like a baby.

Usually he went to sleep the moment his head hit the pillow. Tonight he tossed and twisted. He just couldn't sleep. The wind whistled around the house. It rattled the windows, but it was not the wind that kept him awake. He was thinking of the beautiful little horse.

Finally he jumped out of bed. He pulled on his clothes and slipped downstairs. Then he ran through the darkness toward the stable.

"Did you think I'd forgotten you?" he began softly as he stepped inside the stable.

Firebrand made a noise. Jemmy spoke to him as he passed his stall, but he didn't stop. Firebrand didn't need any help.

The new horse was stamping and kicking. Jemmy touched him and felt him quiver. As Jemmy kept on petting him and talking to him, however, the horse became quiet.

"I wonder what I should call you," said Jemmy. "Father said only that you are a bay. He means that you're reddish-brown in color. Many words rhyme with bay—hay, way, say, may—I believe I'll make up a little poem about you.

> "I want my bay
> To do my way,
> He must eat his hay
> And here I'll stay!"

He piled straw on the floor and lay down. He went to sleep immediately. Presently the horse moved and wakened him. Again Jemmy quieted the animal. He took another nap. Again he was awakened.

"I thought you were settled for the rest of the night," Jemmy said. "You're as uncertain as—as a candle in the wind. That gives me an idea. I'll call you Bayberry."

Friends in Norfolk had sent the Stuarts some candles made of wax from bayberries. The candles had a pleasant odor when they burned.

"Bayberry," Jemmy repeated. "I like that."

For most of the night Jemmy soothed the horse. When light shone through the door, he said, "I'm thirsty and you'd better be."

At the pump by the horse trough in the yard he filled a bucket. He had to use both hands to hold the bucket up to Bayberry.

"Drink, now. I know you want a drink," he said softly. "Come on, you silly horse. Drink."

Bayberry dipped his nose in the water. Then he lifted his head and looked straight at Jemmy. "Drink. A real drink. Please," begged Jemmy.

Bayberry lowered his head and gulped a good, big drink.

Jemmy's knees shook. He sat down on the stable floor with the empty bucket beside him. That was where he was when Pete came in.

"He drank, Pete! He drank! Now I know I can get him to eat, too."

Pete's eyes opened wide. His jaw dropped. Then he dashed off to tell Mr. Stuart.

Being Practical

For the next week Jemmy spent most of his time in the stable. His lessons were forgotten, but nobody seemed to care.

Every night he lay on the straw beside Bayberry's stall. He slept in short naps. At the first sound, he was on his feet, ready to soothe Bayberry.

The very first day Bayberry had behaved well. He was quiet. He ate and drank.

Happily, Jemmy asked his father and mother to come to the stable to see him.

"You do have a way with horses," his father said. "I feel hopeful about him now."

"We don't need to worry any more about that horse," his mother said. "The idea of killing him! What were you and Pete thinking of?"

Bayberry began to tremble. He snorted and tossed his head. He kicked and Jemmy saw blood coming from his wound. Jemmy's heart sank.

"Oh, I spoke too soon," said Mrs. Stuart. "Why, the horse looks wild! Be careful, Jemmy. He's dangerous. I know he is."

A tight lump swelled in Jemmy's throat. Had all his work been for nothing? Was Pete right?

He felt his father's hand on his shoulder. "Don't be disappointed if you fail, son. We hope you can save him, but we won't be surprised if you don't. There's not much chance."

Bayberry grew quiet after his visitors left. He was usually quiet when Jemmy talked to him. When Jemmy stopped, he began to shake. Sometimes he would eat his oats as he should, but not always. Jemmy didn't know whether he was going to cure Bayberry or not. Certainly he couldn't go on talking to him forever, as he was doing now.

One evening Jemmy went to the house to wash and change his clothes. His mother made him eat supper at the table with the rest of the family.

"Bayberry ate tonight," Jemmy announced. "Pete says——"

At that moment Mandy brought in another plate of hot biscuits. "Pete says that new horse is about to kick down the stall," she said.

Jemmy threw down his napkin and rushed out to the stable. He didn't sleep much that night. But the next day Bayberry was better, and the next day better still.

A week later Jemmy proudly led Bayberry out to the watering trough. The horse still limped, but not badly. For the first time Jemmy got a good look at him. His coat was red-brown, but his legs were black. He was beautiful.

In another week Bayberry was entirely well.

"Come to the porch after breakfast," Jemmy said one morning. "I'll show you a fine horse."

He sat proudly in the saddle as he rode Bayberry around from the stable. Pete followed. He was shaking his head and saying, "I can't believe it."

Jemmy's father, mother and three big sisters came out on the porch. The day was cold. They could see snow on the Blue Ridge Mountains in the west. A north wind rustled the dry vines on the porch pillars. Little Colly pressed her nose against the glass of a front window. She had a cold and could not come out.

"I can't believe it, either," his father said.

"Oh, I want to ride him," Bethenia said.

"We've never had a bay with black legs before," said Ann. "Isn't he a beauty?"

Colly beat on the window. She was saying something that nobody could hear.

"What's she saying?" asked her father.

They all listened. Even Jemmy on his horse could hear her this time. "Is this Jemmy's horse?" Colly yelled at the top of her voice.

Jemmy's heart leaped. With shining eyes he looked at his mother.

"Jemmy saved us a great loss," she said slowly. "But the girls need new dresses for the ball in Taylorsville next month."

Jemmy's heart sank. He knew each dress took fifteen yards of silk, and silk was expensive.

His father was frowning.

"I'm sorry," his mother added, "but we must be practical. We need the money. I think we should sell the horse at once."

Jemmy bit his lips as he leaned over to pat Bayberry on the neck.

"A bay with black points," Jemmy thought. "I've never seen one before." His eyes sparkled. "That's the only kind of horse I'll ever want to own now."

"He is a beauty," said Ann. "Look at him arch his neck. Do I dare pet him?" She put out her hand to stroke his nose, but Bayberry tossed his head and reared.

"I was expecting that," Jemmy laughed. He sat easily in the saddle as he soothed Bayberry. "He's pretty skittish, but I like a horse with plenty of spirit."

"I won't ask if I can ride him," said Bethenia. "He's too lively for me."

"And for me," echoed Mary.

"The horse will bring a better price if he's trained," said Mr. Stuart. "This accident may have frightened him. Jemmy should ride him for a while before we try to sell him. He should make sure the horse can still jump fences."

"Hurrah!" yelled Jemmy. He wheeled Bayberry toward a low place in the hedge. He loosened the reins and clapped his knees tighter on the horse. Under him he felt Bayberry rise easily. Jumping the hedge was like flying.

His sisters clapped their hands. He looked back to wave as he galloped off.

"How straight he sits in the saddle," said Ann.

"He took the hedge beautifully," said his father.

"Jemmy seems to be a part of the horse when he rides," said Mary proudly.

"I wish he could have a horse of his own," Bethenia said.

"So do I," said his mother slowly. "Jemmy's a born horseman."

The only thing Jemmy could hear as he galloped away was his mother's voice. "We must be practical," it said. "We must be practical."

The Highwayman

Jemmy never had liked to go to bed. He had spent many nights on straw in the stable, however. Now he was glad to be in his own featherbed. "I'm glad I don't have to wake up until morning," he thought a few nights later. He pulled the blanket up closer around his neck.

He had slept only a little while when he was wakened by a hand on his shoulder. "Wake up!" He heard Ann's voice. She sounded frightened.

"Bayberry!" said Jemmy, sitting up.

"Colly's sick," Ann exclaimed. "Nothing that Mother or Sally or Mandy can do for her is helping at all. We must have Dr. Melton."

Jemmy's bare feet hit the cold floor. "I'll go get him at once."

"Wait, Jemmy. I know you could, but I'll have to talk to Mother. She's afraid to have you ride so far alone at night. But there's nobody else to go. Pete and the other hands say they'd lose their way."

Jemmy's father was in Taylorsville that night. He was to join a fox hunt in the morning.

Jemmy picked up his shirt. "I'll go across the fields. It's only about four miles that way. Tell Mother I can ride there on Bayberry with my eyes shut."

"Of course you can, but she keeps saying, 'Jemmy is only a child. What can we do?'"

Ann hurried from the room. Jemmy called after her, "Remind her I'll be ten years old!"

He hurried into his clothes, fastening buttons with both hands. When he went downstairs, Ann was poking up the fire in the living room. She was wearing a white night cap and a long blue robe. Jemmy saw a rifle lying on the desk.

Ann picked it up and put it in his hands. "Take this with you," she said breathlessly. "You may need it. You know Father always carries a pistol at night. Mother knows you won't get lost. She's worried about a highwayman."

"A highwayman!"

Ann nodded. "Shelby Carter was robbed the other night near the big oak tree."

"Why, I didn't know that!"

"Father told Mother, but he said not to tell the rest of us. He didn't want us to worry about him when he was on the road. That's why she's afraid to have you go out alone now."

From upstairs Mrs. Stuart called, "Ann, Ann!"

"Coming," Ann answered. At the door she looked back. "So take your gun!" she said.

Jemmy frowned at the long gun in his hand. "This is a clumsy thing for a fight on horseback," he thought. "Why, it's nearly as tall as I am. I wish I had a pistol."

In the fireplace a flame leaped high. Light danced on the sword hanging over the fireplace. Jemmy's heart beat faster as he looked at the sword. Of course! He took the sword and its scabbard down from their resting place.

In the stable yard Pete had Bayberry saddled and ready to go.

"Take care of this rifle for me," Jemmy said. He gave Pete the gun. "Now help me tie this sword to the saddle."

As he trotted down the lane, he drew the sword from its scabbard. He could reach it easily with his right hand. "I can use this if I have to," he thought. He slid it back into the scabbard and rode on through the darkness.

It was very dark. Wind sent black clouds racing across the stars and the moon. It twisted the bushes and trees along the road and blew cold on Jemmy's face.

Jemmy looked sharply to right and left. Familiar things looked strange in the darkness. There was a big oak tree two miles down the road. He would cross the fields there. Before reaching the oak, the road went up a steep hill and then down.

"I can't see a thing except the white bark of the sycamore trees," he thought. "I'll just have to feel when I've gone two miles. The road is level near the oak and that will help."

He passed the hill and the road leveled out. He spurred Bayberry on. "I wish we could run," he said to himself. "If only the moon would shine!"

At that moment the clouds began to part. Presently the moon shone like a round silver tray. Jemmy could see wheel marks in the road. Not far ahead he could see the oak tree.

Suddenly Bayberry snorted, and Jemmy's heart missed a beat. At the left of the road a man was crouching under the big tree.

Jemmy's heart rose in his throat. He began to tremble. Then he grabbed his sword and shouted at the top of his lungs. He spurred Bayberry forward at a gallop. He swung the sword above his head and yelled loudly.

The man jumped up. Jemmy saw that he had a dark cloth tied across the lower part of his face. The man stood still for a moment as if he didn't know what to do. Then he dived into the bushes and disappeared.

Jemmy turned Bayberry off the road and started across the field to the right. He felt warm all over with excitement. He slipped the sword back into its scabbard.

"I'm glad I brought the sword," he said to himself. He grinned and sat a little straighter in the saddle. He felt ready for a dozen highwaymen.

He hurried on as fast as Bayberry could go. In some places the field was frozen, and he could go fast. In other places the ground was softer, and the horse struggled through mud. Jemmy could feel it splashing against his cheeks.

More clouds crossed the sky, hiding the moon. The night was darker than ever now, and Jemmy had to guess his way. He peered ahead into the darkness. He slowed Bayberry to a walk. If he didn't see a house soon, he knew that he had come too far to the right.

Bayberry waded across a narrow brook. On the far side the land rose in a low hill. On top of the hill was a dark shadow, a clump of trees. Jemmy was growing worried now. Surely he had come far enough. He urged Bayberry on.

When he reached the top of the hill, he could see the trees more clearly. Beyond them he could see something else, something dim and white. Then the moon peeped out, and Jemmy saw the tall white house of Dr. Melton.

The trip seemed shorter when Jemmy rode back with the doctor. They met nobody.

Dr. Melton chuckled when Jemmy told him about the highwayman. "I'll bet it was your shout and not your sword that scared him," Dr. Melton said. "You boys can yell like Indians."

Back home, as Jemmy was putting the sword in its place over the fireplace, Ann and Mary came into the room.

"Oh, Jemmy, Dr. Melton says that Colly will be all right," said Ann.

"I know," Jemmy nodded. "Mandy told me."

"But the doctor got here just in time," Mary added. "She might have died if——"

She stopped and her eyes grew wide as she stared at the sword. "What are you doing with that?" she asked.

"You won't believe me," Jemmy said. He told them about the highwayman.

"Jemmy!" Ann gasped.

"Weren't you scared?" Mary asked.

"Well, yes," Jemmy admitted. "But I didn't really have much time to be scared!"

Jeb Is a Good Name

It was the morning of February 6, 1843. "What a way to celebrate my tenth birthday," Jemmy thought as he jumped out of bed.

Yesterday a man had come to look at Bayberry. "I want a horse for my wife," he said. "It must be gentle." Jemmy had hoped that Bayberry would act up. Instead he had been as gentle as a lamb. The man had offered a good price for him.

"Mother said she must talk it over with Father," Jemmy thought. "Why didn't she say that Bayberry wasn't for sale? Will she let me keep him, after all?"

After bringing the doctor home, he had hoped his mother would see that they needed Bayberry.

"Hurry, Jemmy," Colly called up the stairs. "There are birthday presents for you."

Only ten days ago Colly had been very sick. Now she was dancing up and down in the hall below. So was Victoria.

Jemmy put one leg over the stair rail and took make-believe reins in his hands. "Here I come on my horse," he cried. He slid down, face forward. At the bottom he leaped over the stair post.

Colly and Victoria laughed with delight. Then Colly gave him a piece of white paper. A smaller piece of black paper was pasted on it. "It's from Vickie and me," she said. "We made it for you ourselves."

"It's beautiful," said Jemmy, smoothing it out. "Thank you very much."

"I printed my name on the back," said Colly.

Jemmy turned the paper over. There in big capital letters was Colly's real name, Columbia Lafayette Stuart.

"It's such a long hard name, too," said Jemmy. "I'm glad you put it on the picture. Then I won't forget who made it."

"I pasted," said Victoria. She put a fat finger on the black patch.

"Do you know what it is?" asked Colly.

"It's a fine picture," Jemmy answered.

Colly waved her hands. "Tell what it is."

Jemmy hesitated. He didn't want to hurt his sisters. But he didn't know what the black spot was supposed to be. Just then Ann came down the stairs. Jemmy looked at her anxiously. She moved her lips to form the word *Bayberry*.

"Bayberry!" Jemmy exclaimed. Now he could see that the odd shape did have a tail.

"He could tell!" Colly shouted. "He could tell it was Bayberry!" She skipped to the dining room, and the others followed her.

Jemmy's favorite breakfast was waiting for them on the long dining room table. There were fried chicken, ham and grits and gravy. There were hot biscuits, peach preserves and apple butter, too. Beside Jemmy's plate was a pile of presents his sisters had made for him.

Ann had made him a pincushion with red roses on it. Bethenia had painted a picture of a horse in water colors. It was a strange-looking animal, with a big head shaped like a bucket.

Mary had a sampler for him. She had sewed his initials, J. E. B., on a square piece of cloth. Beside them she had put the date of his birth, February 6, 1833.

"Why, your initials spell a name, don't they?" Ann said. "Jeb."

"Mother, why do I have three names? All the rest of you have only two," Jemmy said.

"We named you for Judge James Ewell Brown of Wythe County," said his mother. "We liked the sound of the three names."

"I like the sound of the three initials better," Jemmy said. "Jeb is a good name."

His father handed him a small box. "Your brothers sent you this," he said.

Jemmy's hands trembled a little as he lifted the lid of the box. He couldn't imagine what it contained. Inside he found a pair of silver spurs.

Jemmy couldn't speak. Beautiful silver spurs, and he had no horse! He looked at Bethenia's picture of Bayberry. Then he looked at Colly's poor little cut-out. If only Bayberry were his!

"Did you really know my cut-out was Bayberry?" Colly wanted to know.

"I knew it was a horse right away," Jemmy said. "I had to look at it for a minute to be sure it was Bayberry himself, though."

Everybody laughed, but Jemmy didn't feel like laughing. Everything reminded him that Bayberry might be sold.

His father nodded toward the window and smiled. "Here comes Bayberry himself," he said.

Jemmy sprang to the window. His heart was pounding. Pete was leading Bayberry across the yard, toward the house.

"I'm giving you a new saddle for the horse," Mr. Stuart said.

Jemmy caught his breath and looked at his mother. She nodded. "Bayberry is yours. I don't know what we'd have done without him the other night. We'll just have to afford him."

Jemmy's shout was almost as loud as his yell at the highwayman. He rushed outdoors and threw himself into the new saddle. Then he galloped off for a ride over the farm.

VII
HORSES TO DREAM ABOUT

Heroes in fantasy and fable

IRENE
SMITH

Pegasus, the Winged Horse
A Greek legend

OF ALL THE HORSES THE WORLD HAS KNOWN, FROM THE LONG, LONG AGO to modern times, of those found in stories or living today, the most radiant in beauty and the swiftest in action is the silver-white Pegasus, a steed with a legend of glory. He plunged through the clouds and galloped across the sky like a great bird, borne by the power of his broad wings. That Pegasus lived on Mount Helicon, home of nine sisters whose father was Jupiter, the ancient Greeks knew for a fact. They believed in him as in their gods and goddesses who dwelt on high Olympus. The goddess Minerva herself had tamed Pegasus and given him to those divine maidens called the Muses.

There came a time when a fire-breathing monster, the Chimaero, was wreaking havoc in the land of Lycia. His forepart was both lion and goat and the rest of him was dragon. The ruler of Lycia, Iobates, hoped to find a hero brave enough to destroy this terror to his kingdom.

One day a gallant young warrior called Bellerophon presented himself at the court. He brought a letter of highest recommendation from the king's son-in-law, but treachery was written in the last line. The letter closed with a request that Iobates put Bellerophon to death.

The king did not know what to do. He wished to oblige his son-in-law, who was madly jealous of Bellerophon, but the laws of hospitality were strict. Iobates feared the wrath of the gods if he were to slay a guest who was lodged in his house.

The Chimaero however could do all this for him. So the king begged

Bellerophon to challenge the monster, and the young hero agreed to the undertaking. First, though, Bellerophon consulted a soothsayer, who advised him to seek help from the goddess Minerva, and to try to win the winged horse.

Bellerophon spent that night in the temple of Minerva. As he slept the goddess came to him and gave him a golden bridle. The bridle was more than something in a dream, for next morning it lay in his hand, ready to fit over the proud head of but one horse, the shining Pegasus.

Minerva had told Bellerophon to wait near a certain well where the winged horse came now and then to drink. Pegasus actually appeared overhead, and dropped down toward earth, with the sun flashing on his silvery mane. Lightly he touched the ground, then cantered about in the grass and rolled contentedly, before turning toward the well. When Pegasus came to drink he saw Bellerophon, and the gold bridle which he held. The horse did not falter, but was willing for his new master to fasten it in place, and to spring to seat on his back. They rose together toward the heavens, then soared away to the lair of the Chimaero. When they found their enemy Pegasus drew close and hovered above him while Bellerophon, reaching down, slew the monster with a single stroke.

Iobates now had to look for new ways to destroy the victorious youth, and assigned him many trials and labors. But with Pegasus to carry him through every danger, Bellerophon's successes continued, until the king was convinced that the hero was a favorite of the gods. Iobates thereupon accepted him as his heir, giving him his daughter for wife, and half the kingdom to rule.

With all that now was his, which included still the noble Pegasus, Bellerophon could well have been satisfied. But his brave deeds were so publicly admired, and he was so spoiled by lavish praises, that he at last overreached himself. He boldly commanded Pegasus to carry him to Mount Olympus so that he could see the gods. The horse had to obey, and they began ascending toward the realm of the most high.

Jupiter, seeing all, now had to teach this mortal that he had presumed too much. He sent a gadfly to sting Pegasus, who leaped so violently that his master was thrown from his back. Down, down Bellerophon fell to earth. He did not die but suffered many injuries, and remained lame and blind for the rest of his days.

So the life of the hero ended in loneliness and misery. Never again could he speed aloft on the horse's strong pinions, exulting in the wonder of their flight. The winged Pegasus returned to Helicon, the peaceful mountain, which was the lasting sourceplace of man's poetry and his song.

HENRY
WADSWORTH
LONGFELLOW

Pegasus in Pound

Once into a quiet village,
  Without haste and without heed.
In the golden prime of morning,
  Strayed the poet's winged steed.

It was Autumn, and incessant
  Piped the quails from shocks and sheaves,
And, like living coals, the apples
  Burned among the withering leaves.

Loud the clamorous bell was ringing
  From its belfry gaunt and grim;
'Twas the daily call to labor,
  Not a triumph meant for him.

Not the less he saw the landscape,
  In its gleaming vapor veiled;
Not the less he breathed the odors
  That the dying leaves exhaled.

Thus, upon the village common,
  By the school-boys he was found;
And the wise men, in their wisdom,
  Put him straightway into pound.

183

Then the sombre village crier,
 Ringing loud his brazen bell,
Wandered down the street proclaiming
 There was an estray to sell.

And the curious country people
 Rich and poor, and young and old,
Came in haste to see this wondrous
 Winged steed, with mane of gold.

Thus the day passed, and the evening
 Fell, with vapors cold and dim;
But it brought no food nor shelter,
 Brought no straw nor stall for him.

Patiently, and still expectant,
 Looked he through the wooden bars,
Saw the moon rise o'er the landscape,
 Saw the tranquil, patient stars;

Till at length the bell at midnight
 Sounded from its dark abode,
And from out a neighboring farmyard,
 Loud the cock Alectryon crowed.

Then, with nostrils wide distended,
 Breaking from his iron chain,
And unfolding far his pinions,
 To those stars he soared again.

On the morrow, when the village
 Woke to all its toil and care,
Lo! the strange steed had departed,
 And they knew not when nor where.

But they found, upon the greensward
 Where his struggling hoofs had trod,
Pure and bright, a fountain flowing
 From the hoof-marks in the sod.

From that hour, the fount unfailing
Gladdens the whole region round,
Strengthening all who drink its waters,
While it soothes them with its sound.

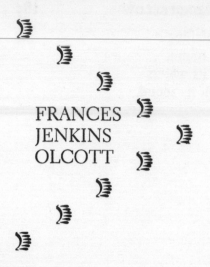

FRANCES
JENKINS
OLCOTT

The Mud Pony

ONCE THERE WAS AN INDIAN CAMP, AND IN IT LIVED A BOY. HIS PARENTS were very poor, and had no ponies. The boy was fond of ponies, and often sat on the bank of the creek, while the other boys were watering theirs.

One day the boy made up his mind to have a pony of his own. He crossed the creek, and got some wood, and built a little corral. He then took a quantity of sticky mud to the corral, and made two ponies of mud. He got some white clay, and put it on the head of one; so that it was white-faced.

Then the boy was happy! Every morning he went to the corral, and carried his mud ponies down to the creek, and dipped their noses in the water. Then he took them back to the corral again. He heaped grass and green cottonwood shoots before them, and took as good care of them as if they were real ponies.

Well, one day the boy went to see his mud ponies, and he found that one of them had crumbled to dust. He felt so badly that he cried; and after that he took even better care of the one that was left. It was the one with the white face.

On another morning, while the boy was in his corral, the people broke camp, and went on a buffalo hunt. The boy's parents looked everywhere for him, and when they could not find him, they had to go away without him. And when he went back to the place where the camp had been, all the people were gone!

He cried and cried, and wandered about picking up pieces of dried meat the people had thrown away. When night came, he lay down and cried himself to sleep. Then he dreamed that a white-faced pony came to him, and said:

"My Son, you are poor, and Mother Earth has taken pity on you, and has given me to you. I am a part of her."

Well, when the boy woke up, it was broad daylight. He rose and went to his corral to look after his mud pony. And what did he see standing in front of the corral, but a fine little pony with a white face! It was pawing the ground and tossing its mane.

The boy rubbed his eyes to see if it was a real pony. He went up to it, and stroked its sides; and it whinnied with joy, and sniffed at his fingers. So he got a piece of rope, and put it round the pony's neck, and led it down to the water.

But the pony would not drink at all, and said like the one in his dream:—

"My Son, you are poor, and Mother Earth has taken pity on you, and has given me to you. I am your Mud Pony."

Then the boy was filled with joy, and rubbed the pony down, and was very proud of it. Just as he was going to lead it back to the corral, the Pony said:—

"My Son, you must do all I tell you to do, and some day you will become a great Chief. Now, jump on my back, and we will find your people. Do not try to guide me, for I know where to go."

The boy, delighted, jumped on the Pony's back, and away they went swiftly over the plain. They travelled all that day, and when evening was come, they reached a place where the people had camped the night before. But they had all gone on farther.

The boy jumped down, and turned the Pony loose to graze, but it would not eat. It only said: "Do not mind me. Go and find something to eat for yourself." So the boy wandered about the deserted camp, picking up bits of food the people had dropped. When his hunger was satisfied, he lay down and went to sleep. In the morning he rose, and jumped on the Pony, and away they went across the plain.

In the evening, the same thing happened as before; they stopped at a deserted camp, the boy ate and slept, and in the morning he and the Pony journeyed on. The next night, they reached the camp where the people were stopping. Then the Pony said:—

"Leave me here outside the camp, and go to your tepee, and wake your mother. I will stay here and take care of myself, for I do not need anything to eat and drink, because I am a part of Mother Earth. All I need is a blanket to keep the dew and rain off me, or I shall melt. Tomorrow, when the people break camp, stay behind, and I will be ready for you."

The boy entered the camp, as the Pony told him to do, and went into his parents' tepee. He sat down, and threw some dried grass on the coals in the fireplace, and the flames blazed up. Then he went to his mother's bed, and woke her, saying, "Mother, here I am!"

His mother opened her eyes, and at first she thought she was dreaming, then she put out her hand and touched him. And when she knew it was really her son, she rose with joy, and waked her husband. He got up, too, and threw logs on the fire, and ran and called the boy's relations. They came crowding in, and were glad to see him safe and well.

The next morning the people broke camp, and the boy told them to go on without him. And they did. The Pony came, and the boy mounted on its back, and away they went swiftly across the plain. At night they caught up with the people, and the Pony stayed outside the camp. In the morning it happened as before. So it was for four days.

On the fourth night, the Pony said: "My Son, take me into the camp, so that the people may see what a nice Pony you have. The Chief will hear about me, and wish to buy me. He will offer you several horses. Take them, and let him have me in exchange. But he will not keep me long!"

So the boy rode the Pony straight into the camp, and the people were astonished to see him on its back. When they examined it, they said: "Why, it looks like a mud pony, such as boys smooth down with their fingers. It is a wonderful pony!"

When the Chief heard about it, he sent for the boy. He welcomed him respectfully and made him sit on a cushion. Then he said:—

"My Son, I have sent for you to eat with me. I wish to tell you that I like your pony, and will give you four of my best horses for it."

The boy replied: "I have listened to the great Chief. I will let the Chief have my pony."

The Chief was pleased, and his wife filled a wooden bowl with dried meat and soup; and put two horn spoons into the bowl. She set this before her husband and the boy, and they ate together.

After that the Chief had the four horses caught, and drove them to the boy's tepee. He took the Pony, and led it to his own corral. He put grass before it, but it would not eat. He piled young cottonwood boughs before it, but still it would not eat.

A few days after, scouts came riding into the camp, and they said that a great herd of Buffalo was near. So the men got on their horses, and rode to the hunt, and the Chief went with them, mounted on the Mud Pony. He soon far outstripped the rest, and killed many Buffalo. But as he was riding over the plain, the Pony staggered and nearly fell. Its feet had become un-jointed, and it was ruined.

The Chief was terribly angry, and, returning to the camp, he ordered the boy to give him back his four horses, and take the Pony. The boy was delighted, and led his Mud Pony home. In a few days it was as well as ever. Then the Chief wished to have it back, but the boy would not give it to him for any number of horses.

Well, from that day on, when the boy went hunting, mounted on the Mud Pony, he killed more Buffalo than the men did. And when he went on the war-path, no one could hurt him, but he always conquered the enemy. After a few years he became a great Chief. He still loved his Mud Pony very much, and tied Eagle feathers on its mane and tail, and covered it carefully at night with a warm blanket.

But one night, he forgot to cover it, and he had a dream. He thought that the Mud Pony came to him and said: "My Son, you are no longer poor. My doings are over. I am returning to Mother Earth, for I am a part of her."

And when he woke in the morning, he found that it was raining hard. He got up and ran to the corral to put a blanket on the Pony, but he could not find the animal anywhere. Then on the side of the hill, he saw a little pile of mud, still in the shape of a pony. And when he saw this, he went home sorrowfully to his tepee.

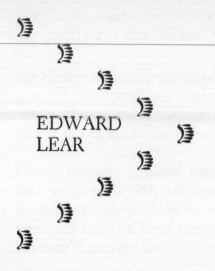

EDWARD
LEAR

The Nutcrackers
and the Sugar-tongs

I

The nutcrackers sate by a plate on the table;
  The Sugar-tongs sate by a plate at his side;
And the Nutcrackers said, "Don't you wish we were able
  Along the blue hills and the green meadows to ride?
Must we drag on this stupid existence forever,
  So idle and weary, so full of remorse,
While every one else takes his pleasure, and never
  Seems happy unless he is riding a horse?

II

"Don't you think we could ride without being instructed,
  Without any saddle or bridle or spur?
Our legs are so long, and so aptly constructed,
  I'm sure that an accident could not occur.
Let us all of a sudden hop down from the table,
  And hustle downstairs, and each jump on a horse!
Shall we try? Shall we go? Do you think we are able?"
  The Sugar-tongs answered distinctly, "Of course!"

190

III

So down the long staircase they hopped in a minute;
  The Sugar-tongs snapped, and the Crackers said "Crack!"
The stable was open, the horses were in it:
  Each took out a pony, and jumped on his back.
The Cat in a fright scrambled out of the doorway;
  The Mice tumbled out of a bundle of hay;
The brown and white Rats, and the black ones from Norway,
  Screamed out, "They are taking the horses away!"

IV

The whole of the household was filled with amazement:
  The Cups and the Saucers danced madly about;
The Plates and the Dishes looked out of the casement;
  The Salt-cellar stood on his head with a shout;
The Spoons, with a clatter, looked out of the lattice;
  The Mustard-pot climbed up the gooseberry-pies;
The Soup-ladle peeped through a heap of veal-patties,
  And squeaked with a ladle-like scream of surprise.

V

The Frying-pan said, "It's an awful delusion!"
  The Tea-kettle hissed, and grew black in the face;
And they all rushed downstairs in the wildest confusion
  To see the great Nutcracker-Sugar-tong race.
And out of the stable, with screamings and laughter
  (Their ponies were cream-coloured, speckled with brown),
The Nutcrackers first, and the Sugar-tongs after,
  Rode all round the yard, and then all round the town.

VI

They rode through the street, and they rode by the station;
  They galloped away to the beautiful shore;
In silence they rode, and "made no observation,"
  Save this: "We will never go back any more!"
And still you might hear, till they rode out of hearing,
  The Sugar-tongs snap, and the Crackers say "Crack!"
Till, far in the distance their forms disappearing,
  They faded away; and they never came back!

BARON MUNCHHAUSEN

The Horse on the Church Tower

I SET OUT ON MY FIRST TRIP TO RUSSIA IN THE DEPTHS OF WINTER. FOR IN spring and fall the roads in Poland, Courland and Latvia are so muddy that it is impossible to make any progress, and in summer they are so bone-dry that you choke and cough all the time. Therefore I traveled in winter, and on horseback, since that is the most practical way to go. Unfortunately, I felt colder and colder every day, for I was wearing only a thin coat, and the whole land was so covered with snow that I frequently saw no trace of a road, no signposts, nothing but snow, snow, snow.

One evening, stiff and tired, I dismounted from my good steed, and fastened the halter to a branch of a tree that was sticking up out of the snow. Then I lay down on my coat, my pistol under my arm, and fell asleep.

When I awoke, the sun was shining. And when I looked around, I had to rub my eyes. For there I was right in the middle of a village. Moreover, I had been sleeping in the cemetery. Thunder and Blitzen, I thought, for what healthy—even if half frozen—man likes the idea of sleeping in a churchyard. My horse had disappeared. And yet I had staked him carefully right beside me.

Suddenly I heard a loud whinnying high above my head. I looked up and saw the poor animal dangling from the weathervane of the church tower. It was whinnying and kicking wildly; naturally, it didn't find the position very comfortable. But how in the world had it got up there on the church tower?

Slowly, the explanation dawned on me. Village and church had been completely snowed in, and what I had in the darkness taken for a branch of a tree was in fact the weathervane of the village church. There had been a sudden thaw and I had sunk down, inch by inch, along with the melting snow, until I woke up among the gravestones.

What was I to do now? Since I am a good shot, I took my pistol, aimed at the halter, and shot it in two. The horse fell upon the soft earth of the cemetery quite unharmed, and very happy he was to have solid ground under his hoofs again. I swung into the saddle and continued on my way.

FLORENCE K.
PETERSON

Carrots and Hay
for Saint Nicholas' Horse

N AME A DATE—THE *best* TO YOU OF ALL THE YEAR—AND 99 OUT OF A HUN-
dred—you're going to say Christmas, December 25th!

Yet here is something which perhaps you did not know. In German and
Dutch households the Feast of Saint Nicholas, December 6th, far over-
shadows Christmas! It is the night that the good Saint, his helper Black
Peter and his horse, make the expected rounds of the homes of every boy
and girl—good and bad.

Excited children whisper, "Will I be given a golden orange because I was
good?" or "Will there be chunks of coal because I was naughty?"

Stockings are hung carefully—but more precisely placed are the shoes.
There is a very special reason for setting them side by side beneath the hearth.
There is Saint Nicholas' horse—faithful and wonderful animal, who has
been carrying a tremendous load of all sorts of things high over the roof
tops.

Such an animal—the bearer of delectable goodies, and the "trusted" of
good old Saint Nicholas and his helper—deserves and earns the affection of
all boys and girls. To be sure that he enjoys a good supper, each child, before
closing his eyes for the wonderful dreams which precede a special day, fills
his shoes with the freshest bits of sweet-smelling hay and the youngest, most
tender carrots he can find . . . all for Saint Nicholas' horse!

194

Whether anyone ever actually saw Saint Nicholas' horse is a great big question. But that he IS is certain . . . and that he is well-fed and happy with his fare of carrots and hay from eager, enthusiastic children is proven by the fact that he reciprocates with gifts of joy and gladness every December 6th.

*   *   *

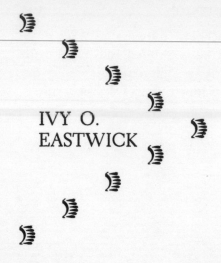

IVY O.
EASTWICK

The Three Horses

THREE HORSES CAME
to the meadow's edge—
they poked their noses
over the hedge.

One was gray,
one was white,
and one was black
as a winter's night.

I patted the white horse,
I stroked the gray,
and I rode the black horse
far away.

We went by the wood,
we went by the hill
we galloped along
by Medlicott Mill.

Oh! if my mother
should question you—
I may be back
in an hour or two.

VIII

HORSES TO THANK

Faithful services to man and country

MARGARET
LEIGHTON

Comanche of the Seventh

(The terrible cavalry encounters of the Civil War took high toll of the horses in this country. Soldiers combed the countryside and took away every horse they could find for service at the front. The Indian Wars followed, climaxed in the valley of the Little Big Horn in Montana, June 25, 1876, when the Sioux destroyed Custer's troops of the Seventh Cavalry. The great horse Comanche was the only survivor of the massacre. Mechanized warfare has mercifully replaced the cavalry and artillery horse.)

THE COLUMN FOUND ITS FIRST SIOUX CAMPSITE BY NOON OF THE SECOND day, and after that the trail left by the hostiles was wide and plain for everyone to see. Comanche snorted and shied wildly as he caught the scent he loathed and feared. His eyes rolled and Keogh had to use his spurs to get him past where the first tepee had stood. "What possesses you? You're getting worse than ever. We'll be following these varmints from now on. You'll have to get used to them," the captain told him sternly. But it took the buckskin the rest of the day's march to become reconciled to the Indians' trail.

The tall, cheerful Crow scouts who had joined with the Arikara now showed the same uneasiness and alarm as their allies at the size of the encampments. "Otoe Sioux! Otoe Sioux!" they exclaimed, over and over again. "Too many Sioux! Too many Sioux!" Nothing they nor Charlie Reynolds could say, however, could convince General Custer that they would find anything

199

he could not handle with ease. "With the Seventh I could lick all the Indians on the plains," he had said, long before, and to him it still seemed true.

The weather was dry and dust billowed chokingly about men and horses. To prevent dust clouds from rising high enough to betray their approach to the foe they were stalking, the different companies were ordered not to march directly behind one another. For further precautions they camped at night in spots as sheltered from view as could be found, lit only small cooking fires which they quenched as soon as possible and discontinued all trumpet calls.

On the evening of the 24th of June, the third day out, Keogh saved a comfortable camping site next to Troop I's bivouac for Captain Benteen's H Company, which had the rear-guard duty. They had barely settled down when an orderly came through the dark to summon the officers to the commander's tent. They groped their way past horse herds, through clumps of sage and bullberry bushes, and over sleeping men to where a single candle gleamed.

"The Indians' trail leads on across the next divide into the valley of the Little Big Horn," General Custer told the assembled officers. "We will take up our march again tonight. I wish to get as close as possible to the Indians before sunrise. Then we'll lie concealed during the day, study the situation and plan our attack for dawn of the 26th."

As they returned to their commands, Benteen clapped Keogh on the shoulder. "It's Troop I's turn for rear guard, I hear," he said. "My sympathy, Captain. You'll have to herd those unspeakable mules, and in the dark, besides. It took me over an hour to get them across the last stream we forded."

"Thanks for your sympathy," Keogh grunted. "I'll be needing it. However, we have some notable curses in the Gaelic which are said on good authority to have set a strong man's teeth six inches back in his head. Would you be thinking I should try them on the mules?"

Benteen laughed and shook his head. "Good old Anglo-Saxon is the only language an American army mule understands," he answered. "I've come to believe that Job in the Bible could never have had anything to do with mules or he wouldn't have kept his reputation for patience. Well, good luck, old man."

The Seventh's pack train had been troublesome from the start. The mules had been trained only to pull wagons. They rebelled at their new duties and used every mulish trick they knew to hamper the packers. They squealed, kicked, bit and humped their backs stubbornly against the packs and, once loaded, did their utmost to shake their burdens loose.

Comanche looked on with well-bred disapproval while Keogh waited for the shouting, sweating men to finish their work. Every line in the horse's frame seemed to show that *he* was a cavalry mount who knew his duty, and that he wished no association whatever with creatures such as mules.

Somehow the pack train was loaded and assembled by the time the regiment moved on again an hour before midnight. It had always lagged far behind the column and in the pitch blackness of this moonless night its difficulties were tripled. During the long dark hours Comanche carried his master many miles farther than the direct distance traveled in his efforts to speed up the pack train and keep it and his rear guard from becoming hopelessly lost from the command.

Crossing Mud Creek in the dark took over an hour and a half of struggle. After this delay it was decided that each troop must take charge of its own pack animals, and the pace increased a bit.

They halted at two o'clock in the morning. Keogh ordered his men to unsaddle in order to rest their mounts. The only water to be found, however, was so alkaline that even Comanche, thirsty though he was, gave one disgusted sniff and refused it. The coffee made with it was undrinkable. The men breakfasted on bacon and hardtack and got what little sleep they could until eight o'clock, when they moved on for ten miles more.

This stop was made in a steep, wooded ravine between two high ridges. There was no water here, either, and orders came to build no fires. The day had dawned clear and bright and the men were now fully awake, excited, and in high spirits. After their months of preparation and the long march from Fort Lincoln, they were to see action at last! If they had really caught up with the Sioux, the next day might mark the end of their chase. All that remained was to herd the hostiles back to the reservations, bringing an early close to the campaign.

Keogh had led his rear guard into the ravine last of all. As he swung wearily out of Comanche's saddle, Captain Yates, of Troop F, hailed him. "Did you see any Injuns behind you? Some have evidently been following us," he said. "A couple of boxes were lost out of one of our packs and I sent Sergeant Curtis with two men back to find them. He found the boxes, all right, but a Sioux brave was sitting on one of them, trying to open it with his tomahawk. He jumped on his pony and galloped out of range, then followed along the top of the ridge, watching us. Looks like we aren't going to surprise Sitting Bull, after all."

Keogh left orders for Comanche's care, then joined a group of officers who stood gathered about the Arikara scouts at one of their ceremonies. The Indians, in full war paint and regalia, were ringed around their medicine man.

While they beat monotonously on their war drums he anointed each one in turn with some substance and chanted in a high, wailing voice.

"Hello, Myles," Tom Custer said. "The old fellow's praying to the Great Spirit to protect his men from the Sioux. How about you and me getting a little of that medicine for ourselves? We may need it," he added, with his abrupt, loud laugh.

Keogh smiled and shook his head. "This is all I'll be using, thanks," he said, touching the medal at his throat. Then he repeated Yates's news, and Tom Custer gave an exclamation. "I'm going to tell that to Autie right away. He's up ahead with Charlie Reynolds, Bloody Knife and the chief Indian scouts, on a peak they call the Crow's Nest."

Within a short time General Custer returned and the officers were summoned. "The scouts have located a Sioux village in the valley of the Little Big Horn," he began, in his brusque, rapid voice. "They seem to think it's a big one, though to tell you the truth I couldn't see it at all and I have as good eyes as anyone. Now Sergeant Curtis's report of Indians in our rear, and those that the scouts have noticed along the ridges mean that there's no further chance to conceal our movements. What's more, since they know we're coming, the Sioux'll doubtless strike camp and scatter, and then the whole job of rounding them up will have to be done over again.

"I mean to cross the divide immediately, ride down into the valley and attack any Indians that may be there before they can get away."

Quickly he rattled out his orders. Each troop must detail seven men to herd their mules with the pack-train. Together with Troop B, now the rear guard, they should be enough to protect the vital ammunition and supplies.

To their intense disappointment and disgust, Mills, McBane and Korn, the blacksmith, found themselves assigned to the pack train. "As if we hadn't had enough of mules last night!" McBane grumbled, watching his comrades ride off up the dusty slope of the divide.

The cavalry column crossed the summit of the ridge and started down into the valley of the Little Big Horn just before noon. A short distance from the top they halted again, while Custer and Lieutenant Cooke, his tall, bewhiskered adjutant, conferred. The regiment was then divided into three sections. Major Reno, with Troops A, G and M was to command the advance. Captain Benteen was given Troops H, D and K, while Custer kept C, E, F, I and L for himself. The pack train was to follow along on their trail.

While the officers were receiving their orders, Charlie Reynolds, Bloody Knife and Bouyer, the half-breed interpreter, rode up to General Custer.

Reynolds was gloomily silent, staring at his horse's ears, but Bouyer spoke up in obvious agitation. "General," he said, "there are more Sioux in that valley than any of us have ever seen before. If we go in there we'll never come out."

Custer gave an impatient exclamation and turned away. After a moment's hesitation, Bloody Knife lifted his dark face to the blazing noonday sun and made a sweeping gesture of farewell. "I shall not see you go down behind the hills tonight," he said in his own tongue. He turned his pony, nevertheless, and followed the general, with the other two scouts behind him.

As the regiment was about to march, Keogh saw Benteen with the three troops of his new battalion start off to the left. Keogh urged Comanche forward to overtake him. "Where are you going, Benteen?" he called.

Benteen waved his arm in the direction of the irregular, broken skyline. "I've got orders to scout for Injuns in those hills and drive them all before me," he shouted back.

The remainder of the Seventh, in column of fours, moved down the slope along the bed of a small creek called the Sundance. Although the ground was rough and thickly timbered they rode at a brisk trot. Men and horses had had little rest and all were parched with thirst, but the thrill of the chase was in their pulses and few of them now felt their weariness.

They were nearly down to the level when another Indian campsite appeared before them. The scouts were already there, examining the still-warm ashes of the campfires. In the center stood a single tepee, a large and handsome burial lodge, containing the body of a dead warrior in full ceremonial dress.

From here they could see some distance down into a wide valley through which curved a blue, tree-bordered stream. "That river's the Little Big Horn," someone said. Above the trees a heavy dust-cloud was rising.

Suddenly a shout reached them from one of the scouts who had climbed a nearby hillock. "There go your Injuns, running like devils!" he yelled.

Custer turned swiftly to Reno, who had reined in beside him. "Take your battalion and go after them. Don't let them get away. I'll support you with the whole outfit," he ordered. "Take all the scouts with you."

Reno signaled his men forward. While the five remaining companies prepared to follow, Lieutenant Cooke, the adjutant, paused on his powerful white charger. "Come along with me, Myles," he said to Keogh. "I'm going after the major to make sure he understood the general's orders. It'll give us a chance to water our mounts."

They caught up with Reno where he sat his restless horse waiting for his troops to cross the river. His sallow face was flushed with the heat and his eyes dark-ringed. "What are you two doing here?" he demanded sharply, at sight of them.

"Why, I'm going in with the advance and Myles Keogh is coming, too," Cooke said, laughing. Then, more seriously, while Comanche and his own horse drank deeply of the clear, swift-flowing water, he gave the general's message. "The village is about two and a half miles away and they are running. General Custer orders you to move at as rapid a gait as you think prudent and charge afterward. You will be supported by the whole outfit."

"Where's Custer?" Reno demanded.

Cooke gestured back toward the column and Reno nodded, then gave his attention to his own men. The two other officers wheeled about, for the leading troop of Custer's section was already in motion.

"Reno looks nervous. Do you suppose the Crows, with their 'Otoe Sioux,' have got him worried?" Cooke commented, his long black side whiskers streaming in the breeze as they trotted along side by side.

"Well, the start of a fight is an anxious time for a married man with a family. I often wonder how they endure it," Keogh said soberly. "That's where we bachelors have the advantage, Cookie. As for me, I have no care in the world, for Comanche here's all the family I've got."

"You've had him a long time, haven't you?" Cooke said, eyeing the buckskin's strong, smooth action. "I think he outranks even Dandy, the general's horse, and he got him before the Washita fight. He's back with the pack train—the general's riding his sorrel, Vic, today."

"Sure and there's no horse in the world outranks Comanche!" Keogh declared, and the buckskin, hearing his name repeated in the conversation, pricked back his ears and tossed his head.

Pounding hoofs behind them caught their attention. It was Girard, one of Reno's scouts. "Lieutenant Cooke!" he called. They slowed their horses and he ranged alongside. "Major Reno wanted me to tell you that the Sioux aren't running. They're coming out in force straight at him—a lot of them," he said. "He thought the general should know."

"All right. I'll tell him," Cooke nodded. Girard turned back to Reno, while the others rode on. They took their places in the column, Cooke beside Custer, Keogh at the head of Troop I. Behind Custer's cavalry flag and fluttering red-and-blue, two-starred pennant, they moved downstream, still on the east side of the river, then turned abruptly to the right and galloped up into the brown bluffs. Dust rose behind them, blotting them from view.

Out of that dust cloud into which they vanished so completely, only two men ever rode back. First, Sergeant Kanipe of C Troop brought a message from the general to hurry the pack train. Later, Trumpeter Martin, Custer's orderly, carried another message to Benteen. "Benteen, Come On, Big Village. Be Quick. Bring Packs. Cooke, Adjutant. P.S. Bring packs," was George Armstrong Custer's last message.

No other man of all those five gallant companies was ever seen alive again. The lone survivor was one horse—*Comanche*.

How they met their end is a mystery that can never be lifted, for Comanche, who alone saw it all and lived, could not speak. Comanche could not tell their story, but a little of it could be pieced together from their tracks along the bluffs, from fragments told long afterwards by the Sioux and Cheyennes who fought them and from the tragic debris left on the battlefield where they died.

They galloped along those sunny bluffs with the dust swirling high and the thunder of hoofbeats in their ears. At a lofty point they paused to look down into the valley and saw, swimming through summer haze, the brown tepees of a vast Indian encampment that stretched into the distance for three miles along the river.

Nearer, in the valley below them, mounted, blue-clad figures were approaching another dust cloud raised by Indian warriors who wheeled their ponies back and forth and howled their shrill, yelping war cries. Reno was charging the Sioux. At this sight Custer took off his hat and waved it in salute while the men behind him broke into a cheer, dimly glimpsed and faintly heard by some of the men below.

On they went, then, along the ridges over ground broken and cut by gullies, dotted with thick, tall patches of sage-brush and cactus and coarse grass. Then, finally, down the slope of a coulee toward the blue river where pony tracks showed that a ford must lie somewhere ahead.

Before they reached the river they were brought to a sudden stop. A host of painted, feathered warriors rose as though from out of the dusty earth of the ravine that opened before them. Others clustered thickly along the slopes of the ridges and more came riding up from the valley.

The village which Custer had been following from the Rosebud was only one of a dozen equally large, already here. Not only many tribes of Sioux, but fierce Northern Cheyennes as well had joined Sitting Bull. They had formed the largest encampment of Indians ever assembled on the plains for a great and final battle in defense of their last hunting grounds. Resolved to fight to the death rather than yield, they had watched Custer's approach along the bluffs, and they were ready for him.

From every hillock and depression, coulee and clump of brush they poured their storms of bullets and arrows. The men of the five doomed companies who survived the shock of that first attack retreated to higher ground. When they dismounted on the L shaped ridge and turned about to fight, however, gunsmoke and dust were so thick in the air that they could barely see each other. It hid the enemies who crept ever closer under the fatally abundant cover, shooting as they came. Even the trumpets, blaring their orders, were all but drowned out by the yells of the savages, the shouts of the troopers, the screams of wounded horses and the deafening crash of gunfire.

More than two hundred troopers, with carbines that jammed when they grew hot, were facing more than ten times that many well-armed warriors!

Troop I had retreated in good order and they fought with stubborn valor under their captain's leadership. They held a steady, desperate line on the lead-swept angle of the ridge where they made their stand. Years afterward the Sioux and Cheyennes told tales of a black-mustached captain in buckskins who rode his mount back and forth between two separated platoons of troopers, trying to draw them together. Time and again he saved men by turning his horse between them and the enemy.

How he stayed alive so long, exposing himself so recklessly, was a wonder to them all. His mount was already bleeding from many wounds, but it responded gallantly to his every signal. Could the horse be bullet proof, like the one the Hunkpapa Sioux had in their camp, long ago? Could the silver medal that flashed at the man's bared throat be medicine strong enough to keep their arrows away? In the end horse and rider went down, swept under with the last few survivors by the charging wave of Gall's warriors.

"The bravest man we ever fought," said Two Moon, the Cheyenne chief.

Comanche had been bowled over and dazed by the rush of the red horsemen. After a while, with a painful effort, he struggled to his feet and stood swaying dizzily. His saddle had turned under his belly, his blanket and pad were gone and one cheek strap of his bridle was cut. His bit dangled loose, although the throat latch kept the bridle on him.

His master lay on the ground, motionless and unresponsive and silent in the midst of other still figures in dusty blue. Beyond, on the highest point of the ridge the horse could see through the smoke and dust where Indians swarmed about a last, small, flag-topped cluster of soldiers.

Gunfire rattled, gradually lessened, then was still. In its place now came the high, exultant war whoops of the victorious Sioux and Cheyennes. General Custer and his five troops of the Seventh Cavalry had fought their last fight.

Somehow Comanche kept his feet in spite of his wounds throughout the rest of the afternoon. All about him Indians galloped their ponies jubilantly over the battlefield, while others scalped, stripped and pillaged the quiet, helpless dead. They passed the buckskin many times but did not harm him further nor try to drive him away.

"He is too badly hurt to be useful to us. See, he bleeds from many places," they said. "He is a faithful horse. Let him stay beside his master. His master was a brave chief."

They looked often at the medal about Keogh's neck, but they did not touch it. "This man's medicine was very strong in battle," they told each other. "It must have come from that round thing he wears that shines like the bright full moon. It would be dangerous to remove it or take his scalp while he wears it."

Dimly Comanche could still hear shooting, but it came from far away, from somewhere up the stream. The sun set in a hot red ball and the Indians went back to their village. With dusk, silence, deep and profound, settled over the battlefield. During the night thirst drove the horse to search for water. He made his way to the river and drank deep, then stood for a long time letting the cool running stream wash about him. Then slowly, agonizingly, he limped back up the slope to take up his vigil again. He was drawn there by a power stronger than his fear and pain—his steadfast devotion to all that was left of his captain.

Below, in the valley, great fires burned in the village, drums beat and Indian women wailed shrilly for their dead. All through the night and the next day Comanche waited, for what he did not know. Toward evening smoke rolled up from the floor of the valley where the Indians had set fire to the grass. Screened by the smoke, they struck their tepees and set off toward the mountains, leaving Custer's dead behind them. They left also the shattered remnants of Reno's and Benteen's battalions and of the pack train. They had beaten them back and held them besieged for two long days and nights on a hill three miles up the river.

The Indians started to march away before sunset and they were still passing when darkness came, a flowing river of people and horses half a mile wide and three miles long, powerful and unhurried as an army division. Their pony herd was like a vast brown carpet dragged up the valley.

Then came another long night, another sunrise and another hot and parching day to be endured. In the middle of the morning a dust cloud appeared on the horizon and moved up the river. Comanche lifted his head and whinnied weakly as he caught the familiar sounds and smells of troops on the march, far below in the valley. They were the men of Terry and Gibbon arriving at last, but far too late. The buckskin tried to take a few steps toward them, but pain overwhelmed him and his head drooped again.

The next day grim-faced men in blue came riding along the bluffs, following the trail Custer's troops had left. Among them were the few survivors of Troop I, living only because they had been assigned to the pack train. Hushed with horror and pity, they set to work at the sad task of burying their dead comrades. Suddenly, on a slope just off the main ridge a trooper caught sight of a buckskin horse. He stood alone, the only erect and living thing on all that silent field. Blood oozed slowly from him; his head hung almost to the ground.

"There's a wounded cavalry horse over here, Lieutenant Nowlan," a man called. "He's in bad shape."

"Poor fellow," Nowlan said. "The kindest thing will be to shoot him and put him out of his misery."

He drew his pistol and moved close. Slowly the animal lifted his head, gave a faint whinny and took an uncertain step toward the officer who had been his master's friend. "Why, it's Comanche!" Nowlan cried, and lowered his pistol. His voice caught in his throat. "It's Keogh's Comanche!" he whispered hoarsely. He put his arms around the buckskin's neck and pressed his forehead against the rough, blood-caked coat. Tears made muddy streaks down the dusty stubble of his face. "Old Comanche, right here with poor Myles to the last."

The other men came hurrying to the scene. "Yes, it's the captain's charger!" Blacksmith Korn exclaimed. "He's hurt bad, sir, but he's lasted this long. I think we maybe could save him, Lieutenant."

"Of course we'll save him!" Nowlan declared. "Try to get him down to the river, Korn. Take it slow and easy."

With eager help from Mills, McBane and the others, Korn led Comanche down the slope to the river, where he gently bathed and dressed his many wounds. Then he led him carefully to where General Terry had set up his camp at the foot of the bluffs on the west bank of the stream. The wounded from Reno and Benteen's battalions had been carried down from their hilltop and now lay there in an improvised field hospital.

Korn, Mills and McBane escorted Comanche, limping slowly and painfully, into the camp. At sight of him the swift word spread. "It's Comanche. It's

Captain Keogh's charger, old Comanche!" Soon all that was left of the Seventh Cavalry and most of Terry's column, too, had gathered around. They touched him gently, reverently. They looked with pity and wonder at his wounds, and spoke to each other in hushed tones almost as though they were in church.

Men who had endured the long ordeal of the battle and held their emotions in check through all that time now felt tears flowing without restraint and without shame. "Good old Comanche!" they said, over and over again.

That night the column started on its way down the Little Big Horn River to where the *Far West* waited at the juncture with the Big Horn. They began their march at night, hoping to spare the wounded men from the withering heat of the day. Carrying them in the darkness proved to be worse, however. The eight soldiers detailed to bear each litter could not see their way and stumbled so often over the rough ground that the wounded suffered intolerably.

The Crow scouts had solved their problem by loading White Swan, their wounded comrade, on an Indian travois dragged behind a pony. The springy poles proved far easier on him than the hand-carried litters. The soldiers, therefore, slung the litters on long poles, also, carried between two horses or mules, and the wounded cavalrymen passed the remaining sixteen miles of the journey to the steamer more comfortably.

Korn, Mills and McBane led Comanche carefully and tenderly, pausing often to let him rest and to give him water. When the column reached the *Far West*, Captain Marsh had comfortable places ready on the vessel for the wounded men. For Comanche, too, there was a bed prepared in the extreme stern. His willing attendants gathered armfuls of the long grass that grew in the flats beside the river to make it soft for him. When he was finally aboard and bedded down, the wounded troopers set up a faint, shaky cheer in his honor.

Veterinarian Stein now attended further to the buckskin's hurts. There were seven major wounds, he reported. Three bone hits and four flesh wounds.

Captain Marsh had held his boat in the treacherous current although the river was receding rapidly from its high level of spring floodtime. When all the wounded were safely stowed, General Terry came aboard.

"Captain Marsh," he said. "You are about to start a trip with fifty-two wounded men aboard your boat. This is a bad river to navigate and accidents are frequent. I beg you to use all the skill you possess, all the caution you can command, to make your journey safely." He paused, then continued even more earnestly. "Captain, you have the most precious cargo a boat ever carried."

Soberly and with emotion the veteran pilot promised. The *Far West* cast off, swung into midstream and began its long journey. The river was full of shallows and whirlpools, rocks and mudbanks. It was necessary, however, to travel "full steam ahead" to hold her to her course in the twisting current. In spite of all Grant Marsh's skill and care the steamer crashed through willows, caromed wildly against mud banks and seemed at every moment in danger of being stranded on rocks or swept away and wrecked in rapids. Down the Big Horn, down the Yellowstone, finally down the Missouri they labored, to arrive at Bismarck safely at last. They had made the 950 mile journey in fifty-four hours.

At Bismarck ambulances transported the wounded men to Fort Lincoln. Comanche was led across a wooden ramp into a wagon and carried to the fort. There a special belly-band sling was constructed for him in which he was suspended for over a year. Dr. Stein and Blacksmith Korn gave him daily care.

John Burkman, Custer's orderly, had brought Dandy safely back to the fort, but Dandy had been shipped back to Michigan to the general's father. A sad souvenir of the battle where the old man had lost three sons, a son-in-law and a grandson! The silent, faithful Burkman had always had the care of Custer's mounts, and now he was assigned to Comanche as the horse's personal attendant.

By the spring of 1878 the buckskin was able to move about without assistance. Colonel Sturgis, who had resumed command of the Seventh, ordered that Comanche be shown special consideration always.

"Comanche, he's the second commanding officer of the regiment," the cavalrymen explained.

On April 10, 1878, Colonel Sturgis issued the following order.

> Headquarters, Seventh U.S. Cavalry
> Fort Abraham Lincoln, Dakota Territory
> April 10, 1878

General Orders No. 7.

1. The horse known as "Comanche," being the only living representative of the bloody tragedy of the Little Big Horn, Montana, June 25, 1876, his kind treatment and comfort should be a matter of special pride and solicitude on the part of the 7th Cavalry, to the end that his life may be prolonged to the utmost limit. Though wounded and scarred, his very silence speaks in terms more eloquent than words of the desperate strug-

gle against overwhelming odds, of the hopeless conflict, and the heroic manner in which all went down that day.

2. The commanding officer of I troop will see that a special and comfortable stall is fitted up for Comanche. He will not be ridden by any person whatever under any circumstances, nor will he be put to any kind of work.

3. Hereafter and upon all occasions of ceremony (of mounted regimental formation) Comanche, saddled, bridled and led by a mounted trooper of Troop I will be paraded with the regiment.

> By Command of Colonel Sturgis
> (signed) E. A. Garlington
> 1st Lt. and Adjutant
> 7th U.S. Cavalry

After that, no horse ever had a pleasanter life than Comanche. He was the pet of the regiment, turned loose every day to graze and frolic as he chose. On one of the first mornings following the general order, Troop I, now commanded by Keogh's friend Lieutenant Nowlan, rode out to the drill ground. Summoned by the same trumpet call came Comanche. Riderless, but with all his old fire and spirit, he took his former place at the head of the troop and went through the different drill formations faultlessly.

Some of the men chuckled, but more found their eyes wet at the sight. "Old Comanche!" Mills said softly. "Look at him arch his neck and prance. Can't you see Captain Keogh riding him, just as plain?"

As time went on the buckskin grew more than a little spoiled. He took advantage of his own freedom to tease and torment the other horses on the picket line by nipping them in the flanks as he passed. A new recruit saw him at this mischief and picked up a clod of earth to throw at him.

"Look out!" an older trooper shouted, just in time. "That's *Comanche*, you fool! Hitting him would get you a court-martial just as quick as striking any other officer."

He begged sugar lumps at the doors of the officers' quarters and if they were not produced promptly he revenged himself by kicking over their garbage pails and feasting on whatever he found there. He waited at the enlisted men's canteen to be treated to buckets of beer. No flower beds or lawns were safe from him, and sunflowers were his special choice. On summer evenings he joined the crowds listening to the band concerts and cropped the grass contentedly around the bandstand. But when they played "Garry Owen" his head came up alertly and his delight was plain for everyone to see.

He had been a one-man horse before, and now Gustave Korn received all his devotion. He followed him everywhere, trotting at his heels like a huge friendly dog. He could often be seen waiting outside the home of Korn's sweetheart for the blacksmith to emerge.

June 25th had become the regimental day of mourning when all duties were suspended. In the ceremonial parade held on that day, Comanche always led Troop I, draped in a black mourning net with saddle reversed and a pair of officers' riding boots in the stirrups. Soldiers stood at attention and other men bared their heads when he passed.

When the regiment went into the field Comanche accompanied Troop I, traveling with the led horses. He marched overland with the regiment when they moved to Fort Totten, then to Fort Meade and finally to Fort Riley, Kansas. He was still Comanche of the Seventh.

The Sioux had scattered after the Big Horn battle. Although they had won a victory, it did them little good, for they were never able to mass in strength again, and the aroused and vengeful Army drove them on to their reservation in the end. In 1890, however, a wave of excitement swept again through the Sioux nation. A group of medicine men, called "ghost dancers," stirred up the warriors to believe that if they wore certain "ghost shirts" the bullets of the white soldiers could not harm them.

In November, 1890, the Seventh Cavalry left Fort Riley and proceeded by rail to Rushville, Nebraska and thence to Pine Ridge Agency. They were sent to help subdue the Sioux who had once more been aroused by the regiment's old enemy, Sitting Bull. The Seventh did not have a chance for a second battle with the great Sioux chief, however. Indian police at Standing Rock Agency made an attempt to arrest him. He signaled to his braves for help and in the resulting fight the Indian police killed him.

"So he's gone!" McBane said, when he heard the news. "I wish it had been us of the Seventh that got him."

Mills nodded, then was silent for a moment. "Still and all . . . Folks are saying now that he was a great man to his people."

"So's an old he-rattlesnake," McBane retorted grimly.

Two weeks after Sitting Bull's death Big Foot, another Sioux chief, started to make trouble. Troop I, with three other companies, was ordered to keep Big Foot and his ghost dancers from escaping to join other hostiles. With Nowlan, now a captain, in command of Troop I, they surrounded Big Foot at a place called Wounded Knee.

Trembling and sweating as the hated scent came to him again, Comanche watched from a distance with the other led horses. He saw the Indians, confident in the power of their "ghost shirts," try to break through the line of troopers. The bullets of the soldiers did their work, but among the battle casualties was Gustave Korn.

After the death of the man to whom he had once again given the devotion of his loyal heart, Comanche seemed to lose his interest in life. Back at Fort Riley he drooped listlessly. He took ill, and now there seemed to be no fight left in him. The men of Troop I and of all the regiment hung about the stable where the veterinarians worked over the brave old charger.

"What would the Seventh be without Comanche?" the troopers said to each other.

At last, on November 6, 1891, those watching him saw his ears twitch forward and a tremor pass through his limbs. They could not know that he was hearing a light step and a long-remembered, lilting whistle, that, suddenly young and strong again, he was prancing down the parade ground to the tune of "Garry Owen," and that the saddle he bore was no longer empty. Comanche had joined his captain.

This was not the end of Comanche's story, however. The men of the Seventh Cavalry refused to give up their cherished mascot, even in death. They had him mounted by the most skillful taxidermist they could find. He is still to be seen in the Museum of the University at Lawrence, Kansas—the most famous and beloved of all cavalry charges—Comanche of the Seventh.

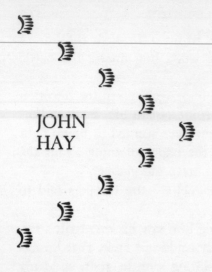

JOHN
HAY

Myles Keogh's Horse

On THE BLUFF OF THE LITTLE BIG-HORN,
  At the close of a woeful day,
Custer and his Three Hundred
  In death and silence lay.

And of all that stood at noonday
  In that fiery scorpion ring
Myles Keogh's horse, at evening,
  Was the only living thing.

Along from that field of slaughter,
  Where lay the three hundred slain,
The horse Comanche wandered,
  With Keogh's blood on his mane.

And Sturgis issued this order,
  Which future times shall read,
While the love and honor of comrades
  Are the soul of the comrade's creed.

He said:
            "Let the horse Comanche,
  Henceforth till he shall die

Be kindly cherished and cared for
   By the Seventh Cavalry.

"He shall do no labor: he shall never know
   The touch of spur or rein;
Nor shall his back be ever crossed
   By living rider again.
And at regimental formation
   Of the Seventh Cavalry
Comanche, draped in mourning, and led
   By a trooper of Company I
Shall parade with the regiment."

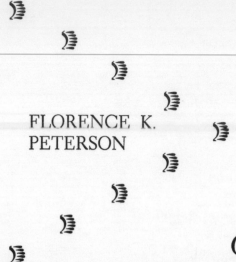

FLORENCE K.
PETERSON

General Putnam's Ride

DURING THE WAR FOR INDEPENDENCE, A HORSE SHARED HONORS FOR bravery with his great General—Israel Putnam.

Here is a story, now almost a legend, which will long be talked about and remembered.

Early one morning, General Putnam and his men were surprised and swiftly chased by a group of expert Red Coat riders. The General spurred on his gallant steed and his mounted men to avoid capture. The hoofs of the pursuers and pursued tossed up pebbles and sent off bright sparks.

It was a wild ride! The Red Coats were gaining, and General Putnam's men scattered to the woods for protection. But not the stalwart General! He and his straining horse continued their frenzied ride along the road, speeding through the town of Stamford, Connecticut. Suddenly Putnam spied, around a hill, a church which had steep steps on one side, leading down to another road.

Never hesitating for a moment, horse and man veered to left, up the slope, and then without missing a beat in the steady sound of flying hoofs, took the steps down to the alternate road.

The Red Coats reined in their horses in astonishment and admiration for so dauntless a pair. They were fearful of leading their horses down the steps and so returned to their camp, deprived of what would have been a prize captive.

The bravery of General Putnam and his horse was the main topic of conversation that night at the campfires of both friend and foe.

HENRY
WADSWORTH
LONGFELLOW

Paul Revere's Ride

LISTEN, MY CHILDREN, AND YOU SHALL HEAR
Of the midnight ride of Paul Revere.
On the eighteenth of April, in Seventy-five;
Hardly a man is now alive
Who remembers that famous day and year.

He said to his friend, "If the British march
By land or sea from the town to-night,
Hang a lantern aloft in the belfry arch
Of the North Church tower as a signal light,—
One, if by land, or two, if by sea;
And I on the opposite shore will be,
Ready to ride and spread the alarm
Through every Middlesex village and farm,
For the country-folk to be up and to arm."

Then he said, "Good night!" and with muffled oar
Silently rowed to the Charlestown shore,
Just as the moon rose over the bay,
Where swinging wide at her moorings lay
The Somerset, British man-of-war;
A phantom ship, with each mast and spar
Across the moon like a prison bar,

And a huge black hulk, that was magnified
By its own reflection in the tide.

Meanwhile, his friend, through alley and street,
Wanders and watches with eager ears,
Till in silence around him he hears
The muster of men at the barrack door,
The sound of arms, and the tramp of feet,
And the measured tread of the grenadiers,
Marching down to their boats on the shore.

Then he climbed to the tower of the church,
Up the wooden stairs, with stealthy tread,
To the belfry-chamber overhead,
And startled the pigeons from their perch
On the sombre rafters, that round him made
Masses and moving shapes of shade—
Up the trembling ladder, steep and tall,
To the highest window in the wall,
Where he paused to listen and look down
A moment on the roofs of the town,
And the moonlight flowing over all.

Beneath, in the churchyard, lay the dead,
In their night-encampment on the hill,
Wrapped in silence so deep and still
That he could hear, like a sentinel's tread,
The watchful night-wind, as it went
Creeping along from tent to tent,
And seeming to whisper, "All is well!"
A moment only he feels the spell
Of the place and the hour, and the secret dread
Of the lonely belfry and the dead;
For suddenly all his thoughts are bent
On a shadowing something far away,
Where the river widens to meet the bay,—
A line of black that bends and floats
On the rising tide, like a bridge of boats.

Meanwhile, impatient to mount and ride,

Booted and spurred, with a heavy stride
On the opposite shore walked Paul Revere.
Now he patted his horse's side,
Now gazed at the landscape far and near,
Then, impetuous, stamped the earth,
And turned and tightened his saddle-girth;
But mostly he watched with eager search
The belfry-tower of the Old North Church,
As it rose above the graves on the hill,
Lonely and spectral and sombre and still,
And lo! as he looks, on the belfry's height
A glimmer, and then a gleam of light!
He springs to the saddle, the bridle he turns,
But lingers and gazes, till full on his sight
A second lamp in the belfry burns!

A hurry of hoofs in a village street,
A shape in the moonlight, a bulk in the dark,
And beneath, from the pebbles, in passing, a spark
Struck out by a steed flying fearless and fleet;
That was all! And yet, through the gloom and the light,
The fate of a nation was riding that night;
And the spark struck out by that steed, in his flight,
Kindled the land into flame with its heat.
He has left the village and mounted the steep,
And beneath him, tranquil and broad and deep,
Is the Mystic, meeting the ocean tides;
And under the alders, that skirt its edge,
Now soft on the sand, now loud on the ledge,
Is heard the tramp of his steed as he rides.

It was twelve by the village clock
When he crossed the bridge into Medford town.
He heard the crowing of the cock
And the barking of the farmer's dog,
And felt the damp of the river fog
That rises after the sun goes down.

It was one by the village clock
When he galloped into Lexington.

He saw the gilded weathercock
Swim in the moonlight as he passed,
And the meeting-house windows, blank and bare,
Gaze at him with a spectral glare,
As if they already stood aghast
At the bloody work they would look upon.

It was two by the village clock,
When he came to the bridge in Concord town.
He heard the bleating of the flock,
And the twitter of birds among the trees,
And felt the breath of the morning breeze
Blowing over the meadows brown.
And one was safe and asleep in his bed
Who at the bridge would be first to fall,
Who that day would be lying dead,
Pierced by a British musket-ball.

You know the rest. In the books you have read,
How the British Regulars fired and fled—
How the farmers gave them ball for ball,
From behind each fence and farmyard wall,
Chasing the Red Coats down the lane,
Then crossing the fields to emerge again
Under the trees at the turn of the road,
And only pausing to fire and load.

So through the night rode Paul Revere;
And so through the night went his cry of alarm
To every Middlesex village and farm,—
A cry of defiance and not of fear,
A voice in the darkness, a knock at the door,
And a word that shall echo forevermore!
For, borne on the night-wind of the Past,
Through all our history, to the last,
In the hour of darkness and peril and need,
The people will waken and listen to hear
The hurrying hoof-beats of that steed,
And the midnight message of Paul Revere.

FRANCES
MARGARET
FOX

The Old Cavalry Horse

AN OLD CAVALRY HORSE WAS MUCH SURPRISED ONE DAY, WHEN HE WAS mustered out of service. It was a fate he could not understand. He had lived long years at a Western post and had always served Uncle Sam faithfully. The old horse loved his garrison friends, because they had always taken good care of him. That is, he loved the old soldiers. Young recruits had so much to learn that he felt superior to them. He believed it beneath his dignity to take orders from newly enlisted men.

Perhaps one reason why the old horse carried himself so proudly was because he had long been the trumpeter's horse. Even so, the day came when he was sold to a milkman and home he went with that milkman to live.

The old cavalry horse must have believed that some officer at the fort had made a bad mistake and that one of his friends would soon come galloping over the hills to his rescue. However, he was kind and polite to the milkman. He didn't hurt his new master's feelings by asking why he didn't blow a trumpet at mealtime and have a little more ceremony in his stable. He didn't object when he was harnessed to the milk-cart, with never the sound of a bugle-call to make the peddling of milk more interesting.

The good old horse peddled milk like a gentleman. The work was easy and there were no young recruits to drive the milk-wagon and tell him when to stop and go. The old horse didn't blame the milkman for the change in his fortunes and he was grateful for kind treatment.

Then one day when the driver was jogging along delivering milk at one

221

door and another, the most upsetting thing happened. As the old cavalry horse approached the drill-ground, where a troop of his garrison friends were drilling, he pricked up his ears and stepped a bit faster. Suddenly the trumpet sounded the order to "Charge!"

Instantly Uncle Sam's old horse obeyed that call. He bounced the milkman off the seat of the cart, and then away he flew to the drill-ground with the milk-cans rattling behind him.

Another minute and the old horse, milk-cart dragging behind, was charging with the cavalry troop. Milk-cans were scattered over the field and the old horse's heels beat like drumsticks on the dashboard.

That was a merry occasion for everyone but the milkman. It gave the old horse something cheerful to think about, while day by day in his stable, far from headquarters, he waited for the trumpeter he loved to come riding over the hills to take him home.

ROSEMARY
and
STEPHEN
VINCENT
BENÉT

Western Wagons

THEY WENT WITH AXE AND RIFLE, WHEN THE TRAIL WAS STILL TO BLAZE,
They went with wife and children, in the prairie-schooner days,
With banjo and with frying pan—Susanna, don't you cry!
For I'm off to California to get rich out there or die!

We've broken land and cleared it, but we're tired of where we are.
They say that wild Nebraska is a better place by far.
There's gold in far Wyoming, there's black earth in Ioway.
So pack up the kids and blankets, for we're moving out today!

The cowards never started and the weak died on the road.
And all across the continent the endless campfires glowed.
We'd taken land and settled—but a traveler passed by—
And we're going West tomorrow—Lordy, never ask us why!

We're going West tomorrow, where the promises can't fail.
O'er the hills in legions, boys, and crowd the dusty trail!
We shall starve and freeze and suffer. We shall die, and tame the lands.
But we're going West tomorrow, with our fortune in our hands.

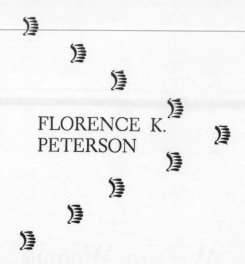

FLORENCE K.
PETERSON

Pony Express Saga

Neither snow nor rain nor sleet nor gloom of night stays these carriers from the swift completion of their appointed rounds.

. . . IS THE MOTTO OF THE WORLD'S GREATEST POSTAL SYSTEM.

It was the speed of horses and the foresighted courage of men who made possible the beginning of fast mail service in the early days of our country.

An Indian trail, called by settlers the "Boston Post Road," was the scene of the first mail route in the Colonies. The Pony Express, established to promote friendly relations between Colonies scattered along the coast between New York and Boston, daily sent out scores of riders, leather saddlebags bulging with mail strapped to their horses. With relays of horses and men, it was possible to send a letter from New York to Boston in two and a half days!

After the discovery of gold in California, the demand for fast mail service was most urgent. No railroads in the West at that time meant that the fleetest of horses and the most adventurous of riders were needed to travel the endless miles of wilderness, woods, desert, mountains and prairies.

Way stations were few and far between. It is said that Buffalo Bill, when he was fourteen years old, rode 322 miles without stopping!

Our fore-fathers, like our present day Americans were ever-eager to surpass themselves in achievement. The Pony Express on the occasion of Abe Lincoln's inaugural address determined to break all records for speed in the delivery of the new president's message. They set what is still the all-time record for fast animal power by covering the vast, hazardous distance of almost

224

2,000 miles between St. Joseph, Missouri and Sacramento, California in 7 days and 17 hours.

Adventure and danger were the daily lot of the brave, youthful couriers. There were the risks of rocky chasms, sand storms, snow slides—the peril of Indian attacks—and the high excitement of starting the great communication system which America now enjoys.

The Pony Express was truly a great success. Those were the days of romance!—of spectacular riding—of bravery beyond belief—of derring-do!

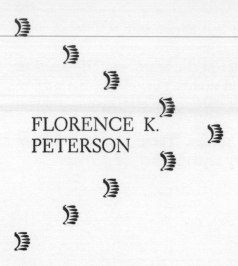

FLORENCE K.
PETERSON

Stage Coach Days

THE REINSMEN OF THE STAGE COACH DAYS WERE PROBABLY THE BEST HORSE-men the world has ever known.

Heroes, everyone of them, they never left their jobs in the early days of the Western Frontier. In their stride they weathered snow slides, the swollen river, washed-out roads, the ever-present danger of hold-up men.

It is difficult in this age of jet travel to understand the wonderment with which people of the 1760's greeted the regular runs of the Stage Coach in America.

Here was progress and the fact that a traveller could go from Boston to New York, from Cumberland to Wheeling, in split second timing, with fresh horses waiting at stages along the road was not only an amazement to all, but kept the Stage Coach business a busy and profitable one.

There was no comfort for the traveller in those days of the corduroy road. Tree trunks were laid side by side and covered with a few inches of dirt which was inevitably washed away by rain. Nor was there comfort for the four or six horse team.

On hundred or more miles of terrain which would seem impassable to us today was the daily hazardous journey of splendid teams of horses. The blare of the bugle from the lips of the Stage Coach driver as he approached a relay station must have trumpeted a "Horse's Heaven." To be bedded down and hayed was bliss—

but there would be tomorrow . . . tomorrow, another driver to whip them on another leg of progress which is America.

226

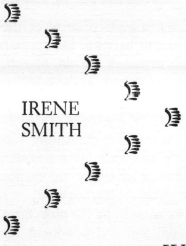

IRENE
SMITH

Not So Long Ago

We Depended on Horses Every Day

(*A hitching post or tie rail was in front of every store, emporium, or other commercial establishment in town, and usually there were posts in front of every house. There was also ample evidence that these were in use. Drinking fountains or troughs abounded at convenient corners in town or forks in the road where there happened to be a spring. No town was too small for a blacksmith shop, a livery stable or two, and the stepping stone out in front was as common as the boot scraper by the door. Any church without a long horseshed could expect few attendants to come from beyond an easy walking distance. Advertisements of spavin cures and liniments lined the roadsides as persistently as the gas and oil signs of today.**)

T HIS WAS THE TYPICAL AMERICAN COMMUNITY IN THE LAST CENTURY, AND for some years after 1900. "Itinerant horse barbers went from farm to farm trimming the fetlocks and often the entire coat of the carriage horses, never failing to finish each job with a call of 'next!' " * Business and social life depended upon horses in innumerable ways, from matters of greatness to trivial details. Saddle horses, buggies, surreys, stagecoaches, wagons, and horse-drawn sleighs filled all the pleasure needs and the necessities that automobiles were later to grasp. Draft horses hauled the loads that motor trucks

* From AS WE WERE by Bellamy Partridge and Otto Bettmann (Whittlesey House) (McGraw Hill) 1946.

227

took over when they appeared on the scene. Tractors replaced most of the farm horses. An era of pleasant, leisurely manners and habits of living came to an end when automobiles frightened the family mares off the old, narrow, uncrowded, unstreamlined roads.

Horses have held their essential place in the American tradition since the country was born. George Washington was an excellent horseman and rode in foxhunts which were popular then as now in the pastimes of wealthy Virginians. Custom-made carriages, rich with hand-crafted details, were available in Europe and America for those who could afford a luxurious conveyance and the handsome pair of matched trotters that would be hitched to it.

Fancy horses had their special role in society, but meanwhile the plain farm horses faced sterner duties and dangers that were real and imminent for many of them. After the American Revolution new wagon trails wound across the forested mountain slopes, to Kentucky and beyond, then forty years later the whole westward movement was in full swing. Covered wagons crept across the broad land, day after weary day, drawn by horses that, like the passengers, endured their limits of hardship. Together they survived blistering sun and desert thirst, or rain, harsh winds, and the high frozen passes; they swam the deep rivers, and escaped Indian arrows, or perished by the wayside.

Homesteaders on the Great Plains established cattle ranches where the wild longhorns could be rounded up, and the cowboy on his horse, riding the open range, was guardian of the herds. Only the all-purpose horses, saddled, or harnessed to the old stagecoaches, kept open the precious, thin lines of communication on lonely western trails.

The farmer's year-long toil depended on his horse, or if possible, horses. They pulled the plows and threshers, and the wagonloads of hay. They hauled the logs for firewood, and heavy grain bags to the mill for flour. Where fields are small and tractors too costly, the good steady draft horses still earn their keep on modest farms. They still give farm children the same safe rides across the meadow and around the barn.

Older people easily remember the long-ago morning, when they awakened to the sound of the milkwagon in the street, making its early deliveries. Not to disturb the sleeping, the milkman's horse wore rubber shoes. He clopped along with slow but steady purpose from house to house, knowing exactly where customers lived. He gave the milkman time to leave milk on each doorstep and bring back empty bottles, then moved on to the next stop. With the route completed the horse could rest in the afternoon and bed down early, for he would be up next morning before the town stirred.

In an old-fashioned buggy, with the horse's reins in his hands and his bag on the seat beside him, the country doctor made his rounds, a comforting and familiar sight on quiet roads. He and his horse answered calls at any hour, day or night, and in all weather. They travelled over muddy, rocky roads when they had to, and forded streams that had no bridges to get to the place where help was needed. Then, while the doctor was with his patient, the horse waited, sometimes for hours, often in rain or snow. But the doctor was mindful of his good partner, and usually there was a blanket in the buggy to be thrown over his horse's back when the weather was bad. Perhaps there was a feed bag too with oats for a meal, when the travels took all day. Intrepid men of medicine also rode horseback, with their instruments and drugs in saddlebags, to reach more remote places. It was a calm, companionable life for the doctor's trusty steed.

Fire horses, on the other hand, lived on excitement. Their performance thrilled spectators and satisfied their own high-spirited natures. When they tore down the street, two or three abreast, with the engine and apparatus clanging behind them, anybody could see that they were just as anxious as the firemen to do their job, and in the same terrific hurry to get to the fire.

A fire horse was trained to spring instantly to his place between the shafts when the alarm sounded, ready for his harness to be fastened, while the firemen slid down the pole. This harness hung from the ceiling, and dropped on the horse's back when a pushbutton released it. The moment a fire horse smelled smoke there was no holding him back. Many stories have been told about old-timers, put out to grass, but trying to answer the call when they caught the scent of fire, or heard the alarm bell ring. They loved their work.

Police horses in the main have held on to their jobs. No motor vehicle gives a policeman the commanding height in a crowd, or provides for the nimble maneuver through a traffic jam that he achieves on a horse. The city "mounties" are able to quell riots and sit tall at parades. They patrol the parks and beaches and larger areas requiring guard. Police horses are splendid specimens and are chosen for intelligence and good nature as well as for their handsome looks. They are trained to remain calm under all conditions. The noise and excitement of mobs, sirens, accidents cannot upset them. When they are standing mid-stream in a roar of traffic, or moving pedestrians back to the sidelines, or marching to the music of a band, these capable horses obey, and conduct themselves with dignity. They learn to back, sidestep, and jump. Like human members of the force, police horses in many cities are retired when they reach a fitting age, with green pastures for their just reward.

The cheerful tingle of harness bells was a common sound on busy streets when trolleys were drawn by horses. Two of them usually could do the job, with a third one for the uphills pulls, and to help in slippery weather. Plodding at a firm gait between the stops, these horses kept the trolley cars going until electric power arrived, able to move them faster.

Horses that work for the circus, or perform to entertain audiences, have the most exacting jobs, and receive the best training. They have to be beautiful, smart, and trustworthy to make good in the theatrical world. The big, handsome Percherons are especially successful in this career. Acrobatic riding takes finished skill on the part of the horse as well as the rider, for both must learn perfect timing. Otherwise the rider falls. Long practice makes excellence, and each is entitled to make the bows when crowds cheer a performance. Circus horses respond to the music and applause as though inspired to do their best when the people watching are pleased with the spectacle.

What goes on in the minds of horses is not for their masters to guess. But in equine society surely the contented members are those kept as family pets, to be ridden for pleasure. A good saddle horse is a valuable property, and a responsible friend. However, great numbers of saddle horses these days are owned by riding academies. People of all ages receive lessons in horsemanship at these academies, and then pay by the hour for their rides on their favorite mounts. The bridle paths in city parks and those less-travelled country roads are goals of the horseback riders on leisure days. Stables with saddle horses for hire are old establishments in their communities, and dude ranches rely on horses as their main attraction to guests eager to ride new trails. At summer camps thousands of boys and girls each summer learn the first principles of horsemanship, and for some it becomes a lifetime's hobby.

We still have a few million horses in this country. Because so many varieties have been imported here, and earnest attention is given to the mixing and breeding of the best strains, the home of fine horses is said to be America. In the building of this country they gave service beyond all measure. Food and care are the least they can be paid, and love is the most that can be added, for their ample reward.

FRANCES
MARGARET
FOX

The Last Run

A NEWSPAPER REPORTER ONCE WROTE A PLEA ON BEHALF OF THE LAST regular team of fire horses in the District of Columbia, begging contributions for the purchase of the beloved old horses, that they might not be sold at auction to the highest bidder. Here is what that kind-hearted reporter said in his paper one June day in 1925.

'Three faithful servants of humanity, the last regular team of Washington's once petted battalion of sturdy fire horses, are stamping the cement floors of unfamiliar stalls today, eagerly listening for the gong that is never again to strike on this earth for them.'

Right there the reporter made a mistake. The gong did strike again for the fire horses, thanks to work done by this very reporter. Something better happened than even he had dreamed of.

The horses' names were Barney, Gene, and Tom. For ten years they had been faithful servants of the fire department on Uncle Sam's payroll in our capital city. Now the fire department would never again require the help of horses in putting out fires. Motor fire-engines had taken their place. Horses must go, and Barney, Gene, and Tom were the last old team to leave the service.

To save these horses from being sold to draymen, the newspaper begged the people of Washington to buy them.

That newspaper article saved the three horses, though not in the way the reporter suggested. The very next day came the good news that the horses were to be given to the Home for the Feeble and Infirm at Blue

Plains, there to live the rest of their days in comfort and happiness. The District Commissioners had so decided. The managers of the farm at Blue Plains, who had seen the newspaper article, had said that they would gladly give the three old horses a good home for life. They could earn their board by taking the old folks out for "straw rides."

The chief of the fire department was glad when he heard these plans. He agreed that it would be a great pity if the faithful old horses should be made wretched by hard work in their old age. They were great pets, and so gentle he was sure the old folks at Blue Plains would enjoy driving out in the sunshine in a big wagon drawn by Barney, Gene, and Tom.

The poor old fellows would live only a short time, he said, if draymen bought them. They were chosen by the fire department in the beginning for their speed and intelligence, and not for their strength. Almost their entire lives had been passed in active fire-service, and they were not fitted for hauling great loads through hot city streets.

Then he declared that the last regular team was to be sent to its retirement with every honor the department can bestow and with the clang of the stirring fire-gong ringing in the horses' ears once more.

"As soon as he learns the day, Superintendent Fay of the farm at Blue Plains will call for the old fellows. He will order them removed to their original stalls," said the chief. "When they leave their former home for the last time, it will be in the shining livery they have worn so well for more than a decade, and in the presence of many of the men who have served along with them, and before the officials of the fire department."

Then said he: "I want to do this, not only for Barney, Gene, and Tom, but to give the people of Washington an opportunity of seeing what a noble crusade this has been. We will have a regular fire-run for those old fellows the last they will ever enjoy, and it will be a sight worth seeing, too."

Next day there was gay news in the paper. The preparations had been made for the retirement of the horses the following Monday morning.

Long before ten o'clock on Monday, thousands of children and grown people were in line to see the dear old horses make their last run.

Meantime, Barney, Gene, and Tom had been taken back to their old home engine-house. There they found their stalls gaily decorated with flowers. The three horses were given a breakfast of oats. The men who had cared for them for seven years dressed them for their farewell party. Their manes were combed and their gray coats curried until they were like satin. The horses' big hoofs were polished until they shone.

At ten o'clock the fire-gong sounded. Barney, Gene, and Tom were ready for the dash the instant their shining harness was snapped on. Nine times the gong sounded, three strokes for Barney, three for Gene, and three for old Tom.

The horses must have believed they were headed for a bad fire.

When the last gong sounded the firemen throughout the city stood at attention for one minute.

In twenty-two seconds from the time the first gong sounded, the three horses were dashing from the engine-house, dragging their old fire-engine behind them.

Thousands of men, women, and children saw the race, and how that crowd cheered! The streets were lined with people. Motion-picture photographers took pictures of the ceremony, that millions of Americans might later see just how those fine horses ran that day.

Perhaps Barney, Gene, and Tom were disappointed when their run ended in front of a fire-hydrant at Lincoln Park, only a few blocks from their engine-house—and no fire in sight.

Anyway, after they had trotted slowly home again, wreaths of roses were hung round their necks and speeches were made. One of the District Commissioners said in the beginning of his speech, as he handed the reins of the glorious trio to Mr. Fay, superintendent of the farm at Blue Plains: "When a fireman has served the department with loyalty, he is pensioned and returned to the rest he has earned in the twilight of his life. These old fellows are no less firemen than the men of our department, and it is only right and fitting that they, too, should be protected now that their service is over."

Barney began to eat the roses in his wreath before the speech was ended, and Gene and Tom were trying to help him, when the fire chief noticed and placed the wreaths out of reach.

The horses then stood at attention while Mr. Fay made a speech, in which he said:

"We accept the trust reposed in us by you and the thousands of admirers and lovers of this wonderful trio of horses. We have afforded refuge to many an old fellow, both man and horse, who have been buffeted by old age and adverse circumstances. You may rest assured that these faithful veterans, like many of their predecessors, will find a haven in the green fields and shady pastures beside the Potomac at Blue Plains."

Then Barney, Gene, and Tom, garlanded with roses, attended by their grooms, walked the five or six miles to Blue Plains, cheered by their admirers all along the line of march to their new home.

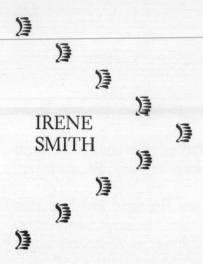

IRENE
SMITH

Old Doctor Dobbin

SOME OF THE FATHERS AND MOTHERS IN A NEW JERSEY SUBURB STILL tell their children about the unusual birthday party to which they were invited when they themselves were very young. It was indeed such an interesting occasion that reporters and newsreel cameramen were there to record its celebration, from beginning to end. The party was held in the biological laboratories of a prominent drug firm in nearby New Brunswick, and the guest of honor was a large black horse. Old Doctor Dobbin, as he was known, or Doc for short, was nineteen years old, and he had been employed at the laboratory for nine of those years. He was the most important one of about a hundred and fifty horses, all chosen for their strong constitutions, that lived in the laboratory's barns and grazed in its fields. Their duty was to supply antitoxin material for the treatment of children against diphtheria. By that time Doctor Dobbin had contributed enough serum to protect thirty thousand of them against the dreaded disease. No other horse had ever given so much to science, and through science, had done so much to help humanity. He richly deserved the attention and compliments he received at that party.

Doctor Dobbin came wearing a huge wreath of flowers around his neck, and was immediately invited to sample the nine red apples spread out for him, one for each of his laboratory years. While a speech was being made about his noble gift to children everywhere, Doc also sampled a few carnations from the bouquet on the table. However it was his party, and his guests were glad he knew how to enjoy it. They received their shares of his enormous birthday cake, which was brought in with candles burning, and they all sang "Happy Birthday, dear Doctor Dobbin, Happy Birthday to You!" That expressed their thanks for his long, faithful service, and for their safety from a once cruel enemy, diphtheria.

Old Doc was a heavy, powerful horse, with a gentle disposition which made him a special favorite among the men in the laboratories. They said his good nature had been born in him, out on the western plains which were his first home. When he died two years after the party, at the fine old age of twenty-one, he had furnished blood for enough serum to treat more than forty-one thousand children. Newspapers published accounts of the death of this great horse and spoke of the debt owed to Doctor Dobbin. School children of his community, who felt that part of him belonged to them, grieved over losing a very famous old friend.

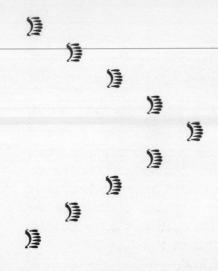

From the Book of Job

Hast thou clothed his neck with the quivering mane?
Hast thou made him to leap as a locust?
The glory of his snorting is terrible.
He paweth in the valley, and rejoiceth in his strength:
He goeth out to meet the armed men.
He mocketh at fear, and is not dismayed;
Neither turneth he back from the sword.
The quiver rattleth against him,
The flashing spear and the javelin.
He swalloweth the ground with fierceness and rage;
Neither believeth he that it is the voice of the trumpet.
As oft as the trumpet soundeth he saith, "Aha!"
And he smelleth the battle afar off,
The thunder of the captains, and the shouting.

IX

HORSES TO KEEP

Beloved friends and pets

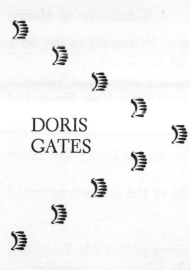

DORIS
GATES

Little Vic

(*The father of Jonathan Rivers had been a jockey, and the orphaned boy, nicknamed Pony, would follow in his steps. He worked as an exercise boy on the Blue Grass farm that owned the great horse, Victory.*)

EACH SPRING A NEW CROP OF COLTS WAS BORN AT SPRING VALLEY FARM. Many of them were the sons and daughters of the farm's greatest treasure, Victory. In the days before he left the track, Victory had been the best known horse in the country next to his father, Man o' War. It was believed that any colt of his would be a great race horse, too. And so his colts were always watched with interest as they grew old enough to train. As colts, they brought large prices in the market. Many of his sons and some of his daughters had already made their marks in the racing world. Spring Valley Farm could be very proud of Victory.

It was because of Victory that Pony Rivers had left the freight at the very spot he did six months back. He had known for years about Spring Valley Farm. He had known that here was where Victory belonged. He had seen Victory race. Pony's father had always hoped that someday he would have a chance to ride Victory, but the chance had never come. Pony's father had not been a great rider and had never ridden any great horses. But he had talked to his small son about riding and had told Pony many good things to know. After he was killed, Pony's mother had talked to him against racing. She had tried to make Pony see that there were other ways of living around horses. Pony didn't care if he never became a rider. All he wanted was to live

239

and work with horses. And he decided, as long as he wanted to live on a horse farm, to choose the one where Victory lived.

Now here he was, the first person to be looking at a new son of Victory's. It was the first of his colts to be born at the farm since Pony Rivers had arrived. Pony thought there could never be a more promising colt born any-where than the lovely little animal he was watching.

After a while he left the barn and went up to the big house. Mr. Barby was there.

"Ginger has her colt," said Pony, very proud to be the first one to spread the good news.

"Are they both all right?" asked Mr. Barby.

"I'll say they are," said Pony. His eyes were shining so that Mr. Barby had to smile. "He's a ringer for his dad. Looks just like Victory, only smaller."

Mr. Barby's smile grew wider. "Sounds like a lucky break for the farm," he said. "And the first one of the season too."

"He's a real little Victory, all right," said Pony. He was watching Mr. Barby's face closely as he said it. But the man seemed not to have heard.

Pony Rivers knew that naming the horses on such a farm as Spring Valley was a very important job. It was always done by the owner or the owner's wife. Then the names had to be given to the people who make the rules about racing in America. He knew that a race horse's name is almost as important as a person's. But he had called the new colt "Little Vic," and he knew that, for him, Little Vic would always be his name.

"Don't you think 'Little Vic' would be a good name for him, Mr. Barby?"

Pony would never know what made him say it. He felt foolish the minute the words were out. He wished with all his heart that he could call them back. He was afraid Mr. Barby would think he was getting too full of him-self. He didn't know what Mr. Barby might say to him. Suppose he had made Mr. Barby mad enough to fire him!

But all Mr. Barby did was to look at Pony in a surprised way, and all he said was, "Let's take a look at the colt."

Pony let out a thankful breath and never said another word all the way to the barn.

Mr. Barby was not very well pleased with Ginger's baby, however. "He looks small," he said, tipping his head to one side and looking at the colt out of the tail of his eye. "He looks small. But then you can't always tell. Some of them, born big, don't shape up well later. Time will tell."

"But don't you think he looks just like Victory?" Pony asked.

Mr. Barby tipped his head to the other side. The colt stared back at him as if waiting for his answer. "Yes," said the man slowly. "He has the same dark coat and the star. But there was something different about Victory when he was born. Can't seem to remember just what it was. Something about the way he held his head perhaps, the flash of his eye. This little fellow doesn't seem to have quite as much class."

He turned to look at the boy standing beside him. It was clear that Pony had stopped listening a good many words back. Now he was just feasting his eyes on the lovely colt. He didn't know it, but a smile was playing around his mouth. He looked like a person who is seeing something wonderful, something that no other person can quite see.

"You look as if you've fallen hard for this colt," said Mr. Barby.

Pony jumped. He had forgotten the man at his side. "Yes," he said quietly. "He's the most beautiful thing in this world."

Mr. Barby laughed and slapped Pony on the back. "All right then. If you feel that way about him, I'll turn him over to you. From this day until he starts training, he's going to be your own special care. See that you do a good job with him."

It had been a long time since Pony's eyes had known tears. And then they had not been happy ones. But now tears were once more filling them, though the boy tried hard to fight them back. Through them, the walls of the box stall became all wavy and Ginger and her colt looked wavy, too. When at last he thought it was safe to speak, his words sounded foolish to him.

"Do you mean it?" he said, and wiped his eyes with the back of his hand.

"Sure, I mean it," said Mr. Barby. He waited a minute for Pony to get hold of himself. "Doc will be along to check them over." He took a quick look at Pony. "Ginger kind of put one over on Doc, didn't she? He wasn't expecting the colt for another week."

Pony Rivers said nothing, but he was thinking, as Mr. Barby walked out of the barn, It wasn't Ginger who put one over. It was Little Vic. He isn't ever going to do anything the way people think he will. But he's going to be great just the same!

The leaves had grown out on the trees. They were a young light green. Robins were singing among their branches. Soon the birds would be building their nests there. Down in the pasture the new grass was unrolling a green carpet over the brown earth. The sun was warm. From the open rolling hills came the sound of tractors. They were at work again, turning up to the sun the earth which had been packed down by the winter snow and rain. Behind

the tractors, clouds of blackbirds settled upon the moist, newly turned ground
to look for earthworms.

Every morning when the dew was gone Pony Rivers led Ginger along the
lane which went from the barn to the pasture. Running at her side and kicking his small hoofs into the air, her colt followed. All day the two stayed
there. Sometimes, tired from play, the colt would curl up in the sun at his
mother's feet and sleep. When he woke up, he would eat hungrily while his
mother stood quietly. Now and then she would swing her long tail lazily to
brush away any fly that might be troubling her baby.

There were other colts in the pasture with their mothers. Ginger's son
played with them. Their play was always the same. They would kick and
nibble and run in the way colts have always done since time began.

Often Pony came and perched on top of the pasture fence to watch them.
Sometimes there would be a little worried look on his face. There was no getting around it. His favorite was smaller than the other colts. Not much, but
a little. Victory was a big horse with powerful shoulders and long legs. Pony
knew it was not always the largest horses who make the best racers, but a big
strong body is an important thing to a race horse. Pony wanted Little Vic
to be big and powerful like his father.

Sometimes when the colt saw Pony sitting there, he would trot toward
him. But he would not go up to the fence unless Ginger came, too. Usually
she did, for Pony always had something in his pockets for her. The boy was
waiting for the time when the colt would be as friendly as Ginger, and he
knew the time would come. But for some strange reason Little Vic was in
no hurry to become close friends with Pony. The other colts would crowd
around him when he came into the pasture, but Little Vic always happened
to be standing so that his mother's body was between him and the boy.

He's different, thought Pony. He does not give his heart so easily as the
others. He does his own thinking, and that is one reason I think he's special.

The colt was a month old when the owner of the farm and his wife dropped
in at Spring Valley Farm for a visit. Sitting on the pasture fence, Pony Rivers
saw a group of people coming toward him down the lane. The women were
all dressed in gay colors, and they made a pretty picture as they came talking
and laughing down the sun-spotted lane to see the new crop of colts. Mr.
Barby was with them. One of the women carried a little dog in her arms.
This was Mrs. Gray, the wife of the owner, but Pony didn't know that yet.

As their voices reached the horses feeding in the pasture, every head was
lifted and every ear was pointed at the strangers. The colts stopped their play
and ran to their mothers. Every eye was round and fixed on the people com-

ing toward them. Pony jumped off the fence and would have run away, but Mr. Barby called to him.

"Go in and bring Ginger over here, Pony. Mr. Gray wants a look at her colt."

Without a word Pony opened the gate and went inside. The horses stood watching his every move. Straight up to Ginger he went, caught her, and started to lead her toward the group waiting at the gate. Behind her the colt came slowly, as if he wasn't quite sure that he wanted to follow.

Pony had almost reached the gate when suddenly the small dog in Mrs. Gray's arms jumped to the ground, shot under the gate, and started toward Ginger's colt. It was a mean little dog and its bark was sharp and frightening.

"Come here," called Mrs. Gray in a voice that rose as loud as a peanut whistle above the barking. "Come back, Baby. Oh, dear, oh, dear, I know those horses will kill him!"

Pony could hardly believe his ears. The silly woman was worried about her dog when she should have been worried about the colt. After all, the dog had not needed to come into the pasture. He had done it all on his own. And he was now barking and snapping at Ginger's colt. Well, he wasn't going to keep that up very long, thought Pony. Anyway, not while he was around!

He let go of Ginger and dived for the dog. He missed. Ginger rose up on her hind feet and the colt took off for the far side of the pasture. The other mares, who until now had been interested only in watching what went on, became excited for the safety of their own colts. They began to run in wide circles. Somewhere in the mix-up of their pounding hoofs was the dog named Baby.

By the time Pony caught up with him, Ginger's colt had run as far as the pasture fence would let him. There he stood pressed into the fence corner, the little dog dancing from side to side in front of him and barking wildly. The colt's eyes showed white and his sides were going in and out from the excitement of the chase. His nose was wide and pointing low at the dog, and he was blowing loudly and stamping his small front feet. Pony longed to go up to him and lay his hands on his back. There were words he longed to say into his stiff little ears, things that would drive away his frightened look. Pony was sure Little Vic would let him come close this time. But there was still the dog. Baby! Of all the names he had ever heard . . .

And then a new thought rushed into Pony's head. The same woman who had wished that name onto a dog, even *this* dog, might pick a name for Victory's son. Pony's own Little Vic might have to live and race under such a name as Sugar Pie or Honey! Pony couldn't bear to think of it. And yet he knew it had happened to horses before now. It could happen again. He didn't see how any horse could be great if it had a silly name. Yet what could he do about it? he asked himself. Nothing. There was just nothing he could do.

He reached down and picked up the little dog. It growled and tried to bite him. But Pony held it tight by the long hair on its neck, and it could not reach him with its flat nose.

It was a very unhappy boy who came back across the pasture, the little dog in his arms. He didn't see Ginger run to her colt. He didn't know that the horses bunched together behind him began slowly to follow after him. He didn't see Ginger's colt working his way through the bunch to watch where Pony was going. All he saw was the crowd of people at the gate. All he heard was the high, excited voice of Mrs. Gray.

"Oh, you brave, brave boy," she was saying. "You saved Baby from being killed. I saw it all, and I want to give you something. You ran after that wild colt that was trying to stamp on my dear little dog, and you saved him. Ducky," she rattled on, turning to her husband, "I want you to make him out a check for a hundred dollars right away. I would not take ten times that much for Baby."

She had rushed up as soon as Pony was through the gate and had taken the dog into her own arms. Now she held Baby to her face and talked to him in such a silly way that Pony had to turn away from her. He caught Mr. Barby's eye. He could not be sure, but it seemed to Pony that Mr. Barby let one lid fall quickly over one eye, and the look on his face was about like the one Pony could feel on his own. It was clear that Mr. Barby was no happier with these goings-on than Pony. What the boy didn't understand was how a man who owned a horse like Victory could have such a silly woman for his wife.

He was about to walk away when suddenly Mrs. Gray left off loving Baby to remember Pony.

"I can't thank you enough," she was saying. "I just don't know what I can do to thank you for saving Baby. Ducky, *do* make out that check."

Mr. Gray was reaching into a coat pocket. Pony could feel his face getting warm. Everyone was looking at him as if he had done something wonderful —that is, everyone except Mr. Barby and Mr. Gray. Mr. Barby realized how Pony felt about Baby. And Mr. Gray was not happy to be passing out so much money to anyone for saving Baby. He didn't think any more of his wife's dog than did Pony and Mr. Barby. But his wife had told him to do so.

What else could he do, with her and her friends looking on? Mr. Gray was a very rich man. He didn't want to look small before these people.

Pony had never felt so uncomfortable in all his life. He knew he had not really earned anything by "saving" Baby. He didn't think Mrs. Gray should even thank him for returning the dog to her. He would like to have thrown Baby to the lions. He had only picked up the crazy dog to get it out of the colt's neighborhood. A dog like that was nothing to have around horses. Some dogs, all right. But not a barking, biting, snapping little animal like this one. The colt might never get over being afraid of dogs for the rest of his days. Whenever he saw one on a track or near it, he might lose his head. You could not tell about such things. Race horses were mighty touchy animals. The more he thought about it, the angrier he got. Right now he would like to give this Baby a good swift kick. And, feeling that way, he had to stand there like a simpleton and watch Mr. Gray reach into his pocket for his checkbook.

All at once Mr. Barby spoke. "I think I know of something Pony would rather have than a hundred dollars," he said.

Mr. Gray's hand stopped halfway to his pocket, and Mrs. Gray let out a kind of squeak.

"Don't tell me," she cried, "that his name is really Pony! My dear, that is too wonderful."

She looked at Pony as if he might have just dropped from the moon. Poor Pony didn't know what to do. What in the world was Mr. Barby talking about? He had never told him about wanting anything. Not, anyway, since he had got this job of taking care of Ginger and her colt. He had enough to eat and a good bed in the house where the farm hands slept. He had all the clothes he needed. What would he do with a hundred dollars? And what was Mr. Barby talking about?

"What is it you want so much?" Mr. Gray asked him.

Pony looked helplessly at Mr. Barby, and the man understood. He smiled at Pony and spoke for him.

"That colt out there," he began, "the one you wanted most to see, Mr. Gray. Ginger's colt. He's a special favorite of Pony's. He has even given him a name. I think Pony would be the happiest fellow in the world if you would let him name that colt for keeps."

Mr. Gray cleared his throat. "What name did you want to give the colt?" he asked.

Pony swallowed to get his heart out of his mouth. "Little Vic," he said.

Mr. Gray turned the words over in his head. At last he spoke. "I think I like that," he said. "*Little Vic*. Not bad at all. He's the son of Victory, so Little Vic fits him very well. Put that down in the book, Barby. See you later, Pony."

He turned away from the pasture gate and the boy who was propping himself against it. Already the others were going back up the lane. Mrs. Gray was talking sweet talk to Baby while the others were expressing themselves on the danger he had just come through.

Pony watched them out of sight and wondered how it could be that people who cared so little about horses could own such fine ones.

"I guess it takes all kinds of people to make a good world," he said out loud. "If that woman had not been just the kind of person she is, and if that dog had not been just the kind of dog he is, then Little Vic might have had the silliest name in the world. You just can't ever tell about things, I guess."

He turned around and let his eyes travel across the pasture until they found Ginger and the small dark colt at her side. He drew in a deep breath and let it out slowly.

"Little Vic," he said. "Little Vic."

From where he stood safely beside his mother, Little Vic watched the boy by the gate. A new idea was taking shape in the colt's head. Until today he had thought that only his mother could save him from danger. But today someone else had saved him—that two-legged animal down by the gate. From now on Pony Rivers was going to be very important to this colt whose name was Little Vic.

"Easy does it, boy."

Little Vic and Pony were in the colt's stall. Little Vic was growing up. He was nearly a year old now and was beginning to look like a race horse. His eyes were brown and deep and quiet. Sometimes the other colts' eyes flashed their whites when they grew excited or jumpy. But Little Vic never seemed to get excited about anything. He would run and kick and lay his ears back when another colt kicked at him in the pasture. And he would throw up his lovely head and point his ears and swell his nose out with interest when he saw something strange and new to him. But he didn't have a mean hair in his whole body, and his eyes showed how gentle he was.

"Easy does it, boy."

Pony's voice was low and slow. He was feeling down Little Vic's strong front legs. The bone felt light, even thin, under his fingers. But Pony knew that Little Vic's legs were strong as a wire is strong. The colt lifted one foot and pawed the barn floor. He looked almost as if he were trying to shake hands with the boy. But Pony knew it was just that Little Vic didn't like having his legs rubbed. He had always been touchy about it, ever since he was a little fellow.

After Pony had looked carefully at each front foot, he moved to the back ones. Again Little Vic showed how little he liked this kind of thing. But he never tried to kick Pony. He would just lift his foot high, then set it down hard.

The boy and the colt had become good friends since that afternoon when Little Vic had received his name. Now when Pony entered the pasture where Little Vic was running, the colt would know it at once and come racing toward him. And Pony always had a piece of carrot ready for him.

No other person on the farm thought of doing anything for Little Vic. Everyone understood the deep love which had grown up between the two. It was almost as if the colt had become the boy's very own. Mr. Barby sometimes laughed at Pony's great love for this son of Victory. Then he would look at Pony in a troubled way. At last one day he spoke to the boy of the danger of loving Little Vic too much. "It will make it harder to lose him later on," the man said kindly.

Pony looked surprised. "What do you mean?" he asked.

"I think Little Vic is one of the colts that Mr. Gray means to sell next spring."

"But Little Vic is the son of Victory," Pony said. "He'll be a great horse someday."

Mr. Barby narrowed his eyes at the colt and looked at him carefully. "That may well be," he answered. "But that colt is small. I don't think we'll keep him."

Now for the first time in a long time Pony was worried. He had not thought about the chance that the colt would be sold. He had even got to thinking of the colt as his very own. But from that day when Mr. Barby warned him of the danger, Pony felt fear like a dull pain eating at his heart. From then on he tried to make Little Vic grow more. He wanted more than anything in the world to have the colt race under Mr. Gray's colors. Not that he cared one way or the other about Mr. Gray, but if Mr. Gray owned Little Vic, Pony would be able to stay near him. Or, at least, that's what Pony thought.

Sometimes at night he would wake from dreaming that Little Vic had been taken from him. For a second or two his heart would thump against his ribs, and his eyes, looking into the darkness, would be round with fear. He would tell himself it was only a dream and would try to go back to sleep again. But it never worked. Always he would have to get up and make his way to the colt's stall. There he would run his hands over the warm body, which felt as smooth as silk to his touch. Little Vic would bump him with his soft nose and nip playfully at his friend's shoulder. For the rest of the night Pony would sleep soundly in a corner of the stall, a smile on his face because Little Vic was safely near him.

But while Little Vic kept strong and well under Pony's care, he still didn't grow as much as Mr. Barby wanted him to. By the time the spring sales were due, there were many finer-looking colts on the farm than he.

Then suddenly, without warning of any kind, Little Vic began to get thin. He seemed perfectly well, as far as anyone could see, but he began to have a bony look. His ribs showed and his hip bones stood out. Pony thought it might be that the colt had begun to grow faster, but Mr. Barby wouldn't even listen to him when he tried to tell him this. Instead he just said that Little Vic was among the colts that Mr. Gray had decided to sell.

The colts, four of them, were shipped away to the place where they were to be sold. Pony and another boy rode with them in a special car that had stalls built in it for horses. There was heat and hay in the car, and the horses seemed as happy as in their stalls at home. As usual, Little Vic showed no fear as the train started. He was interested in his new home and looked around him carefully. But Pony laid a hand on his neck, and Little Vic stood quietly, as if he knew the boy would let no harm come to him.

The bidding on the colts took place in a big tent. It was as big as a circus tent. A crowd of men and women were there to see what this spring's crop of one-year-olds looked like. Most of the colts had come from fine stock, and all of them had their names and the names of their parents entered in the records of the racing board. Some of the people in the crowd already owned many race horses. Others had only one or two. A very few people had come to buy their first race horse. And some were there only becauuse they liked horses and wanted to be in on the show.

At last it was Little Vic's turn to be put on the block. Pony didn't feel the eyes of the crowd on him as he led the colt into the squared-off place where the people could get a good look at him. He was worried that Little Vic might be frightened by the strangeness around him. And he was ashamed that his favorite didn't look better. So many beautiful horses had stood in this same spot while the bidding was going on that poor Little Vic made a sorry picture. There were no ohs and ahs as Pony led him out. The people looked at him, talked about his father, and shook their heads to think that Victory's colt should show so little promise.

Suddenly an exciting new thought came to Pony. Maybe Little Vic would not be sold after all! Maybe he looked so bad no one would want to buy him! Maybe they would be going back together to the farm in the blue grass!

But no, the bidding had started. Even though he did look thin and "off," he was Victory's son just the same. Several voices spoke, making offers for Little Vic, while Pony stood sorrowfully by and tried to swallow the lump in his throat. Once Little Vic bumped him playfully, then rubbed his nose along Pony's sleeve, as if to say, "Cheer up, things always turn out for the best." But Pony seemed not to understand what Little Vic was trying to tell him.

At last a man called out, "Five thousand dollars!" No one made a higher bid, so the bidding on Little Vic was closed and the colt had a new owner.

Sadly Pony led him back to his stall. There the boy smoothed the colt's back while he thought things over. He would have to decide quickly what he was going to do, because any minute now the new owner would be coming along to take his new colt away.

For some reason Pony had got the idea that Little Vic would somehow know and object to having a new owner. It would have made Pony feel better if the colt had acted as if he felt bad too. But Pony's love for Little Vic had made him forget for the moment that Little Vic was, after all, a horse. So now Little Vic just nibbled at his oats and looked around in quiet surprise when Pony, feeling lonelier than he had ever felt before, crossed his arms on Little Vic's back and laid his head down.

He was still standing this way when the new owner arrived at the stall. Hearing footsteps, Pony made a slap at his eyes, then turned quickly to face the new owner.

"He's not much for looks, is he?" the man said to Pony.

"He's the best," the boy replied in a shaky voice.

The man looked more closely at the boy. "What makes you think so?"

Pony took a deep breath, and when he spoke his voice was almost his own again. "Can't tell for sure. Just something about him. He kind of thinks things out for himself. He isn't mean, ever. There's something about him that says"—here Pony stopped and searched inside him for just the right words—"something that says, 'Just give me time and I'll show you.'"

Pony looked quickly at the stranger, wondering if he might be laughing at him. But the man was looking at the colt, and Pony couldn't be sure that he had even taken the trouble to listen. So Pony took this chance to look over Little Vic's new owner.

He was a small man with dark hair and eyes. He was wearing a gray hat pulled low over his forehead. A long, dark topcoat covered his suit. It was well cut and hugged his shoulders smoothly. His black shoes were shining. On the little finger of his left hand was a gold ring with a blue stone set into it. He looked very fine and rich. But his eyes, as they passed back and forth over Little Vic, were hard, and he made no move to pet the colt.

Soon he was joined by another man, who looked enough like Little Vic's new owner to be his brother. He even wore the same kind of clothes and the same kind of ring.

"Hello, Lefty," said the new man. "Feeling lucky today?"

"Hello, Bill," said Lefty. He moved his head toward the colt. "Had a feeling about him. Think I'll send him down to Jack Baker. He may be able to turn him into a race horse someday."

"Five thousand dollars is a lot of money to take a chance on," Bill said.

Lefty gave a short laugh. "I've lost more than that on one race. Besides he was a good buy. Son of Victory."

"He don't look so good," said the other.

Lefty narrowed his eyes and answered, "I like 'em thin."

Pony Rivers had been listening carefully to the talk. He had seen a lot of men like Lefty and his friend around the race tracks. They were always heavy betters. They made a business of race-track betting. Sometimes they owned a race horse or two. But they cared nothing for the horses. Horses, to them, were just another way of making money quickly and easily. It hurt Pony that Little Vic had been sold to one of these.

As the two were turning to leave, Pony spoke at last. "Mister Lefty, please."

The man turned and looked at Pony, a smile turning up one side of his thin mouth. "What's on your mind?" he asked. He ran the words all together so that they sounded like one word. This was because it was a question he asked many times during the day. Usually people who spoke to him as Pony had just spoken needed some money. Lefty was known in his crowd as a "soft touch." So now he waited to see whether Pony wanted one dollar or five.

It took Pony several seconds to get the answer out, but Lefty waited. He even got a little fun out of watching Pony's struggle. People usually didn't have any trouble leading up to a "touch."

"I'd like to stay with the colt," said Pony.

A line appeared quickly between Lefty's hard eyes. This was not what he had expected, and the unexpected had a way of making him angry. He was not a man who liked being taken by surprise.

"How you mean?" asked Lefty.

"Well, you see, Mister Lefty," Pony began, his eyes watching the man's face for any slightest signal of anger, "it's me that's taken all the care of Little Vic since the morning he was born. He hasn't been handled by anybody but me. And, of course, Mr. Barby," he added, wanting to be quite truthful.

He stopped, and the man looked from Pony to the colt. He seemed to be turning over what Pony had said, so the boy decided to give his chances a telling push.

"I wouldn't want anything but enough to eat and a pair of jeans now and then."

Lefty looked for a long minute into Pony's round, steady eyes. At last he said, "Okay. I'm shipping the colt to Jack Baker's training farm. You go along. And if Jack says you can stay, it's okay by me."

"Thank you, Mister Lefty." Pony's smile was a wonderful thing to see. "I'll take care of him like he was my brother. I promise."

"I want you to take care of him like he was your meal ticket," returned Lefty. "What's your name?"

"Pony Rivers."

Lefty did not seem surprised. There were names even stranger than that in this crowd. He reached into an inside pocket and took out a flat leather billfold. From it he took a five-dollar bill and flipped it toward the boy.

"There'll be a truck along in a little while. If you get the colt into it without his hurting himself and deliver him safe to Jack Baker, there will be another one like that waiting for you when you get there."

Pony took the bill and looked at it without saying a word. It was the first five-dollar bill he had ever owned. He was still looking at it when the men went away. At last his eyes lifted from the greenback to the colt standing beside him. He stuffed the bill into a pocket of his jeans and gently laid his hand along the colt's neck.

"Did you hear him, Little Vic? He said he'd give me another five for getting you there safe. Can you beat that? *Paying* me to see that nothing bad happens to you! Some folks don't understand anything except money, do they?"

To the boy's delight, Little Vic moved his head up and down as if he were agreeing with every word.

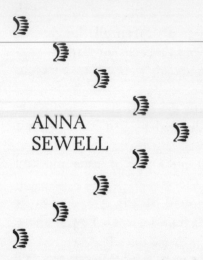

ANNA
SEWELL

Black Beauty

Introduction by Noel Streatfield

Anna Sewell, who was born in England in 1820, spent her early years in a poor section of London. From the time Anna could understand words, her mother told her stories of the country and brought her up to understand that animals—particularly horses—have feelings and should be treated with love and kindness.

In a period when all traffic was pulled by horses, Anna saw animals brutally mistreated. With horror she watched overloaded carts sliding down on to the horses pulling them. She saw exhausted horses being beaten as they dragged coal carts over the slippery cobbles. She would watch, her nose pressed to a window, as hackney-carriage horses waited hour after hour in rain or sleet for a fare, and she suffered with them.

At her grandfather's farm, on the other hand, Anna had a chance to ride horseback and to see horses well treated. When she was twelve her parents moved to a former coach house where the old harness was still hanging, and where she could piece together the history of the horses who had been stabled there.

Two years later, running home from school to get out of a storm, Anna slipped and badly twisted both ankles. Probably she did not receive proper medical attention, for she was a cripple from that day onward. Now from being a doer Anna was forced to become a listener. It must have been very hard for her, for she had a violent temper and a jealous streak that did not make it easy for her to watch others enjoying themselves when she could not.

Her family moved several more times. Anna was delighted when they moved to a house in the country, where she could have a pony and carriage. There are no words to describe what that pony meant to Anna. He allowed her to come and go as she wished, just like other people. He made it easier for her to talk to people, for a horse helps to break down barriers. And, thanks to that pony, Anna's ear was able to record the talk of ostlers, grooms, and stable boys, which was later to help make BLACK BEAUTY *such an outstanding book.*

In 1857 she went by herself to Germany to visit a doctor who might cure her ankles. He could not cure them entirely, but for a time they were so much better that Anna was able to walk a little and—joy of joys—to ride horseback.

Meanwhile, Anna's mother had become a professional writer; one of her poems, "Mother's Last Words," sold over a million copies, and others of her verses sold extraordinarily well. When Anna returned from Germany, she began to help her mother in preparing her verses for the press, and in correcting proof.

When Anna was fifty-one, she knew that she was at the begining of her last illness and would never go out again. Her first concern was for her old pony. She found him a happy home where others would love him as much as she had. Then she settled down to what looked like a life of complete invalidism.

But she wrote in her journal: "I am writing the life of a horse." Anna was so ill that the book took five years to write. At times, she could not hold a pen but dictated the story to her mother.

BLACK BEAUTY *was published late in 1877. The reviews rolled in, and everyone praised her. By the following April, the book had sold 90,000 copies and Anna was famous.*

Anna died that same April. But BLACK BEAUTY *has never died.*

Horses play an important part in the lives of most people in Britain. There are horse shows all over the country which families for miles around attend. Also, in London on the Monday after Whit Sunday there is a special show for working horses—those who draw the milk carts, brewers' drays, and the costers' barrows—just the type of horse in fact that in Anna Sewell's day so often was cruelly treated. Such horses now have no need of defenders, for they are cherished friends of their owners, and loved by the public. Recently when a mare unexpectedly foaled in a London street, people came running from every house carrying coats and rugs to keep the mother and child warm, until a horse ambulance arrived.

Horse riding, at one time exclusively an amusement of the rich, is now within the reach of all, for there are inexpensive riding clubs on the outskirts of most cities, and at horse shows the competitors come from every walk of life.

In this wonderful change in less than a hundred years BLACK BEAUTY *has played a large part. The book is widely known, for not only is it in all children's libraries, but is a school reader. In fact so popular is it with British children that in many homes* BLACK BEAUTY *does not seem a fictional character, but as much part of the family as their pet cat or dog. Wouldn't Anna Sewell be pleased?*

My Early Home

THE FIRST PLACE THAT I CAN WELL REMEMBER WAS A LARGE PLEASANT meadow with a pond of clear water in it. Some shady trees leaned over it, and rushes and water lilies grew at the deep end. Over the hedge on one side we looked into a field, and on the other we looked over a gate at our master's house, which stood by the roadside; at the top of the meadow was a plantation of fir trees, and at the bottom a running brook overhung by a steep bank.

While I was young I lived upon my mother's milk, as I could not eat grass. In the daytime I ran by her side, and at night I lay down close by her. When it was hot, we used to stand by the pond in the shade of the trees, and when it was cold, we had a nice warm shed near the plantation.

As soon as I was old enough to eat grass, my mother used to go out to work in the daytime, and came back in the evening.

There were six young colts in the meadow besides me; they were older than I was; some were nearly as large as grown-up horses. I used to run with them, and had great fun; we used to gallop all together around and around the field, as hard as we could go. Sometimes we had rather rough play, for they would frequently bite and kick as well as gallop.

One day, when there was a good deal of kicking, my mother whinnied to me to come to her, and then she said:

"I wish you to pay attention to what I am going to say to you. The colts who live here are very good colts, but they are cart horse colts, and, of course, they have not learned manners. You have been well bred and well born; your father has a great name in these parts, and your grandfather won the cup two years at the Newmarket races; your grandmother had the sweetest temper of any horse I ever knew, and I think you have never seen me kick or bite. I hope you will grow up gentle and good, and never learn bad ways; do your work with a good will, lift your feet up well when you trot, and never bite or kick even in play."

I have never forgotten my mother's advice; I knew she was a wise old horse, and our master thought a great deal of her. Her name was Duchess, but he often called her Pet.

Our master was a good, kind man. He gave us good food, good lodging, and kind words; he spoke as kindly to us as he did to his little children. We were all fond of him, and my mother loved him very much. When she saw him at the gate, she would neigh with joy, and trot up to him. He would pat and stroke her and say, "Well, old Pet, and how is your little Darkie?" I was a dull black, so he called me Darkie; then he would give me a piece of bread, which was very good, and sometimes he brought a carrot for my mother. All the horses would come to him, but I think he liked us best. My mother always took him to the town on a market day in a little gig.

There was a farm boy, Dick, who sometimes came into our field to pick blackberries from the hedge. When he had eaten all he wanted, he would have what he called fun with the colts, throwing stones and sticks at them to make them gallop. We did not much mind him, for we could gallop off; but sometimes a stone would hit and hurt us.

One day he was at this game, and did not know that the master was in the next field; but he was there, watching what was going on: over the hedge he jumped in a snap, and catching Dick by the arm, he gave him a heavy blow on the ear that made him roar with the pain and surprise. As soon as we saw the master, we trotted up nearer to see what went on.

"Bad boy!" he said, "bad boy! to chase the colts. This is not the first time, nor the second, but it shall be the last. There—take your money and go home, I shall not want you on my farm again." So we never saw Dick any more. Old Daniel, the man who looked after the horses, was just as gentle as our master, so we were well off.

My Breaking In

I was now beginning to grow handsome; my coat had grown fine and soft, and was bright black. I had one white foot, and a pretty white star on my forehead. My master would not sell me until I was four years old; he said lads ought not to work like men, and colts ought not to work like horses until they were quite grown up.

When I was four years old, Squire Gordon came to look at me. He examined my eyes, my mouth, and my legs, and then I had to walk and trot and gallop before him. He seemed to like me, and said, "When he has been well broken in, he will do very well." My master said he would break me in himself, as he should not like me to be frightened or hurt, and he lost no time about it, for the next day he began.

Every one may not know what breaking in is, therefore I will describe it. It means to teach a horse to wear a saddle and bridle and to carry on his back a man, woman, or child; to go just the way they wish and to go quietly. Besides this, he has to learn to wear a collar, a crupper, and a breeching, and to stand still while they are put on; then to have a cart or a chaise fixed behind him, so that he cannot walk or trot without dragging it after him. And he must go fast or slow, just as the driver wishes. He must never start at what he sees, nor speak to other horses, nor bite, nor kick, nor have any will of his own, but always do his master's will, even though he may be very tired or hungry. But the worst of all is, when his harness is once on, he may neither jump for joy nor lie down for weariness. So you see this breaking in is a great thing.

I had of course long been used to a halter and a headstall, and to being led about in the field and lanes quietly, but now I was to have a bit and a bridle. After a good deal of coaxing, my master got the bit into my mouth, and the bridle fixed, but it was an unpleasant thing! Those who have never had a bit in their mouths cannot think how bad it feels; a great piece of cold hard steel as thick as a man's finger to be pushed into your mouth, between your teeth and over your tongue, with the ends coming out at the corner of your mouth, and held fast there by straps over your head, under your throat, around your nose, and under your chin; so that no way in the world can you get rid of the cold hard thing. It is very bad! yes, very bad! at least I thought so; but I knew all horses wore them when they were grown up. And so, what with the nice oats, and what with my master's pats, kind words, and gentle ways, I got to wear my bit and bridle.

Next came the saddle, but that was not half so bad. My master put it on my back very gently, while old Daniel held my head. He then made the girths fast under my body, patting and talking to me all the time, then I had a few oats, then a little leading about. This he did every day until I began to look for the oats and the saddle. At length, one morning my master got on my back and rode me around the meadow. It certainly did feel queer—but I must say I felt rather proud to carry my master, and as he continued to ride me a little every day, I soon became accustomed to it.

The next unpleasant business was putting on the iron shoes. That, too, was very hard at first. My master went with me to the smith's forge, to see that I was not hurt or frightened. The blacksmith took my feet in his hands one after the other, and cut away some of the hoof. It did not pain me. Then he took a piece of iron the shape of my foot, and clapped it on, and drove some nails through the shoe right into my hoof, so that the shoe was firmly on. My feet felt very stiff and heavy, but in time I got used to it.

And now, having got so far, my master went on to break me to harness; there were more new things to wear. First, a stiff heavy collar just on my neck, and a bridle with great side-pieces against my eyes called blinkers, so that I could not see on either side, but only straight in front of me. Next, there was a small saddle with an unpleasant stiff strap that went right under my tail; that was the crupper. To have my long tail doubled up and poked through that strap was almost as bad as the bit. I never felt more like kicking, but of course I could not kick such a good master, and so in time I got used to everything, and could do my work as well as my mother.

I must not forget to mention one part of my training, which I have always considered a very great advantage. My master sent me for some days to a nearby farmer's, who had a meadow which was skirted on one side by the railway. Here were some sheep and cows, and I was turned in among them.

I shall never forget the first train that ran by. I was feeding quietly near the railings which separated the meadow from the railway, when I heard a strange sound at a distance, and before I knew from where it came—with a rush and a clatter, and a puffing out of smoke—a long black train of something flew by, and was gone almost before I could draw my breath. I turned, and galloped to the further side of the meadow as fast as I could go. In the course of the day many other trains went by, some more slowly. These drew up at the station close by, and sometimes made an awful shriek and groan before they stopped. I thought it very dreadful, but the cows went on eating very quietly, and hardly raised their heads as the frightening black thing came puffing and grinding past.

For the first few days I could not eat in peace; but as I found that this terrible creature never came into the field, or did me any harm, I began to disregard it, and very soon I cared as little abot the passing of a train as the cows and sheep did.

To this day, thanks to my good master's care, I am as fearless at railway stations as in my own stable.

My master often drove me in double harness with my mother, because she was steady and could teach me best. She told me that it was wisest always to do my best to please my master. "But," said she, "there are a great many kinds of men; there are good, thoughtful men like our master, that any horse may be proud to serve—but there are also bad, cruel men, who never ought to have a horse or dog to call their own. There are a great many foolish men, as well, who never trouble themselves to think; these spoil more horses than all, just for want of sense. I hope you will fall into good hands; but a horse never knows who may buy him, or who may drive him. Do your best, wherever it is, and keep up your good name."

Birtwick Park

Early in May, a man came from Squire Gordon's, and took me away to the Hall. My master said, "Good-bye, Darkie; be a good horse, and always do your best." I could not say "good-bye," so I put my nose into his hand; he patted me kindly, and I left my first home.

As I lived some years with Squire Gordon, I may as well tell something about the place. Squire Gordon's Park skirted the village of Birtwick. It was entered by a large iron gate, at which stood the first lodge, and then you trotted along on a smooth road between clumps of large old trees; then another lodge and another gate which brought you to the house and the gardens. Beyond this lay the home paddock, the old orchard, and the stables. There was room for many horses and carriages; but I need only describe the stable into which I was taken; this was very roomy, with four good stalls; a large swinging window opened into the yard, which made it pleasant and airy.

The first stall was the largest and shut in behind with a wooden gate. It had a low rack for hay and a low manger for corn. It was called a loose box, because the horse that was put into it was not tied up, but left loose, to do as he liked. It is a great thing to have a loose box.

Into this fine box the groom put me. It was clean, sweet and airy and I could see all that went on through the iron rails that were at the top.

He gave me some very nice oats, and then went away.

When I had eaten my oats I looked around. In the stall next to mine stood a little fat gray pony, with a thick mane and tail, a very pretty head, and a pert nose.

I said, "How do you do? what is your name?"

He said, "My name is Merrylegs. I carry the young ladies on my back, and sometimes I take our mistress out in the low chair. They think a great deal of me, and so does James. Are you going to live next door to me in the box?"

I said "Yes."

"Well then," he said, "I hope you are good-tempered; I do not like any one next door who bites."

Just then a horse's head looked over from the stall beyond; the ears were laid back, and the eye looked rather ill-tempered. This was a tall chestnut mare, with a long handsome neck. She looked across to me and said:

"So it is you who have turned me out of my box; it is a very strange thing for a colt like you, to come and turn a lady out of her own home."

"I beg your pardon," I said, "the man who brought me put me here, and I had nothing to do with it; and as to being a colt, I am turned four years old, and am a grown-up horse. I never had words yet with horse or mare, and it is my wish to live at peace."

"Well," she said, "we shall see. Of course I do not want to have words with a young thing like you." I said no more.

In the afternoon when we went out, Merrylegs told me all about it:

"Ginger has a bad habit of biting and snapping—that is why they call her Ginger. And when she was in the loose box, she used to snap very much. One day she bit James in the arm and made it bleed, and so Miss Flora and Miss Jessie, who are very fond of me, were afraid to come into the stable. They used to bring me nice things to eat, an apple or a carrot, or a piece of bread, but with Ginger in that box, they dare not come, and I miss them very much. I hope they will now come again, if you do not bite or snap."

I told him I never bit anything and could not think what pleasure Ginger found in it.

"Well, I don't think she does find pleasure," said Merrylegs. "It is just a bad habit; she says no one was ever kind to her, and why should she not bite? but I am sure, if all she says is true, she must have been very ill-used before she came here. John and James do all they can to please her, and our master never uses a whip if a horse acts right; so I think she might be good-tempered here. You see," he said with a wise look, "I am twelve years old. I know a great deal, and I can tell you there is not a better place for a horse all around the country than this. John is the best groom that ever was, he has been here fourteen years; and you never saw such a kind boy as James is, so that it is all Ginger's own fault that she did not stay in that box."

Liberty

I was quite happy in my new place but I missed my liberty. For three years and a half of my life I had had all the liberty I could wish for; but now, week after week, month after month, and no doubt year after year, I must stand up in a stable night and day except when I was wanted, and then I must be just as steady and quiet as any old horse who has worked twenty years. Straps here and straps there, a bit in my mouth, and blinkers over my eyes. Now, I am not complaining, for I know it must be so. I only mean to say that for a young horse full of strength and spirits who has been used to some large field, where he can fling up his head, and toss up his tail and gallop away at full speed—I say it is hard never to have liberty to do as he likes. Sometimes, when I had had less exercise than usual, I felt so full of life and spring that when John took me out to exercise, I really could not keep quiet. Do what I would, it seemed as if I must jump, or dance, or prance—and many a good shake I know I must have given him, especially at the first. But he was always good and patient.

"Steady, steady, my boy," he would say. "Wait a bit, and we'll have a good swing, and soon get the tickle out of your feet." Then as soon as we were out of the village he would give me a few miles at a brisk trot, and then bring me back as fresh as before, but clear of the fidgets, as he called them. Spirited horses, when not enough exercised, are often called skittish, when it is only play and some grooms will punish them; but our John did not—he knew it was only high spirits. Still, he had his own ways of making me understand by the tone of his voice or the touch of the rein. If he was very serious and quite determined, I always knew it by his voice, and that had more power with me than anything else, for I was very fond of him.

I ought to say that sometimes we had our liberty for a few hours. This used to be on fine Sundays in the summertime. The carriage never went out on Sundays, because the church was not far off.

It was a great treat for us to be turned out into the Home Paddock or the old orchard. The grass was so cool and soft to our feet, the air so sweet, and the freedom to do as we liked so pleasant, we could gallop, lie down, and roll over on our backs, or nibble the sweet grass. Then it was a very good time for talking, as we stood together under the shade of the large chestnut tree.

A Stormy Day

One day late in the autumn, my master had a long journey to make. I was put into the dogcart, and John went with his master. I always liked to go in the dogcart, it was so light, and the high wheels ran along so pleasantly. There had been a great deal of rain, and now the wind was very high, and blew the dry leaves across the road in a shower. We went along merrily until we came to the tollgate, and the low wooden bridge. The bridge was so low in the middle that if the river was full, the water would be nearly up to the woodwork and planks. But as there were good substantial rails on each side, people did not mind it.

The man at the gate said the river was rising fast, and he feared it would be a bad night. Many of the meadows were under water, and in one low part of the road the water was halfway up to my knees. The bottom was good, and master drove gently, so it did not matter.

As the master's business engaged him a long time, we did not start for home until rather late in the afternoon. The wind was then much higher, and I heard the master say to John, he had never been out in such a storm; and so I thought, as we went along the edge of a wood, where the great branches were swaying about like twigs, and the rushing sound was terrible.

"I wish we were well out of this wood," said my master.

"Yes, sir," said John, "it would be rather awkward if one of these branches came down upon us."

The words were scarcely out of his mouth, when there was a groan, and a crack, and a splitting sound, and crashing down among the other trees came an oak, torn up by the roots, and it fell right across the road just before us. I will never say I was not frightened, for I was. I stopped still, and I believe I trembled; of course, I did not turn around or run away; I was not brought up to do that. John jumped out and was at my head in a moment.

"That was a very near thing," said my master. "What's to be done now?"

"Well, sir, there is nothing to do but to go back to the four crossroad, and that will be a good six miles before we get around to the wooden bridge again. It will make us late, but the horse is fresh."

So back we went, and around by the crossroads. By the time we got to the bridge it was very nearly dark. We could just see that the water was over the middle of it; but as that had happened before, master did not stop. We were going along at a good pace, but the moment my feet touched the bridge, I knew there was something wrong and stopped dead. "Go on, Beauty," said my master, and he gave me a touch with the whip, but I did not stir. He gave me a sharp cut, I jumped, but I dared not go forward.

"There's something wrong sir," said John, and he sprang out of the dog-cart and came to my head and looked all about. He tried to lead me forward. "Come on, Beauty, what's the matter?" Of course I could not tell him, but I knew very well that the bridge was not safe.

Just then the man at the tollgate on the other side ran out of the house, tossing a torch about like a madman.

"Stop!" he cried.

"What's the matter?" shouted my master.

"The bridge is broken in the middle and part of it is carried away; if you come on you'll be into the river."

"Thank God!" said my master. "You Beauty!" said John, and took the bridle and gently turned me around to the other road. The sun had set some time, the wind seemed to have died down. I trotted quietly along, the wheels hardly making a sound on the soft road. For a good while neither master nor John spoke, and then master began in a serious voice. I learned that, if I had gone on as the master wanted me, most likely the bridge would have given way under us, and we would all have fallen into the river; and as the current was flowing very strongly, and it was nearly dark, it was more than likely we would all have been drowned. Master said God had given men reason, but He had given animals knowledge which did not depend on reason, and which was much more prompt and perfect in its way, and by which they had often saved the lives of men. John had many stories to tell of dogs and horses, and the wonderful things they had done; he thought people did not value their animals half enough, nor make friends of them as they ought to do. I am sure he made friends of them if ever a man did.

At last we came to the Park gates, and found the gardener looking out for us. He said that mistress had been in a dreadful way ever since dark, fearing some accident had happened. We saw a light at the hall door and at the upper windows, and as we came up mistress ran out, saying, "Are you really safe, my dear? Oh! I have been so anxious. Have you had an accident?"

"No, my dear; but if Black Beauty had not been wiser than we were, we would all have been drowned at the wooden bridge."

I heard no more, as they went into the house, and John took me to the stable. Oh! what a good supper he gave me that night, a good bran mash and some crushed beans with my oats, and a thick bed of straw. I was glad of it, for I was tired.

"This book should be required reading for every college student. I wish I'd had a copy back when I was in school!"

—*Gregory J. P. Godek*
best-selling author of 1001 Ways to Be Romantic

"A valuable and enthusiastic guide that can benefit every student, whether you want strategies for acing your courses, suggestions on daily college living, or if you just want to hone your social skills. We highly recommend it for any person going to or planning to attend college."

—*Dr. Charles Zastrow and R. Dae H. Chang*
coauthors of The Personal Problem Solver

"GREAT PURCHASE. For the price of a CD, you can clinch four years of success with the *Complete Guide*."

—*Sandy Ann Cho*
student, University of California at Berkeley

"The provocative 'DATING, RELATIONSHIPS, AND SEX' chapter will make you think. Find out where you really stand."

—*Patrick S. Alexander*
student, Carleton College

"Enlightening, empowering, and fun to read. This is the material they don't teach you in school."

—*Ivan G. Burnell*
author of The Power of Positive Doing

"This book vividly and accurately represents the voice of college America. It belongs in every book bag, dorm room, and orientation class."

—*Dr. Kee Park*
educational psychologist, Boston School Department

"Richard Newman is most effective in presenting information that parents wish their college-bound kids knew as well as answering questions students want, but often hesitate, to ask upperclassmen. I recommend *The Complete Guide to College Success* to everyone from parents who wish to send their college-bound kids off with a parcel of good advice to students interested in getting the most from their college experiences, and to anyone committed to achieving their goals and developing better personal relationships."

—*Janine J. Weins, Ph.D.*
columnist and radio talk-show host of the Twin State Journal

The Complete Guide to College Success

What Every Student Needs to Know

▲

▲

▲

▲

RICHARD NEWMAN

NEW YORK UNIVERSITY PRESS
New York and London

NEW YORK UNIVERSITY PRESS
New York and London

Library of Congress Cataloging-in-Publication Data
Newman, Richard, 1969–
The complete guide to college success : what every student needs
to know / Richard Newman.
p.   cm.
Includes bibliographical references and index.
ISBN 0–8147–5783–9. — ISBN 0–8147–5784–7 (pbk.)
1. College student orientation—United States.   2. College
students—United States—Attitudes.   3. Study skills.   I. Title.
LB2343.32.N48   1996
378.1'98—dc20   95–4426
                    CIP

New York University Press books are printed on acid-free paper,
and their binding materials are chosen for strength and
durability.

Manufactured in the United States of America

10   9   8   7   6   5   4   3   2   1

To my father, who gave me his strong work ethic and wisdom.

To my mother, who provided me with an abundance of love and caring.

To my brother, who supported and encouraged my efforts.

To all of my fellow college students, who have inspired these ideas.

And, above all, to my higher power . . . I dedicate this book.

CONTENTS

Part 3 Academic Success

ACKNOWLEDGMENTS

This book was by no means a one-man project. Many minds came together to create this unique college guide. For that, I am ever grateful.

I would especially like to thank the following people who each have contributed, directly or indirectly, to the book and to my life: Niko Pfund, Colin Jones, Antionette Matlins, Lenny Dave and everyone at Argonaut Entertainment, Ken and Mary Brown, Brenda Blakeman and everyone at First Impressions, Frank and Tina Kastor, Lana Lowell, Jenny Gibbs, Denise Rogers, Kenneth McKenzie, Uncle Jack and Aunt Ruth, Richard Bach, John and Ruth Coultis, the entire "AH-SO crew" and their loyal customers, Stanley Alexander, Glen Secor, everyone at NYU Press, Lucy Joo, Gail Bowen, Mark Miles, Wayne Dyer, David Collins and everyone at the KU MBA program, Anita Skeen, Jason Yi, Ms. Incog, Charles Zastrow, Dharma DeSilva, Jay Robinson, Michael Sabatino, Jeff Graber, Joe Bosco, Mike Swearingin, Todd Pettigrew, Warren Wandling, Jin Wahn Doh, P. M. Dawn, Miah Kim, all of the student quote contributors, Scott Nickel, Rick Yust, Catherine Chung, Dot Moran, the Dartmouth College DRS group, Ramsey Hraibi, Michelle Hetherington, Jennifer Yeoman, Robin Parsely, Josephine Choy, Kathy Kim, Tom Gibson, Joan Lawrence, the College Success cartoonists, Mark Miles, the Momsens, Terri C., Janine Weins, Kay Kim, John Cogswell, Billy Momsen, Pete Porter, Tae Won Park, Evander Holyfield, St. John's Church in Boston, Young Namkung, and all of the student quote contributors.

DREAM BIG

If there were ever a time to dare,
to make a difference,
to embark on something worth doing,
it is now.
Not for any grand cause, necessarily —
but for something that tugs at your heart
something that's your dream.

You owe it to yourself
to make your days here count.
Have fun.
Dig deep.
Stretch.

Dream big.

Know, though, that things worth doing
seldom come easy.
There will be good days.
And there will be bad days.
There will be times when you want to turn around,
pack it up,
and call it quits.
Those times tell you
that you are pushing yourself,
that you are not afraid to learn by trying.

Persist.

Because with an idea,
determination,
and the right tools,
you can do great things.
Let your instincts,
your intellect,
and your heart
guide you.

Trust.

Believe in the incredible power of the human mind.
Of doing something that makes a difference.

Of working hard.
Of laughing and hoping.
Of lazy afternoons.
Of lasting friends.
Of all the things that will cross your path this year.

The start of something new
brings the hope of something great.
Anything is possible.
There is only you.
And you will pass this way only once.
Do it right.

—APPLE MACINTOSH COMPUTERS

INTRODUCTION

I am just like you, a college student who wants to get the most out of the college experience. Since my senior year of high school, I have bought or have received as gifts many books on college life. And being the enthusiastic student that I am, I have actually taken the time to read several of these books from cover to cover.

They all served their purpose. However, I always found myself looking for a *different kind* of college life book—one that didn't focus only on study skills, one that wasn't made only for first-year students, and definitely one that wasn't written by some forty- or fifty-year-old author.

What I was looking for was a contemporary, custom-made college success guide—one that covered the entire spectrum of the college experience. In essence, I wanted *one book* that integrated the personal, social, interpersonal, and academic aspects of college life together in a comprehensive manner.

But I was never able to find one.

That frustrating search served as the catalyst for this book. I, and virtually every other college student I talked to, was interested in a success guide of this nature. Yet there was a one-book gap in the college student market—a gap that needed to be filled. I thought, "Who better to fill it than a college student?"

The result of that thought is the book you are holding in your hands: a culmination of time-tested strategies and winning philosophies—all geared toward, you guessed it, college success. The ideas of this book were inspired by college students just like you and me, from all over the country. You will find quotes interspersed throughout the book by students who wanted to express their views on various college life issues. What sets *The Complete Guide*

to College Success apart from the others is the fact that it was written *for* college students *by* college students.

Throughout the production of this book it was my goal to create a tried-and-true *success* guide. For years I have noticed that there are many books covering the themes "how to *survive* your college experience" and "how to *cope* with college life." I did not set out to produce another "survival" guide, nor did I want to put together a "how to cope" book. You will not find anywhere in the text a single occurrence of the word *surviving* or the word *coping* or anything of that flavor. This is a book about college *success,* nothing less. I hope you enjoy reading it as much as I've enjoyed writing it.

Oliver Wendell Holmes once said, "A moment's insight is sometimes worth a life's experience." My wish is that this book may provide you with several such moments.

Part **I**

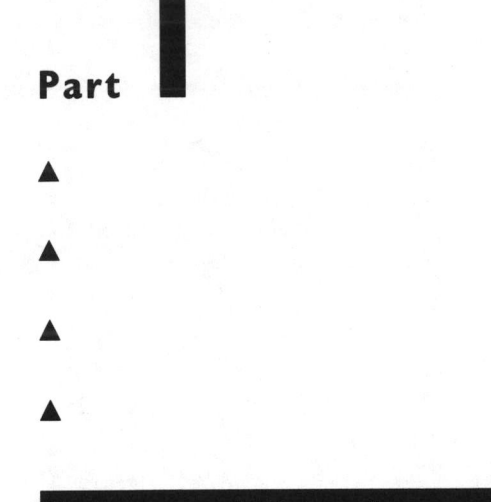

Personal Development

▲ If students believe college is an unstable roller coaster ride, then most likely it will be. But if students believe college is a fast-moving freeway with exhilarating scenery and an occasional speed bump, then college will become the ride of their lives.

JASON LARABEE
University of Oklahoma

▲ The primary cause of any belief or emotion is not outside events, people, or things. Rather, our beliefs and emotions are a result of the self-talk that we give ourselves about those outside events, people, or things. The way to change deleterious beliefs and unwanted emotions is by changing our thinking in a more positive direction. This requires communicating with ourselves in energizing, empowering ways. Through repetition and intensity, any verbal message conveyed will become a belief; and through our beliefs, we ultimately create our own realities.

DR. CHARLES ZASTROW
University of Wisconsin, Whitewater

▲ I've read that the average person is told the word "No" at least 150,000 times by the age of eighteen. As an estimate, we have been told that we were either doing something wrong or unable to do something right 23 times a day, every day, month after month, year in and year out. It is no wonder we have difficulty believing in ourselves. We've been conditioned negatively since day one.

CRISSY LEE
Bennett College, North Carolina

▲ Jesus once said, "As you think, so shall ye be." I wonder if Napoleon Hill had that in mind when he wrote, "What the mind of man can conceive and believe, the mind of man can achieve." It seems to me that the world's most cherished souls and highest achievers always have the same philosophy on belief.

LOUISE LOWELL
Boston University

I

THE POWER OF BELIEF

We can do only what we think we can do.
We can be only what we think we can be.
We can have only what we think we can have.
What we do, what we are, what we have,
all depend upon what we think.

ROBERT COLLIER

My first college advisor told me, "If you truly believe that you can succeed here, you will. Everything starts 'upstairs,' in the brain." Those words meant a lot to me as a wide-eyed freshman.

And now, several years later, I am an advisor of sorts myself; and it's my turn to pass on that powerful philosophy.

The starting point of any success in college is a strong sense of belief in ourselves and in our abilities. But believing extends far beyond accepting the fact that anything is possible. Believing, in this sense, means two things: (1) that you *know* in your heart you can accomplish what you set out to accomplish, and (2) that you expect things will work out for the best in the long run.

I firmly believe that each of us has unlimited potential for greatness and success. Each of us has a special, unique gift to contribute to the world. Some

of us may be destined for excellent careers in medicine, business, or education. Others of us may hope to one day go into professional singing, writing, athletics, or acting. Whatever, we all have our own individual dreams for the future. *To live out these dreams we must first believe in our ability to make them happen.*

And *now* is the time.

College is where we come to discover our lifelong dreams and work toward turning them into realities. That sounds good in theory, but it's not always so easy to apply on a daily basis. There will be a number of times throughout our college experiences when we will be put to the test—personally as well as academically. This chapter is about taking these tests of life, succeeding at them, and actualizing our dreams through the power of belief.

▲

How High Can You Jump?

A typical ninth-grade science experiment can clearly demonstrate the belief concept. If you put a flea in a small jar and close the lid, you will witness an interesting phenomenon. At first the flea will try to escape by jumping out of the jar. Every time it jumps, it will hit its head on the lid. Time after time the flea will jump, but because of the lid it will not be able to get out.

Eventually, the flea will begin to believe that it is impossible to jump any higher than the lid. From that point on you can take the lid completely off the jar and the flea will *still* not be able to escape. It has come to believe that it cannot jump higher than the lid, so it never does. It may jump up to the lip of the jar, but it will never do what it is perfectly capable of doing—jumping *out* of the jar to freedom.

The point here is simply that any limitations you think you have during college will be *self-imposed*. Arnold Schwarzenegger put it best when he said, "The mind is the limit. As long as the mind can envision the fact that you can do something, you can do it—as long as you really believe 100 percent." A simple truth, from one college student to another: we can do absolutely anything we set our minds to, if only we believe that it's possible.

And Now, an Example You Can Really Sink Your Teeth Into

Belief is such an important concept because it—and it alone—is what unifies the mind and the body in pursuit of a dream. For example, an athlete could be blessed with the best runner's physique in the world; but if she does not believe that she can win an Olympic race, all of her physical superiority won't make a bit of difference—and she *won't* win the Olympic race, or any other for that matter. The mind and body function together like that, always working jointly to turn a person's beliefs into realities.

Let's illustrate the association between mind and body with a simple example. Right now, I want you to just relax and slowly read the next paragraph. Close your eyes after each sentence (at the "•") and really visualize the sequence of events taking place. Incorporate as many physical senses— sights, sounds, tastes, smells, feelings—as you can into your imagination.

Imagine yourself cutting a lemon into thick wedges with a knife. • Notice that fresh "ssssshhhk" sound that is made as you slice into it. • Next, pick up a lemon wedge and slowly bring it toward your face. • Notice how sour and tart the lemon smells. • Squeeze the lemon wedge in your hand. • Feel its juice seeping down onto your fingers. • Stick out your tongue and lick some of the sour juice off of your index finger. • Now imagine yourself putting that big, juicy lemon wedge . . . right . . . into . . . your . . . mouth. • Quick, force yourself to bite down on it hard! •

Do you notice anything happening inside your mouth?

This mental exercise will make you salivate, especially if you imagine the scenario vividly. The question is, what causes that mini-gush of saliva? After all, there was no knife and no lemon. Everything that happened took place in your mind.

And *that's* the key, just exactly as my former advisor said; "Everything starts 'upstairs,' in the brain." Whatever you believe in your mind to be true will somehow manifest itself in your body and in your actions. This means simply that if you believe you can achieve success in college, success will become a part of your daily life.

In the providence of the mind, what one believes to be true either is true or becomes true.

JOHN LILLY

Value Rigidity

By the time we enter college, many of us think we know what we are capable of accomplishing and, just as important, what we are *not* capable of accomplishing. These beliefs are deeply rooted in our personal value systems—which have been evolving since childhood.

Should you ever find yourself questioning your ability to succeed at *anything* in college, most likely there is a negative value system at play. Yet it is part of our nature to cling to our values—even if they are negative and disempowering—because they are what we are used to.

The field of psychology affirms that when negative values are too rigid, they can not only prevent us from achieving success, but they can also keep us from living freely and happily. Robert M. Pirsig, author of *Zen and the Art of Motorcycle Maintenance,* gives his take on this concept:

> the most striking example of value rigidity I can think of is the old South Indian Monkey Trap, which depends on value rigidity for its effectiveness. The trap consists of a hollowed-out coconut chained to a stake. The coconut has some rice inside which can be grabbed through a small hole. The hole is big enough so that the monkey's hand can go in, but too small for his fist with rice in it to come out. The monkey reaches in and is suddenly trapped—by nothing more than his own value rigidity. He can't revalue the rice. He cannot see that freedom without rice is more valuable than capture with it.

Now obviously, we're not a bunch of monkeys in South India. But the passage raises a crucial question for each of us.

Are you holding on to any negative beliefs about yourself?

Think about it. Is there anything you think you can't do? A good place to start is to consider your GPA. Do you think you can't make the honor roll? Or the Dean's List? Or straight A's? If the words "I can't . . ." are etched into your value system, you'll cling to those beliefs, and you will prove yourself right, every time.

Of course that same concept works just as well in reverse. If the words "I can . . ." are etched into your value system, your beliefs will reflect that power. And once you believe that you *can* make the honor roll, or the Dean's List, or straight A's, or whatever else, you may soon find yourself a prophet.

There's nothing I can't do. There are plenty of things I won't do. But the word "can't" isn't even in my vocabulary.

DOT MORAN, Northeastern University

Believe Also in Reality

This chapter is not about seeking or expecting perfection in everything you do. You and I and every other student in the world will make our fair share of mistakes and will experience failures as we go through college. But that's all right, as long as we always keep in mind that short-term experiences—both good and bad—pave the way to long-term success.

The most inspiring people in history have all had powerful beliefs in themselves and their dreams. Their beliefs carried them through the rough times and eventually brought them the greatness and successes they deserved. For example:

> Colonel Sanders, founder of Kentucky Fried Chicken, wanted to sell his idea for a unique chicken recipe. As an old, retired man sleeping in his car and living off social security checks, the colonel and his recipe were rejected 1,009 times before the first deal was closed.
>
> Abraham Lincoln was determined to persevere in his political career, even after the following heartbreaking defeats: lost a legislative race (in 1831), lost a congressional race (in 1843), lost another congressional race (in 1845), lost a senatorial race (in 1854), lost another senatorial race (in 1858). He was finally elected as the sixteenth president of the United States in 1860.
>
> Thomas Edison, famous innovator and inventor, failed a whopping 9,999 times before he successfully developed the electric light bulb.

Speaking of Thomas Edison, he gave the world a bit of insight that serves as the perfect wrap-up for this chapter: "If we did all the things we are capable of doing we would literally astound ourselves."

Believe it.

Believe in yourself.

And you are certain to achieve great success in college.

Who Controls Your Life?

Instructions: Read the following statements and indicate whether you agree more with choice A or choice B.

	A	**B**
	I more strongly believe that:	OR

1. Promotions are earned through hard work and persistence. | Making a lot of money is largely a matter of getting the right breaks.

_____

2. In my experience I have noticed that there is usually a direct connection between how hard I study and the grades I get. | Many times the reactions of teachers seem haphazard to me.

_____

3. The number of divorces indicates that more and more people are not trying to make their marriages work. | Marriage is largely a gamble.

_____

4. When I am right I can convince others. | It is silly to think that one can really change another person's basic attitude.

_____

5. In our society a man's future earning power is dependent upon his ability. | Getting promoted is really a matter of being a little luckier than the next guy.

_____

6. If one knows how to deal with people they are really quite easily led. | I have little influence over the way other people behave.

_____

7. In my case the grades I make are the results of my own efforts; luck has little or nothing to do with it. | Sometimes I feel that I have little to do with the grades I get.

_____

8. People like me can change the course of world affairs if we make ourselves heard. | It is only wishful thinking to believe that one can really influence what happens in society at large.

_____

9. I am the master of my fate. | A great deal that happens to me is probably a matter of chance.

_____

10. Getting along with people is a skill that must be practiced. | It is almost impossible to figure out how to please some people.

_____

This forced-choice scale has been developed to measure your locus of control. Give yourself one point for each time you answered A. Your score can then be interpreted as follows:

8–10 = High internal locus of control
6–7 = Moderate internal locus of control
5 = Mixed
3–4 = Moderate external locus of control
1–2 = High external locus of control

The higher your score, the more you believe that you control your own life and your own destiny. The lower your score, the more you believe that what happens to you in your life is due to luck or circumstance.

Sources

Cousins, Norman. *Anatomy of an Illness as Perceived by the Patient*. New York: Bantam Books, 1981.

Hiltner, Pearl N. *Vignettes*. Coshocton, Ohio: Shaw-Barton, 1983.

Pirsig, Robert M. *Zen and the Art of Motorcycle Maintenance*. New York: Bantam Books, 1984.

Robbins, Anthony. *Unlimited Power*. New York: Fawcett Columbine, 1986.

▲ When it comes down to it, you are the only one who takes care of you. The courage to do that comes from knowledge about who you are, and an unending belief in what you're all about.

JOLINE F. HEINTZ
University of Wisconsin, Whitewater

▲ By making it a habit to express courage in your life, you can achieve your goals faster because you don't waste time in contemplation. Why take the dirt path when you can take the superhighway to success?

STEVE ALEXANDER
Bethel College, Kansas

▲ You find out what your real strengths are after you test your own limits. And if you don't try, you will never feel like you succeeded. Your most rewarding successes are the ones that don't come easily, where you know there is a possibility of failure. Facing up to those possibilities requires inner strength which is based on courage.

JODI YARNELL
Pennsylvania State University

▲ The bravest man I've ever known was my father, who had an amazing ability to bounce back from adversity and failure. He taught me that any personal defeat can leave a scar on your heart. But if that experience was born of courage, the scar is no flaw, it's more of a growth mark—one that proves your maturity, one that only you know exists. Being bold enough to admit a defeat is a victory in itself.

LUCY COLL
Champlain College, Vermont

COURAGE:

THE FOUNDATION OF COLLEGE SUCCESS

We must cultivate our garden.

VOLTAIRE

Nothing nurtures success in college more than courage. It is often considered the most important quality that a college student can possess. As the old saying goes, "No guts, no glory."

With courage on our side, there are literally no limits to what we can accomplish—it leads us down pathways of success in life and keeps us on track as we pursue our goals. On the grand tour of college life, courage is our guide.

Before we begin, a quick side note: *Courage* is a rarely used word nowadays. It has become one of those outdated, corny "Leave It to Beaver"–type terms mostly used by the elderly. On a college campus *courage* is used in conversation about as often as are words like *groovy, swell,* or *peachy-keen.*

In the 90's the idea of courage is represented by names of various body parts.

"COURAGE" = HEART as in "Denise has a lot of *heart.*"
  = GUTS as in "Mike is a *gutsy* person."

= BACKBONE as in "Kristen's got real *backbone*."
= BALLS as in "Bill's got some big *balls*."

Whichever term you use in describing the idea of courage is fine. For the purposes of this chapter, they all mean the same thing. The actual word used doesn't make a bit of difference. It's the *concept itself* that matters. After all, this isn't a TV show and you're no Beaver Cleaver. I chose the title "Courage" because, well, "Big Balls" would have been a pretty stupid-sounding name for this chapter.

▲

What Exactly Do You Mean by Courage?

Courage is . . .

Courage is *the ability to act in spite of fear or discomfort*. It is the willingness to do what needs to be done, even in the face of great difficulty. Courage gives us strength to stand up to our fears and move past them. It allows us to handle uncomfortable situations with poise and confidence. Things that seem beyond your reach are often attainable, with courage.

Courage is not . . .

Courage is not, as many students think, the *absence* of fear or the *absence* of discomfort. *Everyone* feels fear and discomfort, even the most courageous people in the world. If you never felt them, you wouldn't be human.

Courage is not a lot of other things, as well. For example, courage is not being rash, placing yourself in dangerous situations just for the sake of the thrill; courage is not being overly assertive, always trying to show that you have more bravery than those around you; courage is not taking foolish risks, doing things without using your head; and courage is not being a hot-headed, confrontational, overly aggressive egomaniac.

Putting It All Together

In a nutshell, having courage in college means that *you do what you believe to be right*. It means that you call the shots. Just you.

Courage means having a strong desire to improve yourself, to learn and grow in all areas of your life—intellectually, physically, socially, emotionally. It means aspiring, reaching, following through. It means looking your fears in the eye and spitting, and moving forward. It means having grace under pressure.

Most importantly, courage means that you *follow your heart*.

Although the whole "follow your heart" idea may sound like a cliché, it is founded on more literal grounds. The word itself comes from the Old French *couer,* which means "heart." Your courage, then, reveals an inner strength to trust and follow your heart, above all else. That's a powerful concept, when you think about it.

Courage takes two different forms—*encourage* and *discourage*. It is a good idea to understand and recognize both; for in college they relate to us every day, in every way.

Encourage vs. Discourage

Placing *en-* in front of *courage* gives us *encourage*. The prefix *en-* means, among other things, "to be at one with." Let's do a little addition. Being encouraged means *utilizing* our courage; it means *being at one with our hearts*. Yeah, that's exactly what we want.

In order to succeed we must *en*list as much *en*couragement as we can for our use. When we do, we *en*able ourselves to *en*large our stores of courage. Through encouragement we become strong.

And with that, we find the first component of an awesome college experience: *en*hanced *en*couragement.

> *Courage is rightly esteemed the first of human qualities because it is the quality which guarantees all others.*
>
> WINSTON CHURCHILL

Placing *dis-* in front of *courage* gives us *discourage*. One of the meanings of *dis-* is "to rid of" or "to dislodge from." Again, a little addition. Being discouraged means *detaching* ourselves from courage; it means that our hearts aren't totally in what we're doing—like they're placed on a backburner. That's exactly what we *don't* want.

It's equally important to *dis*card as much *dis*couragement as we can from our college experiences. When we do, we begin to *dis*sociate ourselves from our fears—and consequently, we *dis*engage much of the power that our fears possess.

Mathematics teaches us that when two negative forces collide, they can create a positive. When we *dis*card *dis*couragement, the negative *dis*es cancel each other out, leaving us with a positive: courage.

Herein we discover the *second* component of a positive college experience: *dis*regarded *dis*couragement.

I am not discouraged, because every wrong attempt discarded is another step forward.

THOMAS EDISON

▲

Getting Practical: What Part Does Courage Play in *My* Life?

Courage is an essential ingredient for college success, no doubt about it. You make use of it hundreds of times every week. Courage is used whenever you

- Introduce yourself to others and socialize
- Reach out to new experiences
- Get involved in campus activities and organizations
- Speak up in class
- Ask someone out on a date
- Stand up for your beliefs
- Talk to professors
- Solve problems and learn from mistakes
- Set challenging goals
- Express feelings to roommates, girlfriends, boyfriends, or family members
- Walk into any exam, turn in any paper, or give any speech

These are some healthy experiences that all college students should have. They all contribute to *some form* of college success (academic, social, or personal). Through them we grow, we learn, we achieve; we become strong, skillful, confident. Yes, these types of experiences are invaluable to us.

And yet, sometimes we find ourselves avoiding some or even all of these situations. Something gets in the way. Something holds us back.

"Hmmmmm. What could it be?" you ask.

Well, take another look at the list. You'll notice that all of the examples have three things in common:

1. They can cause *DISCOMFORT*
    (giving a speech in class can be uncomfortable for us)
2. They can generate *FEAR*
    (taking a series of final exams can be downright scary)
3. They involve some *RISK*
    (asking someone out on a date can be risky)

The way you feel about discomfort, fear, and risk says a lot about you. To a large degree these three principles blend together to form your current level of courage, your personality, and your demeanor.

The Three Principles of Courage

Discomfort, fear, and risk cause students to avoid or back down from situations more than anything else. That's no big eye-opener. After all, it's uncomfortable being uncomfortable, and it's no fun being scared.

But ironically, these three principles are much more beneficial to students than they are harmful—when used correctly. The only problem is, our first reaction to uncomfortable, scary, or risky situations is usually to stop, turn, and walk away.

The paradox is that when we habitually avoid such situations, we put distance between ourselves and our personal goals and ambitions. Only by taking a courageous stand to fearful, uncomfortable, and risky situations can we attain the success we desire in our college lives.

THE COURAGE
DIAGRAM

That's what the next three chapters are all about.

In achieving anything worthwhile—and I do mean *anything*—somewhere along the line we *will* encounter some discomfort and fear, and we *must* take some risks. That's a given.

Think about it. Can you have a special, loving relationship with someone without ever taking any risks? Can an Olympic gold medalist achieve her dreams without ever managing fears? Can a student pull a 4.0 GPA without dealing with some discomfort? Of course not.

I have found that the most accomplished and respected college students have a unique attitude about fear, risk, and discomfort. They view the three principles as allies rather than enemies. They have learned to understand them for what they truly are: valuable tools to be used in developing a successful college career.

Let's make sure that *our* attitudes about the THREE PRINCIPLES OF COURAGE empower us to fulfill our goals and dreams. This can best be done by acquainting ourselves with each of the principles individually. So let's make tracks and check 'em out . . .

▲ "Conservatism" and "personal growth" have an inverse relationship; the less you have of one, the more you have of the other. To grow as a student and graduate as a well-rounded person, we need to take chances, we need to open ourselves to plenty of new experiences, and we all need to go out of our depth every once in a while. Life is really just a bunch of moments. Make them add up to something.

JENNY GIBBS
Babson College, Massachusetts

▲ It is sometimes a risk just being yourself.

MATT JOHNSON
Pomona College, California

▲ The problem with risk-averse students is that because of their ultracautious natures, they are not action oriented. Their motto is "Ready, aim, aim, aim . . ." and they never pull the trigger. Action always requires some sort of change, and, sadly, it's true what they say: "Most people don't welcome change unless it jingles in their pockets."

KEVIN BELLOMA
State University of New York, Utica

▲ At times, life can be a shit-sandwich where every day seems to be another bite. But one needs to remember that there's a new and different menu every place you go.

JACQUELINE WHITE
American University

▲ Learn to balance self-restraint with self-expression.

CHRISTOPHER M. SWIFT
Dartmouth College

TAKING RISKS

Often the difference between a successful man and
a failure is not one's better abilities or ideas,
but the courage that one has to bet on his ideas,
to take a calculated risk—and to act.

MAXWELL MALTZ

Risk taking is a fun and essential part of college life. Simply put, it is impossible to grow and prosper without taking some chances. There is tremendous value in taking calculated risks every now and again.

But then again, we often avoid taking risks during college. And can you guess why? Here's a hint: it's a nasty, four-letter word that begins with F.

Now can you think of the word? Fffff, ffff, ffff. . . .

Ffff . . . FEAR.

Risk-taking fear comes in many forms—fear of the unknown, fear of embarrassment, fear of failure . . . even fear of fear, and fear of fear of fear, and so on.

When we are faced with new challenges or are given opportunities to explore new possibilities, we often stop dead in our tracks out of fear. We pause, worry, contemplate. We think, "Uh, I'll pass on this one," and walk

away. Perhaps too often in college, we students choose to play it safe, stick to our old and familiar ways, fail to venture out, and suck on security like a baby on a nipple.

Any risk implies uncertainty, vulnerability. That's why we avoid risks—we never know what's going to happen. And it's always possible that things may turn out badly. We could enter a student council election and be *beaten*; we could ask someone out on a date and be *turned down;* we could try a new activity with some new people and totally *hate the experience. Anything's* possible when we take a risk. That's the whole point.

Indeed, we can come up with a whole host of reasons why we *shouldn't* take risks in life. But, as the experts tell us, there are even more reasons why we *should* take risks.

▲

The Importance of Taking Risks in College

Taking risks builds character. Authorities on the subject of risk taking regard it as a healthy and beneficial practice for college students. They say risk taking develops courage, raises self-confidence, spurs creativity, and, obviously, keeps life exciting. Plus, it gives us a better understanding of our strengths and reveals to us possible areas of improvement.

"Opportunities to take conscious, calculated risks should be *embraced* rather than *avoided,*" Denise Rogers, a psychologist at the University of Kansas told me in an interview. "Students who never let themselves take conscious risks are more prone to taking imprudent, *un*conscious risks such as partying too wildly, starting arguments and fights, and picking up hazardous habits like smoking or excessive drinking."

> *Don't play for safety—it's the most dangerous thing in the world.*
>
> HUGH WALPOLE

Understand that it's okay to go out on a limb sometimes. Through those risky experiences you can discover ways of surpassing your normal limits, and you can learn better methods of achieving your goals. Risk taking is one of the very best ways to learn what works in life and, just as importantly, what *doesn't* work.

"Yeah, but What If I Take a Risk and Fail?"

For a moment, let's think about the worst possible outcome of taking a calculated risk. Let's say you take a risk and fail. In fact, let's say you don't just fail, you fail *miserably*. You walk into a new situation wide-eyed and walk out with egg all over your face. You strike out. You screw up. You bite the dust.

So? So what? Taking risks—winning some, losing some—is all part of a healthy college experience. At this time in our lives it would be a mistake to get totally wrapped up in security and perfection myths. That's not what college is all about.

Our college years are supposed to represent a time of taking chances, of venturing out, of discovering what we're all about. This means taking risks. It requires some trial and error, success and failure. If you are not making mistakes, you probably aren't learning very much. The only real failures are experienced by those students who never take chances in the first place.

> *You have to take risks in order to experience life. You lose out on 100 percent of the things you don't try.*
>
> CYNTHIA L. NAYLOR, *Mercyhurst College, Pennsylvania*

Even Bad Risks Can Create Good Results

What if I take a risk and it turns out badly? Is there any advantage to that at all?
    You bet.

Every calculated risk aimed at improving ourselves benefits us, regardless of the outcome. If we take a chance and things go the way we want, then, of course, we get a lot out of it. If we take a chance and things *don't* go the way we want, we *still* get a lot out of it.

    "*How?*" you ask.

1. We Learn and Expand Our Potential

You see, every time we venture out into a new situation, we gain wisdom and experience—two things that can't be obtained any other way. We then carry that new wisdom and experience with us into the other areas of our lives. We prepare ourselves for the challenges we'll face in the future.

Think of any calculated risk that you've taken. Maybe you tried out for the cheerleading squad or the football team. Maybe you gave a speech in class or moved away from home. Regardless of the outcome, wasn't it an act of

courage just to make the effort? You bet it was. It strengthened you more than you probably realize.

On the flip side, a student who constantly avoids risks tends to struggle intensely when placed in new situations. Studies indicate that students who are willing to take chances function better in a variety of new situations and are more capable of handling new and unusual challenges.

2. We Become Fulfilled, Not Regretful

Many people who never take chances harbor deep regrets. They walk around thinking in terms of *what could have been* and browbeat themselves with "If only I had . . ." or "why didn't I just . . ." or "I knew I should've . . ." Now, *that* situation is far worse than taking some chances and getting a few bad outcomes.

> *Regret for the things we did can be tempered by time; it is regret for the things we did not do that is inconsolable.*
>
> SYDNEY J. HARRIS

Don't be afraid to take some chances in your life. If you want to try your hand at a new experience, why not go for it? Take a deep breath, roll the dice . . . and bet on yourself!

The Do's and Don'ts of College Risk Taking

Do Have an Objective
Risks should be taken with a goal or end result in mind. Randomly taking chances is meaningless as well as hazardous.

Don't Expect Perfection
First of all, there is no such thing as perfection. Second, no one succeeds all the time. Don't expect that of yourself. Step up, be brave, and make a good effort. That's all you ever need to do.

Do Listen to Your Heart
Always be sure the time is right for you to take risks. Some days you'll feel more daring, and you will be more open to taking chances. Other days you'll choose a safer route and be more conservative. Whatever you're feeling at that moment, go with it.

Don't Go Overboard

Taking risks is good, as long as you don't overdo it. For example, you know you've gone too far when you schedule rock climbing, hang gliding, stock car racing, and underwater boa constrictor wrestling into a single afternoon.

Do Play the Percentages

Try to determine the odds involved. Weigh the pros and cons *before* you commit. Measure the risk and weigh it against possible gains and losses. Taking risks is a lot like playing the stock market—the bigger the risk, the bigger the reward and, yes, the bigger the potential loss.

Don't Take Risks for the Wrong Reasons

Never take risks out of anger, depression, or guilt. In other words, never act blindly from an emotion. If you are angry because you did poorly on a calculus exam, don't risk your education by cheating on the next exam.

Do Start Out Small and Work Your Way Up

If you would like to add spice to your life, but you're ultraconservative by nature, bull fighting or sky diving may not be the best place to start. If you take big risks before you're ready, the experience can be overwhelming. Begin with a small, minor risk. If you enjoy it, take a larger one. Enjoy the process and work your way up gradually.

Don't Engage in Reckless Risk Taking

Stay away from risky situations that endanger your physical or mental well-being. Being courageous isn't slamming ten beer-bongs and doing wheelies around town on a motorcycle or anything quite so melodramatic.

Do Learn from the Past

Try to learn something from each risk you take. That way you become smarter and better prepared the next time around.

Don't Forget to Ask Relevant Questions

What do I want out of it? What's the best-case scenario? The worst-case scenario? What are the potential gains and losses? How far am I willing to go? How much safety do I need? Should I get support from others or should I go it alone? How much fun will it be?

Do Take Some Silly Risks

You don't have to have a productive *reason* for everything you do. Maybe you just want to have fun. Maybe you just *feel* like doing something silly. Go ahead! Have a water fight, go skinny-dipping, watch a Jim Carey movie.[1]

A Little Experiment

Change and growth take place when a person has risked himself and dares to become involved with experimenting with his own life.

HERBERT OTTO

Hey, do you always

- hang out with the same circle of friends?
- go to the same restaurants and eat the same foods?
- listen to the same music?
- watch the same TV shows?
- wear the same style of clothes?
- read the same magazines?
- go out with the same people to the same bars or clubs?
- spend your free time with the same set of extracurricular activities?

It may be fun to take some risks. Taking a chance on something new can open your eyes to a whole new world, so I ask you: *What is the one thing you've always wanted to try?*

For one week, consciously take some calculated risks and write 'em down. Start today! They can be smaller risks like meeting a new person or trying a new kind of food. Or they can be larger ones like trying out a new sport or joining a new club.

_____

_____

_____

_____

_____

_____

Note

1. Thanks to David Viscott for the idea of the Do's and Don'ts in the preceding section. David Viscott, *Risking* (New York: Pocket Books, 1977).

Sources

Dyer, Wayne. *Your Erroneous Zones*. New York: Avon Books, 1976.

Golin, Mark, Mark Bricklin, and David Diamond. *Secrets of Executive Success*. Emmaus, Pa.: Rodale Press, 1991.

Riley, Pat. *The Winner Within*. New York: G. P. Putnam's Sons, 1993.

Viscott, David. *Risking*. New York: Pocket Books, 1977.

▲ If there were ever a time to learn how to confront your fears it is *now*, during your college years. As a senior about to graduate, I look back at my first year of school laughingly because I really was scared of a lot of experiences. In so many incidents throughout college I found myself at a crossroads—I could take either the high-road and move past my fears or I could take the low-road and avoid the situation altogether. It is in those moments of decision that a powerful character is formed.

SARAH WALKER
Western Oregon State College

▲ My favorite movie line comes from *The Snows of Kilimanjaro* where Casey Robinson says, "It's when you run away that you're most liable to stumble." Your capacity to move forward in the face of fear depends on your point of focus. So I say, focus on the direction in which you want to go instead of the awkwardness of the situation. Regardless of where you aim your attention, however, don't ever back away from a fear. Withdrawal is not an option for the truly aspiring.

JANET BESSERER
LaSalle University, Pennsylvania

▲ The worst kind of fear is fearlessness. Everyone is afraid of something, and the only way to overcome your fears is to confront them. If you are fearless, you deny your fears, and hence, can never overcome them.

CHUCK COLLINS
Tulane University

▲ I have only one real fear, I'll call it *monotonophobia*: fear of having a tedious and unfulfilling college experience. But every day I take steps against this phobia by considering my time here precious and acting accordingly.

"SMITTY"
Claremont McKenna College, California

4

OVERCOMING
COLLEGE-RELATED
FEARS

You gain strength, courage and confidence by every experience in which you really stop to look fear in the face . . . You must do the thing you think you cannot do.

ELEANOR ROOSEVELT

Fear. The word conjures up vile images for each of us. When I think of the word "fear," I envision slasher movies, statistics exams, heights, being married with children. . . , you know, brrrrr, really *scary* thoughts.

But what *is* fear? For being such a common student concern, it's pretty hard to define. I am sure you have a good sense of its meaning in your own mind. But for just a moment, I want you to forget everything you know about fear. Too many college students have false ideas of what fear is, and that misunderstanding often contributes to a lack of success unnecessarily. So let's start with a clean slate.

In college we face two kinds of fear: *legitimate fear* and *delusionary fear*. They are radically different and should be treated as such. It's a great advantage to understand the difference because, as Plato said, courage is knowing *what* to fear.

Legitimate fear is caused by *actual,* imminent danger. We all have fear of doing anything physically or mentally harmful. Fear of jumping off a cliff, going to jail, or swimming in a piranha tank is *legitimate fear.* Such fear is helpful. It forewarns us of danger and prevents us from doing things that we wouldn't want to do in the first place.

Delusionary fear (usually called anxieties), on the other hand, is caused by *false perceptions* of imminent danger. It tries to convince us that dangers exist *when they really don't.* Fear of speaking in front of the class, fear of talking to professors, fear of introducing ourselves to new people, and fear of asking someone out on a date are examples of delusionary fear. Such fear discourages us from doing things that we *want* to do, things that benefit us in some way.

Have you ever really wanted to do something but were just too scared to do it? Yeah, we all have. This section is about overcoming these fears. In college most of our day-to-day fears are delusionary in nature. In fact about 95 percent of them are nothing more than overconcern for the way *other people perceive us.* Is this real danger? Not hardly!

▲

The Wall of College Fear: Fact or Fiction?

A delusionary fear often acts like a wall, impeding our progress. Sometimes we can find imaginary graffiti on this imaginary wall, delivering imaginary warnings: "Stop! Don't do it, you won't fit in," "Stop! Don't do it, you'll mess up," "Stop! Don't do it, people will laugh at you," "Stop! Don't do it, you'll be rejected for sure."

Don't believe the hype; if you do, it might deceive you.

If you want to believe *something* about fear, here are some insightful acronyms:

FEAR = False Evidence Against Reality

or

FEAR = False Expectations Assumed to be Real

Understand that as real as the wall of fear may *seem* at the time, it is merely a delusion. The only way *any* fear can stop you from moving forward is if you let it. As Bertrand Russell put it, "Fear is the main source of superstition. . . . To conquer fear is the beginning of wisdom." Shakespeare put an even better spin on the idea when he wrote, "Our doubts are traitors, and make us lose the good we oft might win by fearing to attempt."

Fear Is a Self-Fulfilling Phenomenon

When we fear something unnecessarily, we empower it, and it becomes worthy of fear. Yet, when we courageously face our fears, we often find that there was nothing *to* fear, and that we're much stronger than we earlier thought. That's always an empowering realization! When Franklin D. Roosevelt advised, "The only thing we have to fear is fear itself," he was right on the money.

We all have to deal with our fair share of college-related challenges, concerns, and anxieties. That's reality. So how are some students able to take action in spite of the fears they feel, while others turn and walk away at the first sign of fear?

Again, it all boils down to courage. The truth of the matter is, you can handle anything that comes your way. And when you actively move forward and push against your fears, eventually you will overcome them.

A Call to Action

Ain't nothin' to it but to do it.

MAYA ANGELOU

Which situations cause us college students to feel fear and anxiety? Some common ones are taking exams, giving presentations in front of the class, engaging in certain social events, and confronting roommates, boyfriends, or girlfriends about problems.

When you experience one of these trying situations, you can actually *feel* your body going through a series of internal changes. Here's some of what happens: your heart rate increases, enhancing blood flow and circulation; your breathing quickens, allowing you to take in oxygen faster; your eyesight sharpens; your muscles become warm and more responsive; your mind becomes sharper, more attentive, and more aware.

In other words, when you face your fears, you get a boost of adrenaline just when you need it! Further, your body produces glucose, a powerful energy-producing compound, and releases it into and circulates it through your bloodstream. It's your body's way of telling you, "I know you're feeling a little anxious right now, so here's some extra energy to help you out. Use it, and you'll be able to handle anything."

It's interesting. We have learned to think of fear in such negative ways—as if it were something we have to avoid at all costs. But the truth is, fear is *not* something that we need to habitually avoid. Not by a long shot.

In the proper context fear is a valuable emotion, a facilitator of peak performance. It has one specific purpose: to supply us with the extra energy we need to perform well in new or challenging situations.

Take another look at the physiological changes that occur when you experience fear. *These are the same changes that take place within your body when you feel enthusiasm, delight, or excitement.* The physiological sensations themselves are the same. The only difference is the way we *perceive* those feelings. Again, Shakespeare: "There is nothing either good or bad, but thinking makes it so." So, is fear good or bad? You make the call.

For any fearful situation: *feel the fear and take action in spite of it.* Use the extra energy you've been given in a positive way. If, instead, you choose to walk away from the thing you fear, that same extra energy will be spent worrying about the fear later on. I mean, really, wouldn't you rather conquer a fear than worry about it? I'm not saying that it's always easy. But it is the best, most empowering choice you can make.

> *Do the thing you fear, and the death of fear is certain.*
>
> EMERSON

The next time you encounter a situation that causes you some fear or anxiety, *feel* what is taking place within your body. Notice the heightened awareness, the quickened heartbeat, the warmed muscles. Realize that these feelings are there for a reason. They are there to help you do your best in the situation you face. They represent *a call to action.* So, by all means, act on the call! Take action, conquer your fears.

Proving Grounds

> *Aim for success, not perfection. Never give up your right to be wrong, because then you will lose the ability to learn new things and move forward with your life. Remember that fear always lurks behind perfectionism. Confronting your fears and allowing yourself the right to be human can, paradoxically, make you a far happier and more productive person.*
>
> DR. DAVID M. BURNS

Jot down three to five things that you would be proud of yourself for doing. They can be minor anxieties such as speaking up in English class. Or they can be larger delusionary fears such as visiting with an intimidating professor.

☐ _____

☐ _____

☐ _____

☐ _____

☐ _____

This week, make an active effort to do the things you listed. Put a checkmark by the ones that you do. Prove to yourself that you can move through any college-related fear or anxiety. It's all a matter of exercising the courage you already possess.

Sources

Dyer, Wayne. *The Sky's the Limit*. New York: Pocket Books, 1980.

Gross, John. *The Oxford Book of Aphorisms*. New York: Oxford University Press, 1987.

Jeffers, Susan. *Feel the Fear and Do It Anyway*. New York: Ballantine, 1987.

McWilliams, John-Roger, and Peter McWilliams. *The Life 101 Series*. Los Angeles: Prelude Press, 1991.

Noe, John R. *Peak Performance Principles for High Achievers*. New York: Berkley Books, 1984.

▲ The most mature mind has learned to embrace, not just deal with, change in all its forms. Uncertainty is the only thing in life you can be certain of. You might as well make it your friend instead of your foe.

JOHN ROPER
Wichita State University

▲ It is of utmost importance to retain the wonder of life and people you had when you started college, especially in your most jaded and cynical finishing years. Even when you get to the "I-just-want-to-finish.-All-of-academia-is-self-serving-mental-masturbation" point of your education, keep challenging yourself. Do not surrender to complacency and apathy. It is easy to fall into that trap or to get sucked in under the swell of your numb peers. Let everything amaze you as those syndicated reruns and Saturday morning cartoons did when you were a latchkey kid. Even if you're the most acerbic cultural critic or astute political satirist, it's fascination with life and a desire to learn that will drive you to success.

JOANNA CHOY
University of California, Berkeley

▲ My jeans are the most comfortable thing I own. But if I wore them every day, I would begin to smell something fierce, so I don't. When something becomes too comfortable, you know it's time to change.

JEFF HARRISON
Carnegie Mellon University

▲ You don't "pay the price for success." You enjoy the process of getting there.

ELLEN PASSERA
Castleton State College, Vermont

EXPANDING YOUR
COMFORT ZONE

The ultimate measure of a man is not where he stands in the moments of comfort and convenience, but where he stands in times of challenge.

MARTIN LUTHER KING, JR.

Each of us has a personal zone of comfort within which we like to operate. If we venture out beyond this *comfort zone,* we begin to feel, well, *un*comfortable. For example, studying twenty minutes for a quick and easy algebra quiz may be well within our zone of comfort. But staying up until 4:00 A.M. every night for a week studying for an accounting final exam . . . that's another story.

Generally, an activity is out of our comfort zone if (1) we have never done it before, (2) we *have* done it before and didn't like it, or (3) it seems difficult, challenging, or intimidating in any way. Some of our most common comfort zone trials include keeping on top of our homework and reading assignments, exercising regularly, waking up early for morning classes, watching our diets, and pulling late-night study sessions.

These things often exist *outside* our zone of comfort because they pose difficult challenges for us. They require discipline. In order to do them, we have to put up with some *dis*comfort.

And, really, why should we have to do that?

Success in college is really a comfort zone issue. *In order to succeed, we have to be willing to accept the inevitable discomforts that college life brings*—the long hours of studying, the stresses of taking exams, the anxieties of the social scene, and all the other pressures that go along with living in a college environment.

Does that seem like a hard pill to swallow? Does all this talk about long hours of studying, stress, anxiety, and pressure make you feel just the least bit uncomfortable? Good. It's supposed to. No student is supposed to feel totally at ease when thinking about demanding personal challenges. But daily challenges are what college is all about. And since your comfort zone is the key to successfully meeting all of those challenges, it pays to expand it as much as possible.

But we have to understand before we can expand, so let's get into a little comfort zone theory.

▲

The Nature of the Zone

In their best-selling *Life 101 Series,* John-Roger and Peter McWilliams describe the comfort zone as being "a dynamic, living thing, always expanding or contracting." The moment-to-moment choices we make every day affect the size of our personal comfort zones—which, in turn, affect our ability to tackle the unavoidable struggles of college life.

For example, when we do something challenging or uncomfortable for a good cause (forging ahead), we *expand* our comfort zones and become more self-assured, more competent students; this gives us the confidence to manage future challenges with less apprehension and more grace. But when we succumb to our nagging inclinations to *just stay comfortable* in spite of our cause (blowing things off), our comfort zones shrink—and we lessen our abilities to adapt to change and handle difficulty.

Now I realize that is all a bit philosophical, so let's illustrate the concept metaphorically. Think of your comfort zone as a muscle. The more you exercise it, the larger and stronger it becomes; you bulk up with courage, and normal challenges become just a little less difficult.

In a similar light, the *less* you exercise your "comfort muscle," the smaller and weaker it gets; atrophy sets in, and you become uneasy at the very thought of taking on a tough college challenge. Instead, you would opt for a more comfortable choice, such as spending more time on the couch, rapping on the phone, or parking your brain in front of the TV.

Your comfort zone is intimately related to your successability—your ability to achieve success. A large, ever-expanding comfort zone is what will guarantee successability in any college setting. And applying the concepts of this chapter can help you reach that point.

We will see how the comfort zone concept can be used directly in college life situations. But first, some advice from professional business consultant Debra A. Benton, author of *Lions Don't Need to Roar:*

> Old habits are comfortable. Because you are used to them, the same old things *feel* right—even when they're wrong. You *became used* to those actions by repeating them, and you can become used to new behaviors in the same way. Take on a behavior that doesn't quite fit you and practice it until it does. If you go through the motions physically, your attitude and emotions eventually catch up.

The Fountain of Truth

So far, we have gone over the idea that success in college is based on our willingness to both *expect* and *accept* some discomfort in our daily lives. How can this concept be applied to a real life challenge?

Here's a true story that highlights this concept.

> It was one of the greatest world heavyweight championship bouts of all time. A packed house. A pay-per-view event. Millions of dollars on the line. In one corner stood a lean and determined Evander Holyfield; in the other, a colossal, intimidating George Foreman. Twelve rounds of hard-hitting, pulse-pounding, heart-racing action ensued before the final bell sounded. After the dust cleared, the two exhausted fighters stood at center ring, anxiously awaiting the decision from the judges. A hush descended over the fervent crowd as the announcer approached the house mike. "Ladies and gentlemen, the judges have come to a final decision . . . winner, and *still* heavy-weight champion of the world, EVANDER HOLYFIELD!!"
>
> The crowd went crazy; thundering applause from all sides.
>
> After the bout the question was often asked: how was Holyfield able to defeat a larger, stronger, and far more experienced opponent? Conditioning? Sure. Determination? You bet.
>
> But many boxing experts believe his real edge came from his unique training regimen. Over and above his vigorous boxing-skills training, Holyfield had spent months learning a host of other disciplines to supplement his talents—not the least of which was, believe it or not, ballet dancing! $\longrightarrow$

On the surface ballet doesn't seem to have any place in a professional boxer's training regimen. But—whether they knew it or not—Holyfield and his trainers were applying the comfort zone principle and using it to their advantage. After hours upon hours of arduous boxing-skills training, Holyfield wouldn't pack it up and go home. Instead, he would don some funky leotards and head straight for ballet practice.

Through those lessons Holyfield was able to expand on his list of resources and learn skills that he could take to the ring with him. Ballet taught him how to keep balanced in awkward positions, how to stay light on his toes, how to increase his flexibility, and how to focus and stay mentally composed—skills that ultimately helped him retain his world championship title.

The point of this story is that it probably would have been more comfortable for Holyfield to put in his expected training time and then call it a day. But in lieu of comfort he chose a more challenging and empowering route. Evander Holyfield drank deeply from the fountain of truth. He made it his mission to constantly expand his comfort zone in preparation for the fight, and it paid off for him—both literally and figuratively.

Ladies and Gentlemen, the Morals of the Story . . .

There are two major lessons to be learned from this story:

Lesson Number One: *You can expand your comfort zone by challenging yourself to do more than you normally expect yourself to.* Take a good, honest look at your old habits. Pinpoint the areas of your life that you would like to improve. Then set out to make your moment-to-moment decisions based on the comfort zone theory.

> *Hold yourself responsible for a higher standard than anybody else expects of you. Never excuse yourself.*
>
> HENRY WARD BEECHER

Every day you will find opportunities to expand your zone of comfort. You can identify them by noticing those little tinges of discomfort urging you—against your better judgment—to "pack it in," "call it quits," or "blow it off."

During those times, think about your comfort zone and *challenge yourself.* Have you been studying physics for two hours? Make it two and a half. Have you been on the exercise bike for forty minutes? Stay on for another ten. Are you feeling too lazy to get up for today's 8:00 A.M. English class? Think comfort zone, and prod yourself to rise up out of bed.

Lesson Number Two: *You can expand your comfort zone by periodically challenging yourself to try an activity that doesn't come naturally.* Consider the Evander Holyfield example. I don't know about you, but the thought of a 200-plus-pound, Herculean fighting machine dancing around in pink, pointy little shoes doesn't seem very natural to me.

Such is the way to build a powerful comfort zone.

Take yet another good look at yourself. What do you feel you're *not* good at? Do you think of yourself as *not* being musically inclined? Then consider taking a one-credit-hour guitar or piano class. Do you think you're *not* good at playing in team sports? Then join an intramural or neighborhood softball or basketball team. What about singing? Or writing poetry? Or dancing? Or public speaking?

Whatever you feel you are not good at is something you should think about learning—at least in part—during college. This will stretch your mind and expand your comfort zone faster than anything else.

Do what you think you can't.

SUNNY CHO, *Northern Illinois University*

Side Note: before trying out a new activity, refer to the "Do's and Don'ts of College Risk Taking" section of chapter 3.

Wrapping It Up

This chapter deals with an essential concept for all of us. College is a time for us to find out what we are made of and improve in the areas of our lives that we may not be completely satisfied with. As a professor once told me, "There is no place for complacency here."

However, always keep in mind the *comfort-zone-is-a-muscle* metaphor. If you work it too hard or too fast, you will end up causing more harm than good. It is always a good idea to expand your zone of comfort gradually—at a pace and in an amount that is right for you. Strike a balance in your efforts, and this concept will be your ace in the hole as you strive toward college success.

Mission Possible

Life is either a daring adventure or nothing.

HELEN KELLER

In the spaces below, write down four things that you feel you're not very good at. Every semester, make it your mission to learn one activity or skill that doesn't come naturally to you.

_____

_____

_____

_____

Also, actively look for moment-to-moment opportunities to expand your comfort zone. At least six times this week, motivate yourself to work just a bit longer and harder, past your normal zone of comfort, and record them below. Even smaller triumphs like "studied 20 minutes past the point of discomfort" or "worked out 15 minutes more than usual" deserve to be written down.

_____

_____

_____

_____

_____

_____

Sources

Benton, Debra A. *Lions Don't Need to Roar*. New York: Warner Books, 1992.

McWilliams, John-Roger, and Peter McWilliams. *The Life 101 Series*. Los Angeles: Prelude Press, 1991.

Steinem, Gloria. *Revolution from Within*. Boston: Little, Brown, 1993.

▲ Nutrition was never really an issue for me while I was living at home. Whatever my parents served for dinner was what I ate, no questions asked. Now that I'm living in a dorm, I can eat anything I please. That's great and all, but I've found that there is a subtle kind of pressure that goes along with being in total control of my own diet—a perfect example of the expression, "With newfound freedom comes greater responsibility."

TRISH HALL
Clarion University of Pennsylvania

▲ After my very first meal in the dorm, I went to my floor's community bathroom and on the wall—right above the toilet—a scribbled message read, "FLUSH TWICE! It's a long way to the cafeteria." Right at that moment, I knew I was in for a full year of dietary hell.

MARK WRIGHT
University of Vermont

▲ I have discovered that daily eating habits in college are such a mental thing. We eat not only to satisfy physical needs, but also to fill emotional voids. Bored, we entertain ourselves with a bag of Fritos. Depressed, we lift our spirits with a banana split. Stressed out, and right away we're dialing for a pizza. The best thing any student can do for his or her health is to learn how to distinguish bona fide physiological hungers from psychological ones.

JANET SIMMONS
University of Washington

▲ If the formula for a great body came in a package or a bottle, everybody would have one. Quick-fix solutions have no place in a person's overall health. You have to approach fitness from two different fronts. The forging of the ultimate physique doesn't just take place at the dinner table. It also takes place in the gym.

RAMSEY HRAIBI
St. Michael's College, Vermont

DIET AND EXERCISE

The body is a test tube. You have to put in exactly the right ingredients to get the best reaction out of it.

JACK YOUNGBLOOD

This chapter introduces you to the Food Guide Pyramid. The Pyramid illustrates the research-based food guidance system developed by USDA and supported by the Department of Health and Human Services (HHS). It goes beyond the "basic four food groups" to help you put the Dietary Guidelines into action.

The Pyramid and this chapter will help you choose what and how much to eat from each food group to get the nutrients you need and not too many calories or too much fat, saturated fat, cholesterol, sugar, sodium, or alcohol.

The Pyramid focuses on fat because most Americans' diets are too high in fat. Following the Pyramid will help you keep your intake of total fat and saturated fat low. A diet low in fat will reduce your chances of getting certain diseases and help you maintain a healthy weight.

This chapter will also help you learn how to spot and control the sugars and salt in your diet and make lower sugar and salt choices. It concludes by

enumerating the many benefits of regular exercise. Specific books are also recommended for a number of diet and exercise needs.

The pages that follow will show you how regular exercise, in conjunction with a healthy diet, will keep you healthy, fit, and looking great throughout your years in college . . . and beyond.

▲

What's the Best Nutrition Advice?

There are seven guidelines for a healthful diet. By following the Dietary Guidelines you can enjoy better health and reduce your chances of getting certain diseases. These guidelines, developed jointly by USDA and HHS, are the best, most up-to-date advice from nutrition scientists and are the basis of federal nutrition policy.

1. *Eat a variety of foods* to get the energy, protein, vitamins, minerals, and fiber you need for good health.
2. *Maintain healthy weight* to reduce your chances of having high blood pressure, heart disease, a stroke, certain cancers, and the most common kind of diabetes.
3. *Choose a diet low in fat, saturated fat, and cholesterol* to reduce your risk of heart attack and certain types of cancer. Because fat contains over twice the calories of an equal amount of carbohydrates or protein, a diet low in fat can help you maintain a healthy weight.
4. *Choose a diet with plenty of vegetables, fruits, and grain products,* which provide needed vitamins, minerals, fiber, and complex carbohydrates, and can help you lower your intake of fat.
5. *Use sugars only in moderation.* A diet with lots of sugars has too many calories and too few nutrients for most people and can contribute to tooth decay.
6. *Use salt and sodium only in moderation* to help reduce your risk of high blood pressure.
7. *If you drink alcoholic beverages, do so in moderation.* Alcoholic beverages supply calories but few or no nutrients. Drinking alcohol is also the cause of many health problems and accidents and can lead to addiction.

What Is the Food Guide Pyramid?

The Pyramid is an outline of what to eat each day. It's not a rigid prescription, but a general guide that lets you choose a healthful diet that's right for you.

Food Guide Pyramid
A Guide to Daily Food Choices

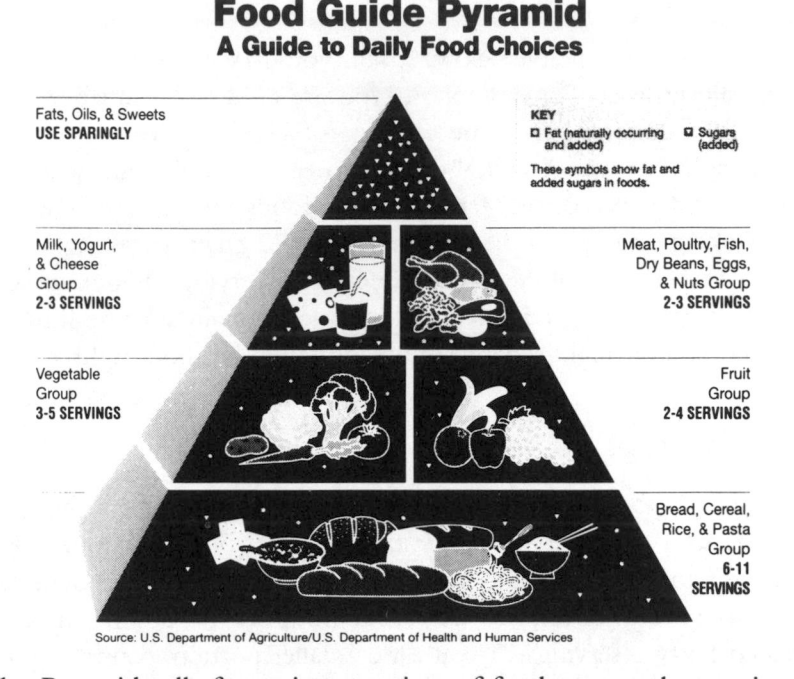

Fats, Oils, & Sweets
USE SPARINGLY

KEY
▢ Fat (naturally occurring and added)   ▢ Sugars (added)
These symbols show fat and added sugars in foods.

Milk, Yogurt, & Cheese Group
2-3 SERVINGS

Meat, Poultry, Fish, Dry Beans, Eggs, & Nuts Group
2-3 SERVINGS

Vegetable Group
3-5 SERVINGS

Fruit Group
2-4 SERVINGS

Bread, Cereal, Rice, & Pasta Group
6-11 SERVINGS

Source: U.S. Department of Agriculture/U.S. Department of Health and Human Services

The Pyramid calls for eating a variety of foods to get the nutrients you need and at the same time the right amount of calories to maintain a healthy weight.

How Many Servings Are Right for Me?

The Pyramid shows a range of servings for each major food group. The number of servings that are right for you depends on how many calories you need, which in turn depends on your age, sex, size, and how active you are. Almost everyone should have at least the lowest number of servings in the ranges.

The following calorie level suggestions are based on recommendations of the National Academy of Sciences and on calorie intakes reported by people in national food consumption surveys.

For Adults and Teens

- 1,600 calories is about right for many sedentary women and some older adults.
- 2,200 calories is about right for most children, teenage girls, active women, and many sedentary men. Women who are pregnant or breastfeeding may need somewhat more.
- 2,800 calories is about right for teenage boys, many active men, and some very active women.

For You

Now take a look at the table below. It tells you how many servings you need for your calorie level. For example, if you are an active woman who needs about 2,200 calories a day, nine servings of breads, cereals, rice, or pasta would be right for you. You'd also want to eat about six ounces of meat or alternates per day. Keep total fat (fat in the foods you choose as well as fat used in cooking or added at the table) to about 73 grams per day.

If you are between calorie categories, estimate servings. For example, some less active women may need only 2,000 calories to maintain a healthy weight. At that calorie level, eight servings of breads would be about right.

What Is a Serving?

The amount of food that counts as a serving is listed under the question "What Counts as One Serving?" If you eat a larger portion, count it as more than one serving. For example, one-half cup of cooked pasta counts as one serving in the bread, cereal, rice, and pasta group. If you eat one cup of pasta, that would be two servings. If you eat a smaller portion, count it as part of a serving.

Q: *Isn't six to eleven servings of breads and cereals a lot?*

A: It may sound like a lot, but it's really not. For example, a small bowl of cereal and one slice of toast for breakfast are two servings. A slice of bread is one serving, so a sandwich for lunch would equal two more servings.

SAMPLE DIETS FOR A DAY AT THREE CALORIE LEVELS

	LOWER (about 1,600)	MODERATE (about 2,200)	HIGHER (about 2,800)
Bread group servings	6	9	11
Vegetable group servings	3	4	5
Fruit group servings	2	3	4
Milk group servings	2–3[a]	2–3[a]	2–3[a]
Meat group[b] (ounces)	5	6	7
Total fat[c] (grams)	53	73	93
Total added sugars (teaspoons)	6	12	18

[a]Women who are pregnant or breastfeeding, teenagers, and young adults to age 24 need 3 servings.
[b]Meat group amounts are in total ounces.
[c]See the Pyramid Food Choices Chart for details on how to count total fat.

And if you have a cup of rice or pasta at dinner, that's two more servings. A snack of three or four small plain crackers adds yet another serving. So now you've had seven servings. It adds up more quickly than you think!

Q: *Do I need to measure servings?*

A: No. Use servings only as a general guide. For mixed foods, do the best you can to estimate the food group servings of the main ingredients. For example, a generous serving of pizza would count in the bread group (crust), the milk group (cheese), and the vegetable group (tomato); a helping of beef stew would count in the meat group and the vegetable group. Both have some fat—fat in the cheese on the pizza and in the gravy from the stew, if it's made from meat drippings.

Q: *What if I want to lose or gain weight?*

A: The best and simplest way to lose weight is to increase your physical activity and reduce the fat and sugars in your diet. But be sure to eat at least the lowest number of servings from the five major food groups in the Food Guide Pyramid. You need them for the vitamins, minerals, carbohydrates, and protein they provide. Just try to pick the lowest-fat choices from the food groups.

To gain weight, increase the amounts of foods you eat from all of the food groups. If you have lost weight unexpectedly, see your doctor.

Q: *What counts as one serving?*

A: The breakdown is as follows:
- *Breads, Cereals, Rice, and Pasta*
  1 slice of bread
  ½ cup of cooked rice or pasta
  ½ cup of cooked cereal
  1 ounce of ready-to-eat cereal
- *Vegetables*
  ½ cup of chopped raw or cooked vegetables
  1 cup of leafy raw vegetables
- *Fruits*
  1 piece of fruit or melon wedge
  ¾ cup of juice
  ½ cup of canned fruit
  ¼ cup of dried fruit
- *Milk, Yogurt, and Cheese*
  1 cup of milk or yogurt
  1½ to 2 ounces of cheese
- *Meat, Poultry, Fish, Dry Beans, Eggs, and Nuts*
  2½ to 3 ounces of cooked lean meat, poultry, or fish
  Count ½ cup of cooked beans, or 1 egg, or 2 tablespoons of peanut butter as 1 ounce of lean meat (about ⅓ serving).

- *Fat, Oils, and Sweets*
  LIMIT CALORIES FROM THESE, especially if you need to lose weight.

Side Note: The amount you eat may be more than one serving. For example, a dinner portion of spaghetti could count as two or three servings of pasta.

Fats

Q: *How much fat can I have?*

A: It depends on your calorie needs. The Dietary Guidelines recommend that Americans limit fat in their diets to 30 percent of calories. This amounts to 53 grams of fat in a 1,600–calorie diet, 73 grams of fat in a 2,200–calorie diet, and 93 grams of fat in a 2,800–calorie diet.

You will get up to half this fat even if you pick the lowest fat choices from each food group and add no fat to your foods in preparation or at the table.

You decide how to use the additional fat in your daily diet. You may want to have foods from the five major food groups that are higher in fat—such as whole milk instead of skim milk. Or you may want to use it in cooking or at the table in the form of spreads, dressings, or toppings.

How to Check Your Diet for Fat

If you want to be sure you have a lowfat diet, you can count the grams of fat in your day's food choices, using the Pyramid Food Choices Chart, and compare them to the number of grams of fat suggested for your calorie level.

You don't need to count fat grams every day, but doing a fat checkup once in a while will help keep you on the right track. If you find you are eating too much fat, choose lower-fat foods more often.

HOT TIP: You can figure the number of grams of fat that provide 30 percent of calories in your daily diet as follows:

A. Multiply your total day's calories by .30 to get your calories from fat per day. *Example: 2,200 calories X .30 = 660 calories from fat.*

B. Divide calories from fat per day by 9 (each gram of fat has 9 calories) to get grams of fat per day. *Example: 660 calories from fat / 9 = 73 grams of fat.*

Q: *Are some types of fat worse than others?*

A: Yes. Eating too much saturated fat raises blood cholesterol levels in many people, increasing their risk of heart disease. The Dietary Guidelines recommend limiting saturated fat to less than 10 percent of calories, or about one-third of total fat intake.

All fats in foods are mixtures of three types of fatty acids—saturated, monounsaturated, and polyunsaturated.

Saturated fats are found in largest amounts in fats from meat and dairy products and in some vegetable fats, such as coconut, palm, and palm kernel oils.

Monounsaturated fats are found mainly in olive, peanut, and canola oils.

Polyunsaturated fats are found mainly in safflower, sunflower, corn, soybean, and cottonseed oils and some fish.

Q: *How do I avoid too much saturated fat?*

A: Follow the Food Guide Pyramid, keeping your total fat within recommended levels. Choose fat from a variety of food sources, but mostly from those foods that are higher in polyunsaturated or monounsaturated fat.

Cholesterol

Q: *What's the scoop on cholesterol?*

A: Cholesterol and fat are not the same thing. Cholesterol is a fatlike substance present in all animal foods—meat, poultry, fish, milk and milk products, and egg yolks. Both the lean and the fat of meat and the meat and the skin of poultry contain cholesterol. In milk products, cholesterol is mostly in the fat, so lower-fat products contain less cholesterol. Egg yolks and organ meats, like liver, are high in cholesterol. Plant foods do not contain cholesterol.

Dietary cholesterol, as well as saturated fats, raises blood cholesterol levels in many people, increasing their risk of heart disease. Some health authorities recommend that dietary cholesterol be limited to an average of 300 milligrams (mg) or less per day. To keep dietary cholesterol to this level, follow the Food Guide Pyramid, keeping your total fat to the amount that's right for you.

It's not necessary to eliminate all foods that are high in cholesterol. You can have three to four egg yolks a week, counting those used as ingredients in custards and baked products. Use lower-fat dairy products often, and occasionally include dry beans and peas in place of meat.

Sugars

Q: *What about sugars?*

A: Choosing a diet low in fat is a concern for everyone; choosing one low in sugars is also important for people who have low calorie needs. Sugars include white sugar, brown sugar, raw sugar, corn syrup, honey, and molasses; they supply calories and little else nutritionally.

To avoid getting too many calories from sugars, try to limit your added sugars to six teaspoons a day if you eat about 1,600 calories, twelve teaspoons at 2,200 calories, or eighteen teaspoons at 2,800 calories. These amounts are intended to be averages over time. The patterns are illustrations of healthful proportions in the diet, not rigid prescriptions.

Added sugars are in foods like candy and soft drinks, as well as in jams, jellies, and sugars you add at the table. Some added sugars are also in foods from the food groups, such as fruit canned in heavy syrup and chocolate milk.

Salt and Sodium

Q: *Do I have to give up salt?*

A: No. But most people eat more than they need. Some health authorities say that sodium intake should not be more than 3,000 mg a day; some say not more than 2,400 mg. Much of the sodium in people's diets comes from salt they add while cooking and at the table. (One teaspoon of salt provides about 2,000 mg of sodium.)

Go easy on salt and foods that are high in sodium, including cured meats, luncheon meats, many cheeses, most canned soups and vegetables, and soy sauce. Look for lower-salt and no-salt-added versions of these products at your supermarket.

Breads, Cereals, Rice, and Pasta

Q: *Why are breads, cereals, rice, and pasta important?*

A: These foods provide complex carbohydrates (starches), which are an important source of energy, especially in lowfat diets. They also provide vitamins, minerals, and fiber. The Food Guide Pyramid suggests six to eleven servings of these foods a day.

Q: *Aren't starchy foods fattening?*

A: No. It's what you add to these foods or cook with them that accounts for most of the calories. For example: margarine or butter on bread, cream

or cheese sauces on pasta, and the sugar and fat used with the flour in making cookies.

- To get the fiber you need, choose several servings a day of foods made from whole grains, such as whole wheat bread and whole grain cereals.
- Choose most often foods that are made with little fat or sugars. These include bread, English muffins, rice, and pasta.
- Baked goods made from flour, such as cakes, cookies, croissants, and pastries, count as part of this food group, but they are high in fat and sugars.
- Go easy on the fat and sugars you add as spreads, seasonings, or toppings.
- When preparing pasta, stuffing, and sauce from packaged mixes, use only half the butter or margarine suggested; if milk or cream is called for, use lowfat milk.

Vegetables

Q: *Why are vegetables important?*

A: Vegetables provide vitamins, such as vitamins A and C, folic acid, and minerals, such as iron and magnesium. They are naturally low in fat and also provide fiber. The Food Guide Pyramid suggests three to five servings of these foods a day.

Q: *What counts as a serving?*

A: One cup of raw leafy vegetables; one-half cup of other vegetables, cooked or chopped raw; three-fourths cup of vegetable juice.

HERE ARE SOME SELECTION TIPS:

- Different types of vegetables provide different nutrients. For variety eat dark green leafy vegetables (spinach, romaine lettuce, broccoli), deep yellow vegetables (carrots, sweet potatoes), starchy vegetables (potatoes, corn, peas), legumes (navy, pinto, and kidney beans, chickpeas), and other vegetables (lettuce, tomatoes, onions, green beans).
- Include dark green leafy vegetables and legumes several times a week— they are especially good sources of vitamins and minerals. Legumes also provide protein and can be used in place of meat.
- Go easy on the fat you add to vegetables at the table or during cooking. Added spreads or toppings, such as butter, mayonnaise, and salad dressing, count as fat.
- Use lowfat salad dressing.

Fruits

Q: *Why are fruits important?*

A: Fruits and fruit juices provide important amounts of vitamins A and C and potassium. They are low in fat and sodium. The Food Guide Pyramid suggests two to four servings of fruits a day.

Q: *What counts as a serving?*

A: A medium apple, banana, or orange, ½ cup of chopped cooked, or canned fruit; ¾ cup of fruit juice.

HERE ARE SOME SELECTION TIPS:

- Choose fresh fruits, fruit juices, and frozen, canned, or dried fruit. Pass up fruit canned or frozen in heavy syrups and sweetened fruit juices unless you have calories to spare.
- Eat whole fruits often—they are higher in fiber than fruit juices.
- Have citrus fruits, melons, and berries regularly. They are rich in vitamin C.
- Count only 100 percent fruit juice as fruit. Punches, ades, and most fruit "drinks" contain only a little juice and lots of added sugars. Grape and orange sodas don't count as fruit juice.

Meat, Poultry, Fish, Dry Beans, Eggs, and Nuts

Q: *Why are meat, poultry, fish, and other foods in this group important?*

A: Meat, poultry, and fish supply protein, B vitamins, iron, and zinc. The other foods in this group—dry beans, eggs, and nuts—are similar to meats in providing protein and most vitamins and minerals. The Food Guide Pyramid suggests two to three servings each day of foods from this group. The total amount of these servings should be the equivalent of five to seven ounces of cooked lean meat, poultry, or fish per day.

HERE ARE SOME SELECTION TIPS:

- Choose lean meat, poultry without skin, fish, and dry beans and peas often. They are the choices lowest in fat.
- Prepare meats in lowfat ways: trim away all the fat you can see; broil, roast, or boil these foods, instead of frying them.
- Go easy on egg yolks; they are high in cholesterol. Use only one yolk per person in egg dishes. Make larger portions by adding extra egg whites.
- Nuts and seeds are high in fat, so eat them in moderation.

Milk, Yogurt, and Cheese

Q: *Why are milk products important?*

A: Milk products provide protein, vitamins, and minerals. Milk, yogurt, and cheese are the best sources of calcium. The Food Guide Pyramid suggests two to three servings of milk, yogurt, and cheese a day—two for most people, and three for women who are pregnant or breastfeeding, teenagers, and young adults to age twenty-four.

Q: *What counts as a serving?*

A: One cup of milk or yogurt; one and one-half ounces of natural cheese; two ounces of process cheese.

HERE ARE SOME SELECTION TIPS:

- Choose skim milk and nonfat yogurt often. They are lowest in fat.
- One and one-half to two ounces of cheese and eight ounces of yogurt count as a serving from this group because they supply the same amount of calcium as one cup of milk.
- Cottage cheese is lower in calcium than most cheeses. One cup of cottage cheese counts as only one-half serving of milk.
- Go easy on high-fat cheese and ice cream. They add a lot of fat (especially saturated fat) to your diet.
- Choose part skim or lowfat cheeses when available and lower-fat milk desserts, like ice milk or frozen yogurt.

The following chart lists commonly used foods in each food group and the amount of fat in each. Only a few of the thousands of foods we eat are listed. However, they will give you an idea of foods from each food group that are higher and lower in fat.

The Food Guide Pyramid symbol (^) next to the food item means that food is one of the lowest-fat choices you can make in that food group.

You can use the food label to count fat in specific foods. Many labels on foods list the grams of fat in a serving.

Q: *How much is a gram of fat?*

A: To help you visualize how much fat is in these foods, keep in mind that one teaspoon (one pat) of butter or margarine has four grams of fat.

Q: *What about alcoholic beverages?*

A: If adults choose to drink, they should have no more than one to two drinks a day. Alcoholic beverages provide calories, but little else nutritionally. These standard-size drinks each contain about the same amount of alcohol.

THE PYRAMID FOOD CHOICES CHART

For this amount of food . . .	count this many . . .	

Bread, Cereal, Rice, and Pasta Group

Eat 6 to 11 servings daily	Servings	Grams of Fat
^Bread, 1 slice	1	1
^Hamburger roll, bagel, English muffin, 1	2	2
Tortilla, 1	1	3
^Rice, pasta, cooked, ½ cup	1	Trace
Plain crackers, small, 3–4	1	3
Breakfast cereal, 1 oz	1	*
Pancakes, 4″ diameter, 2	2	3
Croissant, 1 large (2 oz.)	2	12
Doughnut, 1 medium (2 oz.)	2	11
Danish, 1 medium (2 oz)	2	13
Cake, frosted, 1/16 average	1	13
Cookies, 2 medium	1	4
Pie, fruit, 2-crust, 1/6 8″ pie	2	19

Vegetable Group

Eat 3 to 5 servings daily	Servings	Grams of Fat
^Vegetables, cooked, ½ cup	1	Trace
^Vegetables, leafy, raw, 1 cup	1	Trace
^Vegetables, nonleafy, raw, chopped, ½ cup	1	Trace
Potatoes, scalloped, ½ cup	1	4
Potato salad, ½ cup	1	8
French fries, 10	1	8

Fruit Group

Eat 2 to 4 servings daily	Servings	Grams of Fat
^Whole fruit: medium apple, orange	1	Trace
^Fruit, raw or uncanned	1	Trace
^Fruit juice, unsweetened, ¾ cup	1	Trace
Avocado, ¼ whole	1	9

Milk, Yogurt, and Cheese Group

Eat 2 to 3 servings daily	Servings	Grams of Fat
^Skim milk, 1 cup	1	Trace
^Nonfat yogurt, plain, 8 oz	1	Trace
Lowfat yogurt, 2 percent, 1 cup	1	5
Whole milk, 1 cup	1	8
Chocolate milk, 2 percent, 1 cup	1	5
Lowfat yogurt, plain, 8 oz	1	4
Lowfat yogurt, fruit, 8 oz	1	3
Natural cheddar cheese, 1½ oz	1	14
Process cheese, 2 oz	1	18
Mozzarella, part skim, ½ cup	1	7
Ricotta, part skim, ½ cup	1	10
Cottage cheese, 4 percent fat, ½ cup	¼	5
Ice cream, ½ cup	⅓	7
Ice milk, ½ cup	⅓	3
Frozen yogurt, ½ cup	½	2

Meat, Poultry, Fish, Dry Beans, Eggs, and Nuts Group

Eat 5 to 7 ounces daily	Servings	Grams of Fat
^Lean meat, poultry, fish, cooked	3 oz*	6
Ground beef, lean, cooked	3 oz*	16
Chicken, with skin, fried	3 oz*	13
Bologna, 2 slices	1 oz*	16
Egg, 1	1 oz*	5
^Dry beans and peas, cooked, ½ cup	1 oz*	Trace
Peanut butter, 2 tbsp	1 oz*	16
Nuts, ⅓ cup	1 oz*	22

* Ounces of lean meat these items count as

Fats, Oils, and Sweets

Use sparingly	Servings	Grams of Fat
Butter, margarine, 1 tsp	——	4
Mayonnaise, 1 tbsp	——	11
Salad dressing, 1 tbsp	——	7

Use sparingly	Servings	Grams of Fat
Reduced calorie salad dressing, 1 tbsp	——	*
Sour cream, 2 tbsp	——	6
Cream cheese, 1 oz	——	10
Sugar, jam, jelly, 1 tsp	——	0
Cola, 12 fl. oz	——	0
Fruit drink, ade, 12 fl. oz	——	0
Chocolate bar, 1 oz	——	9
Sherbet, ½ cup	——	2
Fruit sorbet, ½ cup	——	0
Gelatin dessert, ½ cup	——	0

* Check product label

Q: *What about alcoholic beverages?*

A: If adults choose to drink, they should have no more than one to two drinks a day. Alcoholic beverages provide calories, but little else nutritionally. These standard-size drinks each contain about the same amount of alcohol.

Alcoholic Beverages	Calories
Beer, 12 fl. oz. (1 regular can)	150
Wine, dry, 5 fl. oz	115
Liquor, 1½ oz.*	105

* A mixer such as a soft drink will add more calories.

How to Rate Your Diet

You may want to rate your diet for a few days. Follow these four steps.

STEP 1: Jot down everything you ate yesterday for meals and snacks.

Grams of Fat

_____ _____

_____ _____

_____   _____

_____   _____

_____   _____

_____   _____

_____   _____

_____   _____

_____   _____

_____   _____

_____   _____

_____   _____

_____   _____

_____   _____

_____   _____

_____   _____

_____   _____

_____   _____

_____   _____

_____   _____

Total _____

STEP 2: Write down the number of grams of fat in each food you list. First, use the Pyramid Food Choices Chart to get an idea of the number of grams of fat to count for the foods you ate. Also use nutrition labels on packaged foods you ate to find out the grams of fat they contained.

STEP 3: Answer these questions:

1.   Did you have the number of servings from the five major food groups that is right for you?

	Circle the Servings Right for You	Servings You Had
Bread group servings	6 7 8 9 10 11	_____
Vegetable group servings	3 4 5	_____
Fruit group servings...	2 3 4	_____
Milk group servings	2 3	_____
Meat group servings...	5 6 7	_____

2. Add up your grams of fat listed in step 2. Did you have more fat than the amount that is right for you?

	Grams Right for You	Grams You Had
Fat	53 73 93	_____

3. Do you need to watch the amount of added sugars you eat?

	Teaspoons Right for You	Teaspoons You Had
Sugars	6 12 18	_____

How did you do? Too much? About right?

STEP 4: Decide what changes you can make for a healthier diet. Start by making small changes, like switching to lowfat salad dressings or adding an extra serving of vegetables. Make additional changes gradually until healthy eating becomes a habit.

For more information contact USDA's Human Nutrition Information Service. The address is

> U.S. Department of Agriculture
> Human Nutrition Information Service
> 6505 Belcrest Road
> Hyattsville, MD 20782

And Now, for Exercise

The following exercise information was assembled by Jerry Napp, M.S., Cedric X. Bryant, Ph.D., and James A. Peterson, Ph.D., and appeared in the January 1995 issue of *Fitness Management* magazine.

It has often been said that "it is far better and easier to prevent a problem than to treat one." When it comes to your health, nothing could be closer to the truth.

Fortunately, the three primary steps you can take to prevent a health problem have already been identified: avoid undue risk factors (e.g., smoking, excessive alcohol, unsafe sex, recreational drugs) eat sensibly (consume a nutritionally sound diet—refer to the USDA's food pyramid), and exercise regularly (adhere to the American College of Sports Medicine's guidelines for exercise).

Of these three factors, many individuals would contend that, for whatever reason, the need to exercise has received the least amount of acceptance by the American public. What many Americans have obviously either discounted or failed to fully understand is that exercise offers every individual an array of terrific health-related benefits. At least ninety-five very positive reasons exist concerning why you should exercise. Exercise

1. Improves the functioning of your immune system.
2. Helps you to lose weight—especially fat weight.
3. Improves the likelihood of your survival after a myocardial infarction (heart attack).
4. Improves your body posture.
5. Reduces your risk of heart disease.
6. Improves your body's ability to use fat for energy during physical activity.
7. Helps the body resist upper-respiratory-tract infections.
8. Helps relieve the pain of tension headaches—perhaps the most common type of headache.
9. Increases your maximal oxygen uptake (VO_2max—perhaps the best measure of your physical working capacity).
10. Increases your level of muscle strength.
11. Helps you to preserve lean body tissue.
12. Reduces your risk of developing hypertension (high blood pressure).
13. Increases the density and breaking strength of your ligaments and tendons.
14. Improves your coronary (heart) circulation.
15. Increases your circulating levels of HDL (good) cholesterol.
16. Reduces your circulating levels of triglycerides.
17. Helps you to maintain your weight loss—unlike dieting alone.
18. Helps improve short-term memory in older individuals.
19. Reduces your risk of developing type 2 (non-insulin-dependent) diabetes.

20. Helps relieve many of the common discomforts of pregnancy (e.g., backache, heartburn, constipation, etc.).
21. Reduces your level of anxiety.
22. Helps control blood pressure in hypertensives.
23. Increases your level of muscle endurance.
24. Reduces your vulnerability to various cardiac dysrhythmias (abnormal heart rhythms).
25. Increases the density and breaking strength of your bones.
26. Assists you in your efforts to stop smoking.
27. Helps to boost creativity.
28. Lowers your resting heart rate.
29. Slows the rate of joint degeneration if you suffer from osteoarthritis.
30. Helps you overcome jet lag.
31. Enhances your sexual desire, performance, and satisfaction.
32. Increases your anaerobic threshold, allowing you to work or exercise longer at higher intensity before a significant amount of lactic acid builds up.
33. Helps you to incur fewer medical and health-care expenses.
34. Improves your ability to recover from physical exertion.
35. Increases your ability to supply blood flow to your skin for cooling.
36. Increases the diffusion capacity of your lungs, enhancing the exchange of oxygen from your lungs to your blood.
37. Improves your heat tolerance.
38. Provides you with protection against injury.
39. Reduces the viscosity of your blood.
40. Increases the thickness of the cartilage in your joints.
41. Helps you to more effectively manage stress.
42. Helps you sleep easier and better.
43. Helps you to maintain your resting metabolic rate.
44. Reduces your risk of developing colon cancer.
45. Reduces your risk of developing breast cancer.
46. Reduces your risk of developing prostate cancer.
47. Expands your blood plasma volume.
48. Helps to relieve constipation.
49. Reduces your risk of having a stroke.
50. Helps to alleviate depression.
51. Helps you maintain proper muscle balance.
52. Increases your ability to adapt to cold environments.
53. Helps you to combat substance abuse.
54. Helps to alleviate certain menstrual symptoms.
55. Lowers your heart-rate response to submaximal physical exertion
56. Helps alleviate low-back pain.

57. Helps reduce the amount of insulin required to control your blood sugar level if you are a type 1 (insulin-dependent) diabetic.
58. Improves your mental alertness.
59. Improves your respiratory muscle strength and muscle endurance—particularly important for asthmatics.
60. Reduces the rate and severity of medical complications associated with hypertension.
61. Helps you to burn excess calories.
62. Increases your cardiac reserve.
63. Improves your physical appearance.
64. Increases your tissues' responsiveness to the actions of insulin (i.e., improves tissue sensitivity for insulin), helping you to better control your blood sugar—particularly if you are a type 2 diabetic.
65. Increases your stroke volume (the amount of blood the heart pumps with each beat).
66. Improves your self-esteem.
67. Reduces your susceptibility to coronary thrombosis (a clot in an artery that supplies the heart with blood).
68. Helps you to relax.
69. Offsets some of the negative side effects of certain antihypertensive drugs.
70. Improves mental cognition—a short-term effect only.
71. Maintains or improves your level of joint flexibility.
72. Allows you to consume greater quantities of food and still maintain caloric balance.
73. Helps prevent and relieve the stresses that cause carpal tunnel syndrome.
74. Protects against "creeping obesity" (the slow but steady weight gain that occurs as you age).
75. Makes your heart a more efficient pump.
76. Increases your productivity at work.
77. Reduces your likelihood of developing low-back problems.
78. Improves your balance and coordination.
79. Improves your glucose tolerance.
80. Gives you more energy and vigor to meet the demands of your daily life and provides you with a reserve to meet the demands of unexpected emergencies.
81. Decreases (by 20–30 percent) your need for antihypertensive medication, if you are a hypertensive.
82. Helps to retard bone loss as you age, thereby reducing your risk of developing osteoporosis.
83. Helps to relieve and prevent migraine headache attacks.

84. Reduces your risk of endometriosis (a common cause of infertility).
85. Reduces your level of abdominal obesity—a significant health risk factor.
86. Helps decrease your appetite—a short-term effect only.
87. Improves your pain tolerance and mood, if you suffer from osteoarthritis.
88. Reduces work days missed due to illness.
89. Enhances your muscles' ability to extract oxygen from your blood.
90. Helps you to maintain an independent lifestyle.
91. Improves your general mood state.
92. Improves your athletic performance.
93. Helps to increase your overall health awareness.
94. Reduces your risk of gastrointestinal bleeding.
95. Improves your overall quality of life.

Look for a Better Way

As you can see from this list of health-related exercise benefits, exercise can have a substantial impact in helping you avoid becoming a negative statistic in the ongoing battle for personal wellness.

In the litany of self-help advice books and articles that currently proliferate the marketplace, one of the most common themes to individuals who perceive they are confronted with an insurmountable problem is to "look for a better way." When it comes to your health, the better way has already been identified: exercise regularly. Without question, exercise is medicine . . . preventive medicine.

(Reprinted with permission from *Fitness Management* magazine, Los Angeles, Calif., copyright © 1995 by *Fitness Management*.)

Additional Diet and Exercise Recommendations

The diet and exercise experts have been polled. The following books are frequently recommended for college students.

1. GENERAL NUTRITION

· *The Wellness Encyclopedia of Food and Nutrition*
Sheldon Margin and the editors of the University of California, Berkeley, *Wellness Letter*, Rebus, 1992.

- *Food*
  Susan Powter; Simon & Schuster, 1995.
- *Perfect Weight*
  Deepak Chopra, Harmony Books, 1991.
- *Fit For Life*
  Harvey and Marilyn Diamond, Warner Books, 1985.
- *Nutrition for Women: The Complete Guide*
  Elizabeth Somer, Henry Holt, 1993.
- *Eat Smart Think Smart*
  Robert Haas, HarperCollins, 1994.

2. WEIGHT LOSS

- *Thin for Life*
  Anne M. Fletcher, Chapters Publishing, 1994.
- *Straight Talk about Weight Control*
  Lynn J. Bennion, Edwin L. Bierman, James Ferguson, and the editors of Consumer Reports Books, Consumers Union of the United States, 1991.
- *Get Smart about Weight Control*
  Philip M. Sinaikin, Berkely Books, 1994.
- *Eat More, Weigh Less*
  Dean Ornish, HarperPerennial, 1993.

3. EATING DISORDERS

- *Surviving an Eating Disorder*
  Michele Siegel, Judith Brisman, and Margot Weinshel, Harper & Row, 1988.
- *Breaking Free from Compulsive Eating*
  Geneen Roth, Plume Books, 1993.
- *Anorexia and Bulimia*
  Richard A. Gordon, Blackwell, 1990.
- *Overcoming Overeating*
  Jane Hirschmann and Carol Munter, Addison-Wesley, 1988.

4. GENERAL EXERCISE

- *Smart Exercise*
  Covert Bailey, Houghton Mifflin, 1994
- *Getting in Shape*
  Bob Anderson, Ed Burke, and Bill Pearl, Shelter, 1994.
- *Cory Everson's Workout*
  Cory Everson with Jeff Everson, Berkely Publishing, 1991.

- *The New Fit or Fat*
  Covert Bailey, Houghton Mifflin, 1991.

5. AEROBIC/CARDIOVASCULAR EXERCISE

- *Kathy Smith's Walkfit For a Better Body*
  Kathy Smith with Susanna Levin, Warner Books, 1994.
- *Step Up Fitness*
  Tamilee Webb with D. J. Arneson, Workman Publishing, 1994.
- *Body Shaping*
  Michael Yessis with Porter Shimer, Rodale Press, 1994.
- *Fitness Running*
  Richard L. Brown and Joe Henderson, Human Kinetics, 1994.
- *Ultimate Training*
  Gary Null and Howard Robins, St. Martin's Press, 1993.

6. WEIGHT TRAINING

- *Arnold Schwarzenegger's Encyclopedia of Modern Bodybuilding*
  Arnold Schwarzenegger with Bill Dobbins, Fireside, 1987.
- *Cory Everson's Fat-Free & Fit*
  Cory Everson with Carole Jacobs, Perigee, 1994.
- *Technique!*
  Tony Little with Paula Dranov, Warner Books, 1994.
- *Lean and Mean*
  Morton H. Schaevitz, Berkely Books, 1994.
- *Getting in Shape*
  Bob Anderson, Ed Burke, Bill Pearl, Shelter, 1994.
- *The Gold's Gym Training Encyclopedia*
  Peter Grymkowski, Edward Connors, Tim Kimber, and Bill Reynolds, Contemporary Books, 1984.
- *Working Out*
  Charles Hix, Fireside, 1983.
- *Peak Performance*
  Charles A. Garfield with Hal Zina Bennet, Warner Books, 1984.

▲ To have a winning personality, you must first fully accept yourself, and that means having a relaxed attitude. You should take the components of your being (race, sexuality, gender, class, religion, everything) seriously only if you can see the humor in the fact that they exist.

XIMENA MORGAN
University of California, Berkeley

▲ A true winner understands the principle that it often takes an important student to act unimportant.

TIM COLLINS
Villa Julie College, Maryland

▲ My first intramurals team was named, "WE HAVE MORE FUN." And we did. We didn't care as much about keeping score as we cared about playing together as a team. The only times we felt we lost were when we didn't have fun.

GEORGE MOSS
University of Minnesota

▲ The law of the college jungle: Live your own life for your own reasons, under your own conditions. The real purpose of life, I feel, is to become happy and content with who you are. To do that, you don't ever have to look beyond yourself. You're all you need.

LANA LOWELL
Boston University

ENTERING THE
WINNER'S CIRCLE

Winning isn't everything. It's the only thing.

VINCE LOMBARDI

This chapter is about WINNING—in all areas of your life, all of the time. Sounds like a tall order, I know. But you will be surprised to find that there is a philosophy behind being a winner every single day of your life—a philosophy that's as simple and basic as living and breathing.

During my sophomore year I listened in on a lecture given by the world-famous psychologist Dr. Wayne W. Dyer. The lecture was brilliant, and I believe the heart of its message can be summed up this way: *Winning is an internal process, and it can be experienced in virtually all life experiences.* This is one of the fundamental themes that he writes about in his books and lectures around the world. Such wisdom pertains to every college student.

"Entering the Winner's Circle" asserts an inner-winner approach to college life. First we explode two common myths to which students generally subscribe. They are

You enter the Winner's Circle the moment you transcend these myths and take on a new, broader perspective on the concept of winning.

FYI: This chapter is a tad bit on the philosophical side. So sit back, get comfy, put in an Enya CD, open up your mind . . . and read on.

▲

Myth 1: Winning Is Based on External Measures

We tend to think of winners as people who rank high on *external* scales. That is, winners seem to be distinguished by how much they can outscore their opponents in various sports, how high a GPA they can achieve in school, how many awards and trophies they can accumulate, and how much money they can earn in their professions.

We have come to believe that winning is an external process, based on external measures. Nowhere is this more evident than in our daily lives as college students. Just take a look at our formal education system! We have spent over twelve years of our lives being ranked and categorized in the following way:

A STUDENT = CORRECT >90% OF THE TIME
B STUDENT = CORRECT >80% OF THE TIME
C STUDENT = CORRECT >70% OF THE TIME
D STUDENT = CORRECT >60% OF THE TIME
FAILURE = CORRECT <60% OF THE TIME

From this we learn that the value of a student depends on statistical standings, positions on grade curves, and grade point averages. We naturally develop a kind of "I'll be a winner in college *if and only if* I attain an X.XX GPA; if I don't, I'll just be average" mentality.

In that same tradition we have learned to believe that all other forms of winning are also based on external measures. It's a recurring theme. In the backs of our minds we tend to think, "I'll be a winner *if and only if* such and such rating scale or such and such scoreboard or such and such person tells me I am."

It has been estimated that more than three-quarters of the time we allow

external scales to govern our own sense of worth and significance as human beings. External scales call the shots—a paradoxically unrealistic reality.

As we advance in college and ready ourselves for our future careers, it is supremely important to put this whole external concept into perspective.

A New View on Which to Chew

There are major flaws in the notion that winning is an external process. But unfortunately, these flaws go unnoticed by most people most of the time. So let's shed a little light on the subject.

Author Wess Roberts provides a simple, school-related example that offers some valuable insight:

> Suppose you were taking a course in parachuting and there were 100 things to learn to do successfully; you correctly identified 99 of these 100 items on the written test. But on your first jump, you couldn't remember how to pull the rip cord, which was the item you missed. You'd probably earn a posthumous A for the course from most teachers, but it wouldn't bring you back from the dead.

Roberts's message has significance for all of us. *External measures have limited value.* Yet we place such enormous significance on them in our lives.

In an exhaustive two-year-long research study conducted on ninety-nine college and university campuses, it was found that *more than 55 percent of college students cheat to get better grades.* This is just another example of how much importance students place on external measures. Over half of the entire college population is willing to sacrifice their own internal standards just to look better on some external scale!

True, scales are useful in some respects. But they can never measure what really counts in the heart of a winner: *potential, integrity, level of interest, capacity for growth and expansion, positive outlook, and, most importantly, inner pride.* Nothing that exists outside of you can accurately measure what is inside of you. Only YOU can measure YOU. So always set and follow your own standards *first*; and consider any external measures *afterward*.

Myth 2: Winning Is Comparison-Based

Just as we are inclined to view winning as an external process, we also tend to believe that winning is *based on comparisons*.

By definition, the word *winner* implies that there must also exist the counterpart *loser*. Embedded within this definition is the notion that a winner is someone who is better than another person in a given activity or aspect of life. For example, the winner in a tennis match is the player who has more skill, performs at a higher level, and scores more points than his or her opponent; the player who performs at a lower level carries around the label of loser.

This is the standard view of winning and losing—one we all grew up accepting at face value. If this view represents your *only* angle on the concept, then you are standing just outside of the Winner's Circle. Out there, you have to defeat or "be better" than someone else in order to feel like a winner. But the problem is that *when you take on this attitude, you are allowing another person to control the way you feel about yourself*—and that's a whole lot of power to hand over to someone else, don't you think?

The total winning philosophy of this chapter views winning in a broader, more realistic, way. You can expand your views on winning even further by chewing on another new view.

A New View on Which to Chew 2

You never need to compare yourself with another person in order to be a winner. Period!

In a total winning philosophy, *comparisons* and *winning* are unrelated concepts. *It is simply not possible to feel like a winner every day of your life when your self-respect is being based on other people.* Even when you prove that you are better or more skilled than another person, those winning feelings are only temporary. Next thing you know, the feeling wears off and you have to go find another person to compare yourself with in order to feel like a winner again.

If you are constantly measuring up to other people, then you will always be discontented. Reality tells us that there will always be someone who has more, or at least *appears* to have more, than you do at your current level.

No matter who you are, there will always be someone with greater athletic skills, more money, cooler parents, more popularity, a thinner waist, a more impressive résumé, a cuter mate, or more knowledge in different areas of life. That's just the way it is on a planet with more than five billion people.

Pardon the religious groove, but it's true: *God did not create some people to be superior to others,* just as He did not create some roses to be superior to other roses. It only makes sense to toss out the whole "winning is comparison-based" myth.

These roses under my window make no reference to former roses or to better ones; they are for what they are. . . . There is no time for them. There is simply the rose; it is perfect in every moment of its existence.

RALPH WALDO EMERSON

Getting a handle on all this is especially important for us as students. One of the most difficult aspects of college life is learning how to deal with negative emotions. Jealousy, insecurity, self-doubt, fear of embarrassment, need for approval . . . these all stem directly from a need to compare. So, when next they stem, nip 'em in the bud.

Winning Is an Attitude

Yes, your high school gym teacher was right: winning *is* an attitude. This much we figured through deductive reasoning—winning is *not* based on external criteria. And it is *definitely not* based on comparisons of any kind.

Winning is an internal process based on inner pride. Like I said, it's an attitude—one that YOU, and only YOU, control.

Dr. Wayne Dyer expressed it like this:

Everything you do in life affords you an opportunity to think of yourself as a winner. You can learn from every single experience. And when you use your life experience to provide yourself with motivation for growth rather than as evidence of your deficiencies, you will be on the side of being a one-hundred-percent winner.

That's a key point. Think about it. There are plenty of people in the world who are winners by all external accounts, but whose lives are filled with self-doubt and unhappiness. There are also plenty of people whose lives may be filled with problems, yet they are always self-confident and positive. Paraphrasing psychologist Rita Freedman, *it isn't what you have or what you do, but how you react to who you are that makes you a winner.*

I could go on, but I think the point is made. If you resolve to think of yourself in winning ways, you will always find personal growth opportunities in your experiences. They'll be revealed to you like diamonds in the rough.

Don't Get Me Wrong

So far, we have talked a lot about winning being an internal process. And we have transcended the myths that winning is based on external scales and comparisons.

But keep in mind, there is a difference between winning and success. Winning is, as we've learned, a holistic attitude that you carry with you at all times. It can *spur* success (and usually does). But it is not *the same as* success.

Success is the achievement of specific goals. As such, it *can* be measured by external scales and comparisons. I am not trying to diminish the importance of external measures. They do add value to our lives. And many of the chapters in this book promote success on an external level.

For example, a college GPA is an external measure. Yet we all know how important it is in terms of career opportunities and earning potential. There's no disputing this fact.

Nevertheless, the bottom line in a total winning philosophy will always remain the same: there is no need to use external scales or other people as an index for measuring your value as a person. You have immeasurable value in life. *You are a winner—in every way—simply because you choose to think of yourself in winning ways.*

Your vision will become clear only when you look into your own heart. Who looks outside, dreams; who looks inside, awakes.

CARL JUNG

Living in Winning Ways

We've come a long way in a relatively small number of pages. And we've put a new spin on an old concept. The total winning philosophy of this chapter is now yours. CONGRATS! You have just entered the Winner's Circle. Cigar, anyone?

Having entered the Winner's Circle, you can emerge from any experience feeling like a winner without ever deluding yourself. There's no hocus-pocus involved here. No tricks. There is just enlightened self-awareness and heightened self-knowledge.

Being a winner in life is a matter of choice, not circumstance. You never have to make another person *wrong* in order to be *right*. You never have to gossip and put other people down in order to appear *better* by comparison

And you never have to make another person a *loser* in order to feel like a *winner* yourself.

That's what it means to be a round-the-clock winner, a student who is living in winning ways.

Sources

Dyer, Wayne. *The Sky's the Limit*. New York: Pocket Books, 1980.

Freedman, Rita. *That Special You*. White Plains, N.Y.: Peter Pauper Press, 1994.

Glasser, William. *Schools without Failure*. New York: Harper Colophon, 1975.

Roberts, Wess. *Straight A's Never Made Anybody Rich*. New York: HarperCollins, 1991.

Von Oech, Roger. *A Whack on the Side of the Head*. New York: Warner Books, 1990.

Williamson, Marianne. *A Return to Love*. New York: HarperPerennial, 1992.

▲ Success in college is all a matter of following your own path as you discover it. Find what you like, and go there.

JOSEPHENE CHOY
Dartmouth College

▲ Deciding on a major is like climbing a mountain. There are numerous routes you can follow, some more difficult than others, some less crowded than others. The only true way to find out whether a route fits your skills and interests is to explore it. But as you climb your mountain, beware of fool's gold. There was many a prospector who lost it all chasing after the illusory myth of a quick and easy way to the top.

TOMMY ROBERTS
Alma College, Michigan

▲ You are your own individual person and the future that lies ahead is your own as well. So don't choose a major to make somebody or everybody else happy. In the end, that will get you nowhere except into a mist of uncertainty and unhappiness. Choose a major that will make *you* happy, and career success will be a natural outcome.

APRIL FRANKS
University of Wisconsin, Whitewater

▲ I've heard that people in our generation will have between five and seven totally different careers by the time we retire. The days of choosing one major, getting one job in that field, and then working there until the age of 65 are good and gone. Declaring a major is important but it's not a life-or-death decision by any means. So take your time. It can take you years to figure out what you want to do tomorrow.

NICK LEWIS
University of Central Florida

8

CHOOSING THE
RIGHT MAJOR AND CAREER

The greater thing in this world is not so much where we stand as in what direction we are going.

OLIVER WENDELL HOLMES

One of the most common questions we are asked as college students is "What are you majoring in?" Some of us can respond with iron-clad certainty. For others, the question alone is enough to create severe anxiety and self-doubt. Choosing a major is a decision that every college student makes at least once. But that's not to say the decision is an easy one to make.

It is often said that declaring a major is akin to choosing a spouse: *we may like what we see at the time of commitment, but may not feel the same way about things several years later*. In a world of countless career possibilities, it is essential to choose majors that will *continually* excite, challenge, and fulfill us — ones on which we can build rewarding future professions.

That's the ideal situation, of course, but it is far from the norm. In fact, being trapped in an ill-suited career with an inapplicable major and limited career opportunities is a common predicament among recent college graduates. Four out of five Americans (80 percent of the population) report that they are dissatisfied with their careers.

I don't know about you, but that statistic seems pretty grim to me. One thing I know for certain: *the last thing our generation wants is to become another grim statistic.*

This chapter is about our major and career choices. I would be amiss if I tried to pass it off as a "how to" chapter. There isn't any book or person in the world that can show you "how to" choose a major for yourself. Declaring a major is a decision that you have to make in your own way, in your own time.

What this chapter will provide, however, are ten suggestions for you to consider before you sign your name on the dotted line; take to heart the ideas you like and discard the ones you don't. Your choice of a major is a major choice, so whatever you do, take plenty of time to think over this decision before you make it. Harken to the wise words of Orison Swett Marden: "There are powers inside of you which, if you could discover and use, would make of you everything you ever dreamed or imagined you could become."

▲

Ten Major Suggestions

Visit Your Advisor.   Your advisor's numero uno job is to make sure you get on the right track in your college career. If you have any concerns regarding a possible major—any concerns whatsoever—he or she will be able to assist you in a number of ways. First, your advisor can answer basic questions pertaining to your field of interest, such as:

- what is this major like?
- how many credit hours are required to earn a degree in this major?
- how many students have declared this major?
- what percentage of students drop out of this major?
- what are the core classes for this major?
- what are the requirements to get into grad school?
- what is the average GPA in this major?

Second, he or she will be able to set up a tentative schedule for you to follow in order to satisfy all the requirements of the major and graduate on time. Even if your advisor cannot answer all of your questions, he or she can point you in the right direction to get the assistance you need.

Talk to Professors Who Are Teaching in Your Field of Interest.   These academics have committed their entire professional lives to one particular field of study. They have deep insight into their professions and can candidly tell you

what to expect from the major. Plus, professors often give the most valid, accurate answers to deeper questions like

- what abilities, interests, and values are usually associated with success in this major?
- which careers pertain to this major?
- what are the job markets like in this field?
- what are pros and cons of this field of study?
- how is performance evaluated in this major?

Talk to Competent Students Who Are Majoring in Your Field of Interest. Before you make a final decision, be sure to talk with some *good* students who have already had a year or two of experience in the field you have your eye on. These students are hip to the more functional aspects of the major, such as course workloads and difficulty levels.

You will also find that students really get down to brass tacks when they talk about their personal experiences in their majors. Based on their experiences, they can recommend the best classes and the "easiest" professors just as easily as they can point out the worst classes and the "hardest" professors—this information will be invaluable to you, should you decide on that major.

Spend a Day in Your Possible Future Life. One of the best things you can do in deciding on a major is to *spend one day with someone who is working in the profession you're interested in.*

For example, if you fancy a career in investment banking, spend a day at work with an investment banker; if you are interested in marine biology, go out into the field for a day with a marine biologist; if the idea of graphic design turns you on, spend a day with someone at a multimedia studio or an exhibition design firm. This will give you the most practical insight into that career.

You may be thinking, "Yeah, but how do I get my foot in the door?" Well, if you or your parents do not personally know someone in that profession, don't worry; you can still pull it off by making a simple phone call or sending a brief letter.

You can call virtually any business or organization and get permission to spend a day with a chaperon if you go about it the right way. The best approach is to (1) contact the manager or PR person, (2) introduce yourself and explain your intent, and (3) ask him or her to kindly assign you a chaperon for a day—something like:

Hello, my name is Kori Foster. I am a sophomore at Indiana University and am very much interested in pursuing a career in graphic design. Before

I declare my major, though, I'd really like to observe a typical workday in this profession. Would it be okay if I spent a morning or afternoon with someone in your organization just to quietly watch the day-to-day activities of a graphic designer?

Or, if you'd rather, you can write a brief letter with the same basic message:

Dear Mrs. Baxter,

My name is Phil Deere. I am a freshman at Chapman College and am considering a major in civil engineering. Before I declare a major, however, I would really like to observe a typical workday in this profession.

Your firm has the reputation of having a top-notch engineering workforce. As a college student, I am very interested in pursuing a career in this field.

Would you have any objection to my spending a morning or afternoon with someone in your organization? Since I only wish to *quietly* watch the day-to-day activities of a civil engineer, I can assure you that my presence will be unobtrusive. Even a brief visit with an engineer would be helpful and greatly appreciated.

Many thanks,

You can even be excused from school if you arrange for one day of "fieldwork experience." Many teachers have strict absenteeism policies; but most will be amenable if you explain your purpose and your intent and show them some written documentation.

So make a few phone calls and set up a visit or two. Take in the sights and learn what really goes on behind the scenes in the professions you're interested in. This will help you decide whether or not the career is the right one for you.

Discuss Your Ideas with Your Parents. Let me start off by saying that there are some major pros and cons to talking over your major with your parents. Granted, all of us have different relationships with our parents. But still, any parent/child relationship will have a number of common threads when it comes to discussions about career plans.

First, the pros. Your parents probably know you better than anyone else in the world. They watched you grow and mature; and naturally, they know your dispositions, your strengths, your weaknesses, and your natural talents and abilities. They will surely be able to help you evaluate some future career choices.

Since declaring a major is one of the most important decisions of your life

thus far—and since your parents generally want what's best for you—they will be willing to spend plenty of time talking with you about your dreams and ambitions. Best of all, parents have years of practical work experience to back up any advice they may give.

Finally, your parents can be a wonderful resource. For instance, if you are interested in a career in neurology, your parents may have a friend—or a friend of a friend—who would be able to set up a meet-and-greet with a neurologist.

Now for the cons. A lot of parents—hate to say it—tend to go overboard when it comes to discussing future careers for their children. You see, no matter how old and independent we may become, we will always be our parents' children. And that means we may get way more parental advice than we bargained for.

It is also common for parents to sway their children toward a certain career path simply because *they* think it is best. This is an inclination that has psychological roots. In many ways, parents look to their children as a means of extending and validating their own lives—which can be a sticky situation for you, especially if you have a parent who is one of those *I-want-my-kid-to-become-a-successful-attorney-just-like-his-old-man* types.

Regardless of the pros and cons in your family situation, however, talk this decision over with Mom and Pops. I can all but guarantee that if you visit or call your parents and say, "I'm thinking about majoring in (such and such) and I'd really love some of your advice," your parents will be giddier than Richard Simmons in a jello fight and will help you in any way they can.

Take a Good Mix of Classes. Normally, anywhere from one-fourth to one-half of your classes will be electives (not directly related to your major). It is always a good idea to get exposure to a wide range of classes from various fields of study.

> *Develop the hunter's attitude, the outlook that wherever you go, there are ideas waiting to be discovered.*
>
> ROGER VON OECH

Are most of your academic endeavors geared toward mathematics? Then why not enroll in a music or fiction writing class? Are you a physical science buff? Then try your hand at a philosophy or sociology course. Do you focus mainly on the field of business? Then consider giving a zoology or ethnic studies class a try. You never know, you may find that your true calling is in an area that you have never before considered.

So, before you declare a major, be sure to delve into as many disciplines as you can. You might also consider getting a governmental or departmental

internship in many fields of interest such as journalism, nursing, social work, or urban studies. These golden college years may be your one and only chance to freely explore such a wide range of curricula.

Choose a Field of Study that You Enjoy.   Confucius said: "Choose a job you love, and you will never have to work a day in your life." That's a cute phrase, for sure, but it is impossible to find a major that will bring you total and complete satisfaction.

No matter which major you declare, you will probably not be floating to school on air every day, blissful and breathless with anticipation. Getting a college degree requires a great deal of hard work; a lot of that work isn't always going to be satisfying. It pays to stay true to yourself and get into a field that you enjoy.

This means that you should refrain from choosing a major based solely on market demand. Many people will tell you to go out and examine the Labor Department statistics, find the fields with the highest demand, and then declare your major based on "what's hot and what's not." Don't fall into this trap. Just because, say, Real Estate Law is a hot field now doesn't guarantee that it will be hot ten years down the road. Always focus on what you want to do before you focus on "how much money they're payin' now."

Do Some Vocational Testing.   Many colleges offer vocational counseling services for their students. For a small fee (sometimes free of charge), you can take a series of tests that will evaluate different aspects of your personality, such as how you process information, interact with others, and make decisions.

Based on those evaluations, several career-path suggestions will then be made. Ideally, the results of your tests will measure the probability of success, enjoyment, and personal fulfillment that you would have in certain careers. These tests are very insightful and have helped many students find ideal majors and careers. (If you prefer to do vocational testing at home, I would recommend the book *Do What You Are* by Paul Tieger and Barbara Barron-Tieger.)

Don't Freak Out.   As important as declaring a major is, you needn't ever feel that your entire future hinges on this one decision. If you so choose, you can always change majors; you can always get a double major; you can even get permission to create your own specialized major or interdisciplinary concentration. My point is simply to relax with this decision.

Also keep in mind that the career you ultimately end up with may have little to do with your field of study. For example, many people major in history and then go on to occupations in law or criminal justice. Other people use a chemistry major as a stepping stone to get into medical school. Still others

major in English and later find themselves with excellent careers in business management, journalism, and even acting.

So breathe easy; *you will always have a number of options available to you, no matter which major you choose.*

Think It Through, Long and Hard. Finally, take as much time as you need to reflect on what you really want to do with your life. Be honest with yourself and don't rush this decision, and everything else will fall nicely into place.

> *Realize what you really want. It stops you from chasing butterflies and puts you to work digging for gold.*
>
> WILLIAM MOULTON MARSTON

Career Assessment Test

Instructions: for each statement, circle the answer that most accurately describes your feelings.

SA = Strongly Agree, A = Agree, D = Disagree, SD = Strongly Disagree.

1. I would leave my company rather than be promoted out of my area of expertise. SA A D SD
2. Becoming highly specialized and highly competent in some specific functional or technical area is important to me. SA A D SD
3. A career that is free from organization restriction is important to me. SA A D SD
4. I have always sought a career in which I could be of service to others. SA A D SD
5. A career that provides a maximum variety of types of assignments and work projects is important to me. SA A D SD
6. To rise to a position in general management is important to me. SA A D SD
7. I like to be identified with a particular organization and the prestige that accompanies that organization. SA A D SD
8. Remaining in my present geographical location rather than moving because of a promotion is important to me. SA A D SD
9. The use of my skills in building a new business enterprise is important to me. SA A D SD
10. I would like to reach a level of responsibility in an organization where my decisions really make a difference. SA A D SD

11.	I see myself more as a generalist as opposed to being committed to one specific area of expertise.	SA	A	D	SD
12.	An endless variety of challenges in my career is important to me.	SA	A	D	SD
13.	Being identified with a powerful or prestigious employer is important to me.	SA	A	D	SD
14.	The excitement of participation in many areas of work has been the underlying motivation behind my career	SA	A	D	SD
15.	The process of supervising, influencing, leading, and controlling people at all levels is important to me.	SA	A	D	SD
16.	I am willing to sacrifice some of my autonomy to stabilize my total life situation.	SA	A	D	SD
17.	An organization that will provide security through guaranteed work, benefits, a good retirement, and so forth, is important to me.	SA	A	D	SD
18.	During my career I will be mainly concerned with my own sense of freedom and autonomy.	SA	A	D	SD
19.	I will be motivated throughout my career by the number of products that I have been directly involved in creating.	SA	A	D	SD
20.	I want others to identify me by my organization and job.	SA	A	D	SD
21.	Being able to use my skills and talents in the service of an important cause is important to me.	SA	A	D	SD
22.	To be recognized by my title and status is important to me.	SA	A	D	SD
23.	A career that permits a maximum of freedom and autonomy to choose my own work, hours, and so forth, is important to me.	SA	A	D	SD
24.	A career that gives me a great deal of flexibility is important to me.	SA	A	D	SD
25.	To be in a position in general management is important to me.	SA	A	D	SD
26.	It is important for me to be identified by my occupation.	SA	A	D	SD
27.	I will accept a management position only if it is in my area of expertise.	SA	A	D	SD
28.	It is important for me to remain in my present geographical location rather than move because of a promotion or new job assignment.	SA	A	D	SD
29.	I would like to accumulate a personal fortune to prove to myself and others that I am competent.	SA	A	D	SD
30.	I want to achieve a position that gives me the opportunity to combine analytical competence with supervision of people.	SA	A	D	SD
31.	I have been motivated throughout my career by using my talents in a variety of different areas of work.	SA	A	D	SD
32.	An endless variety of challenges is what I really want from my career.	SA	A	D	SD

33. An organization that will give me long-run stability is important to me.   SA   A   D   SD

34. To be able to create or build something that is entirely my own product or idea is important to me.   SA   A   D   SD

35. Remaining in my specialized area, as opposed to being promoted out of my area of expertise, is important to me.   SA   A   D   SD

36. I do not want to be constrained by either an organization or the business world.   SA   A   D   SD

37. Seeing others change because of my efforts is important to me.   SA   A   D   SD

38. My main concern in life is to be competent in my area of expertise.   SA   A   D   SD

39. The chance to pursue my own lifestyle and not be constrained by the rules of an organization is important to me.   SA   A   D   SD

40. I find most organizations to be restrictive and intrusive.   SA   A   D   SD

41. Remaining in my area of expertise, rather than being promoted into general management, is important to me.   SA   A   D   SD

42. I want a career that allows me to meet my basic needs through helping others.   SA   A   D   SD

43. The use of my interpersonal and helping skills in the service of others is important to me.   SA   A   D   SD

44. I like to see others change because of my efforts.   SA   A   D   SD

This instrument is an expanded version of Schein's five career anchors. It adds service, identity, and variety anchors. Score your responses by writing the number that corresponds to your response (SA = 4, A = 3, D = 2, SD = 1) to each question in the space next to the item number.

1. _____   2. _____   3. _____   4. _____   5. _____   6. _____

7. _____   8. _____   9. _____   10. _____   11. _____   12. _____

13. _____   14. _____   15. _____   16. _____   17. _____   18. _____

19. _____   20. _____   21. _____   22. _____   23. _____   24. _____

25. _____   26. _____   27. _____   28. _____   29. _____   30. _____

31. _____ 32. _____ 33. _____ 34. _____ 35. _____ 36. _____

37. _____ 38. _____ 39. _____ 40. _____ 41. _____ 42. _____

43. _____ 44. _____

Now obtain subscale scores by adding your scores on the items indicated and then dividing by the number of items in the scale, as shown:

Technical competence _____ / 6 = _____
  1, 2, 27, 35, 38, 41

Autonomy _____ / 6 = _____
  3, 18, 23, 36, 39, 40

Service _____ / 6 = _____
  4, 21, 37, 42, 43, 44

Identity _____ / 5 = _____
  7, 13, 20, 22, 26

Variety _____ / 6 = _____
  5, 12, 14, 24, 31, 32

Managerial Competence _____ / 6 = _____
  6, 10, 11, 15, 25, 30

Security _____ / 5 = _____
  8, 16, 17, 28, 33

Creativity _____ / 4 = _____
  9, 19, 29, 34

Briefly, the eight career anchors mean the following:

- *Technical competence.* You organize your career around the challenge of the actual work you're doing.
- *Autonomy.* You value freedom and independence.
- *Service.* You're concerned with helping others or working on an important cause.
- *Identity.* You're concerned with status, prestige, and titles in your work.
- *Variety.* You seek an endless variety of new and different challenges.

- *Managerial Competence*. You like to solve problems and want to lead and control others.
- *Security*. You want stability and career security.
- *Creativity*. You have a strong need to create something of your own.

The higher your score on a given anchor, the stronger your emphasis. You'll function best when your job fits with your career anchor. Lack of fit between anchor and a job can cause you to leave the organization or suffer excessive stress.

Ask yourself now: What jobs fit best with the anchor on which I received the highest score? You can use your analysis to help you select the right job and career for you.[1]

Note

1. Stephen P. Robbins, *Organizational Behavior*. 6th ed. (Englewood Cliffs, N.J.: Prentice-Hall, 1993), 717–18.

Sources

The Bathroom Book. Salt Lake City: Compact Classics, 1992.
Bolles, Richard N. *What Color Is Your Parachute?* Berkeley, Calif.: Ten Speed, 1994.
Brown, H. Jackson. *A Father's Book of Wisdom*. Nashville: Rutledge Hill, 1988.
Motivation Magic. Glendale Heights, Ill.: Great Quotations, 1993.

▲ The most helpful thing I did when I was writing my senior thesis was to set specific and attainable goals. Each Sunday I wrote out a calendar which specified the exact hours I would spend in the library and the computer lab. I didn't stray from my plans, even during those times when I desperately wanted to. The goal was my guide. I finished my work on time, and ended up getting distinction on my senior thesis. If I hadn't set those clear goals, I would probably still be working on the rough draft.

PATRICK S. ALEXANDER
Carleton College, Minnesota

▲ As a kid, I learned an important maxim from watching a *Star Wars* movie — one that stuck with me all the way to college. Yoda said to Luke Skywalker, "There is no try, only do or do not." That is how I approach my goals. I can always say I tried, but I want to be able to say I did.

STAN SMITH
University of Minnesota

▲ Purpose is stronger than outcome.

LIZ KIMBALL
Tulane University

▲ I once wrote a paper on Andrew Carnegie, who was America's first billionaire. Researching this man taught me a lot about how to achieve goals. As successful as Carnegie was, he didn't attribute his wealth and personal success to variables such as luck, "being at the right place at the right time," or even hard work. His strategy for success was to surround himself with intelligent, winning people and to model himself after those who had already achieved what he wanted to achieve; *he* benefited greatly from *others'* experiences. Every college student should have other people as role models and should also be a role model for other people.

KAREN MILLER
Bennett College, North Carolina

GOAL SETTING

This one step—choosing a goal and sticking to it—changes everything.

SCOTT REED

In the hierarchy of personal success strategies, *goal setting* sits close to the top. Setting specific goals for ourselves is an act of personal power—one that can propel us to unexpected heights of success, academically and otherwise.

You see, through the process of goal setting we develop a sense of control, a feeling that we are calling the shots in our own lives. Having a specific goal is like harnessing the power of a laser beam. It gives our minds the focus, direction, and energy needed to home in on a target and hit it dead center.

A famous philosopher once said that the mind will not strive for achievement until it has clear objectives. Makes a lot of sense, yet most students do not set specific goals for themselves in college. The few who do—and write their goals down on paper—are usually the ones who get ahead . . . *way* ahead in life.

Want proof?

Here's the perfect example for every college student: An extensive study was conducted on the graduating class of Yale University in 1953. *It was found that only 3 percent of the graduates had specific, written goals for their lives before*

they went off into the "real world." The other 97 percent of the class had no written goals.

The follow-up study was done twenty years later in 1973. What the researchers found was astonishing. *They discovered that the 3 percent who had committed their goals to paper were worth more in financial terms than the remaining 97 percent of the class combined!* The same 3 percent were also noted as being happier, more fulfilled, and more enthusiastic about their lives than the rest of the alumni.

This research study illustrates the sheer power of goal setting. By establishing clear goals for both our immediate tasks and our long-term endeavors, we set the stage for success in life. This very book, I'm happy to add, serves as testimony for that common law.

So let's set the wheels of achievement in motion by learning all the ins and outs of goal setting. The process begins by taking a journey of six little steps . . .

▲

Six Stepping Stones to Success

Stone 1: Figure Out What You Want
The first step of goal setting is to determine exactly what you want to accomplish. Too often, we live under the philosophies of "going with the flow" and "taking things as they come." In so doing, we become proverbial ships without rudders.

As captains of our own ships, we need to decide on a destination before we can chart a course. So grab a pen and pad and take a couple minutes to brainstorm for goals. What are some personal characteristics or skills that you would like to develop in college? What kind of grades do you want to make? What kind of physical shape do you want to be in? What activities or clubs would you like to get involved with?

Get a firm grasp on what you'd like to achieve, and try to visualize the smaller steps you'll need to take in order to attain it. Then take a second step forward . . .

Stone 2: Get S.M.A.R.T. with Your Goals
Whether your goals are personal, social, or academic in nature, make sure they are structured based on the following five criteria:

Specific   – "I am going to meet at least four new students on campus this week."

Measurable	—	"I will make at least a 3.1 grade point average this semester."
Attainable	—	"I am going to go to the gym and exercise four times per week."
Realistic	—	"I am going to lose five pounds by the end of next month."
Timely	—	"I will finish the rough draft of my English essay assignment by midnight tomorrow."

Use the SMART model to help you construct your goals. Vague or arbitrary objectives such as "making good grades" or "becoming a well-rounded person" won't cut it; they are powerless from a motivational standpoint. Yet they exemplify the extent to which most students set their goals.

Remember: the personal goal that is concrete, explicit, and most importantly, SMART, is the one that will promote success.

Stone 3: Write It Down

Once you set a SMART goal, *get it down on paper!* This is an all-important step—but one that usually gets blown off.

The obvious suggestion here is *not* to overlook it. Remember the outcome of the Yale research study: 97 percent of the grads didn't write down their goals; 3 percent did. The rest is history.

An unwritten goal is just an abstraction in the mind. But when it takes on the physical form of a written statement, it becomes more valid. More *real*. And that in itself takes it another step closer to its realization.

Aside from that fact, taking the time to write down your goal speaks volumes about your level of resolve. It's like making a contract with yourself. You physically and psychologically confirm your commitment to a goal when you jot it down. In his autobiography, Lee Iacocca wrote, "The discipline of writing something down is the first step to making it happen."

Side Note: An excellent place to write down your short-term academic goals is in the Weekly Planner found in chapter 24, "Time Management." The planner contains spaces for two weekly goals and even provides a means for tracking the time you spend working on them!

Stone 4: Make It Positive

Every goal should be written in a positive way—with conviction! *Begin each goal statement with "I am going to . . ." or "I will . . ."* Avoid forming tentative goals such as "I'll try to work out four times each week" and negatively phrased goals such as "I can't allow myself to get a C in Chemistry."

> *Language can either support or thwart your goals. . . . There's a world of difference between I will and I'll try.*

SCOTT NICKEL, Santa Clara University, California

Stone 5: Refer to It Often

Because achieving a goal is a gradual process, it is important to *see* your written goal frequently as you work to achieve it.

Keep in mind that *every time you see your written goal, your mind reaffirms its commitment to it*. There is a psychological factor involved in goal achievement—one that you can use to your advantage.

Top achievers in varying areas of life do just that. Many straight-A students, for example, write their academic goals in daily planners or on the inside covers of their notebooks. Many successful dieters write their weight goals on Post-it notes and stick them on their refrigerators. Many top-producing sales people put their written sales goals on their walls at work and even on their mirrors at home. Many up-and-coming body builders tape up their written workout goals, along with pictures of their role models, in their gym lockers.

What's the point?

Primarily to get leverage on your goals and develop an even stronger desire to see them through. Trust the psychologists and top achievers on this one: *Put your written goals in places where you'll see them often!*

Stone 6: Be Flexible

Always allow for some flexibility. Commitment is important, of course, but, hey, so is reality. Things change. *We* change. Sometimes we may need to alter our goals in order to accommodate changes in lifestyle or shifts of priority. It's not a sin to leave a little room for error. After all, goals are meant to enhance your life, not control it.

I'll Have a Shot of Motivation . . . No, Make That a Double

Achieving goals—especially major ones—takes motivation. Lots of it. But this is a tricky little concept. Not only do we have to find a way to *get* motivated, we also have to find a way to *stay* motivated.

What's the key to it all?

Emotion, plain and simple. *We have to attach some inner emotions to our goals in order to stay motivated.*

Emotions come in two garden varieties: positive and negative. Positive emotions create pleasure; negative emotions create pain.

These are the two driving forces of motivation.

Nature has placed mankind under the government of two sovereign masters, pain *and* pleasure . . . *they govern us in all we do, in all we say, in all we think: every effort we can make to throw off our subjection, will serve but to demonstrate and confirm it.*

JEREMY BENTHAM

If you fundamentalize everything that has been learned about human motivation, you'll discover one universal truth: *our emotions guide our actions.* Everything that we do in life is designed to move us either toward pleasure or away from pain. That's the very crux of our animal instincts.

The point of this little psychophysiological lesson is simple as well as powerful: *give your goals plenty of emotional value, and you'll develop and maintain a peak level of motivation.*

Here's how to imbue your goals with emotional content:

First, actively associate feelings of <u>pleasure</u> with the thought of reaching your goal. Write down every benefit of success you can think of. Really go for it, no holds barred. What reward will you offer yourself once you've achieved your goal? How will you feel about yourself after you've succeeded? In what ways will the achieved goal enrich your life or make it easier? Here are some examples:

> If I finish my term project by next Thursday, I'll buy myself a CD and a new pair of shoes.

> If I get at least a 3.3 GPA this semester, I'll be a shoo-in for grad school.

> If I become Student Senate VP, my résumé will sparkle and I'll make my parents proud.

> If I do the overcoming fear exercise from chapter 4, I'll gain confidence and will feel great about myself.

> If I stick to my study schedule all week, I'll treat myself to a crazy night on the town with all my friends.

Second, actively associate feelings of <u>pain</u> with the thought of not reaching your goal. Write down some possible repercussions. What will you miss out on if you neglect your goal? How will it hamper you in the long run? What future inconveniences will it cause you? How will it make other aspects of your life more difficult? Here are some examples:

> If I don't finish my accounting homework today, I'll have to miss the party tomorrow.

If I don't get involved on campus this year, I won't have any fancy extracurricular activities to put on my résumé.

If I half-ass my midterms, I'll have to work twice as hard during finals to recover.

If I drop my calculus class, I'll have to take summer school or carry an extra-heavy load of classes next year.

If I don't get at least a 2.5 GPA this semester, I'll feel disappointed and so will my parents.

Keep in mind that we all consider such thoughts on a passive, subconscious level. But the trick is to think *actively* of both the pros of reaching and the cons of not reaching your goal. Motivation is an active process. Achieving goals is an active process. So is this exercise.

As you work toward your goal—whatever it may be—use your emotions to create intense drive and passion. Give yourself a double shot of motivation! Use both the pros *and* the cons, the goods *and* the bads, the positives *and* the negatives, the carrots *and* the sticks, the pains *and* the pleasures . . . you get the idea.

Use your emotions.
Energize your motives.
And leave the rest to your instincts.

A Word on Failure

Let's have a quick reality check before we wrap up this chapter . . .

When you set challenging goals for yourself in college, you're not *always* going to end up on top. Sometimes you'll miss your target by just a smidgen; other times you'll miss by a mile. Sometimes failure will rest on your shoulders; other times it'll be caused by circumstances beyond your control.

Whatever the case may be, *it's unrealistic to expect 100 percent success 100 percent of the time*.

The whole concept of failure needs to be kept in perspective. Too many students refuse to set goals because they are petrified of the prospect of failing to reach them. They believe that *failing at a goal* is tantamount to *failing as a person*.

Nothing could be further from the truth.

Every failed effort strengthens you as a person. Barry LePatner aptly remarked, "Good judgement comes from experience, and experience comes

from bad judgement." There is a deep truism here. And if you accept it, you'll find that every short-term failure only serves as a building-block for long-term success.

If you fall short of a goal, (1) ask yourself "what went wrong?" (2) learn something from the experience, and (3) move on to the next challenge. Never allow a failure to immobilize you.

> *If you have made mistakes . . . there is always another chance for you. . . . You may have a fresh start any moment you choose, for this thing we call "failure" is not the falling down, but the staying down.*
>
> *MARY PICKFORD*

Whether you succeed or fail is really a secondary issue. Ultimately, it's the person you become as you work toward your goals—not the actual achievement of those goals—that really matters. So keep reading, fill out a couple of Goal-Setting Rap Sheets, and hit the ground running!

GOAL-SETTING RAP SHEET

Goal: _____

_____

Date: _____

Type: (check one) *Personal* ___   *Academic* ___   *Social/Interpersonal* ___

WHY I AM COMMITTED TO REACHING MY GOAL:

_____

_____

_____

TOP TWO PERSONAL CHARACTERISTICS NEEDED TO REACH THIS GOAL:

1. _____

2. _____

TOP TWO BENEFITS OF REACHING MY GOAL:

1. _____

2. _____

TOP TWO REPERCUSSIONS OF *NOT* REACHING MY GOAL:

1. _____

2. _____

EXTERNAL REWARD(S) TO BE RECEIVED ON ACHIEVEMENT DAY:

_____

_____

GOAL-SETTING RAP SHEET (SAMPLE)

Goal: I will get at least a 3.2 grade point average during the fall semester.

Date: August 19th

Type: (check one) *Personal* ___ *Academic* X *Social/Interpersonal* ___

WHY I AM COMMITTED TO REACHING MY GOAL:

I am not satisfied with the grades I made last year, and want to prove to myself that I can break a 3.0. Plus, I already told my parents I'd make a 3.2!

TOP TWO PERSONAL CHARACTERISTICS NEEDED TO REACH THIS GOAL:

1. Better time management; cut down on Nintendo, TV, etc.

2. Willingness to study; stronger commitment this semester.

TOP TWO BENEFITS OF REACHING MY GOAL:

1. Boost my chances for landing that great summer internship.

2. Build confidence; add to my personal and employment merits.

TOP TWO REPERCUSSIONS OF *NOT* REACHING MY GOAL:

1. Lower my chances of getting into grad school next year.

2. Disappoint myself and my parents.

EXTERNAL REWARD(S) TO BE RECEIVED ON ACHIEVEMENT DAY:

2 new CDs, dinner at TGIF's, and a wild night in the city.

Sources

Chambliss, Arrington, Wayne Meisel, and Maura Wolf. *Light One Candle*. White Plains, N.Y.: Peter Pauper, 1991.

Covey, Stephen R. *The 7 Habits of Highly Effective People*. New York: Fireside, 1990.

McWilliams, John-Roger, and Peter McWilliams. *The Life 101 Series*. Los Angeles: Prelude Press, 1991.

Robbins, Anthony. *Awaken the Giant Within*. New York: Fireside, 1991.

Robbins, Anthony. *Unlimited Power*. New York: Fawcett Columbine, 1986.

Schlenger, Sunny, and Roberta Roesch. *How to Be Organized in Spite of Yourself*. New York: Penguin/Signet, 1990.

Part **2**

▲

▲

▲

▲

Social and Interpersonal Excellence

The Brass & Fern   © Steve Riehm

THE ART OF MAKING A
GREAT FIRST IMPRESSION

You never get a second chance to make a first impression.

UNKNOWN

College provides us with unlimited opportunities to meet new people, make new friends, and start new relationships. It's one of the many perks of being a student.

Friendships, relationships, and popularity are definitely big issues on college campuses. Research shows that people between the ages of eighteen and twenty-two have the greatest desire to make new friends. And, of this age bracket, college students are more motivated to make friends than nonstudents.

Most of us fall within this statistic. We *love* making friends. We treasure our friendships and cherish our relationships. After all, what do we spend most of our free time talking with other students about? Friends and relationships! Luckily, we are at the ideal place and the ideal time for making new friends. It's a situation made to order.

This chapter will show you how to make a great first impression on the people you meet. During your college years you will undoubtedly meet hundreds, even thousands of new people. A good first impression is often the key

that unlocks the door to new friendships and, perhaps, new love. If you think about it, every perfect friend you have was once a perfect stranger.

Making *positive* first impressions is a major factor in being well-liked and highly popular wherever you go. It is also an essential ingredient for success in the business world. Making *poor* first impressions, on the other hand, limits you in terms of friendships and relationships, can hamper you in your future career, and can sabotage you socially.

It's always a good idea to put your best foot forward, especially when meeting people for the first time. The next few pages describe how to do just that. You'll learn the simple, yet often neglected, elements of a great first impression, which can help you win the admiration, respect, and friendship of the people you meet.

▲

Hey There, Stranger!

A first impression is made during the first face-to-face encounter you have with a person you haven't met before. Judging from this first encounter, the other person forms a lasting opinion of you—one that can be difficult, if not impossible, to change. In other words, *first impressions last*.

For example, let's say that you've been introduced to someone who had a bored, disinterested look on his face and acted stuck-up toward you. Regardless of how many times you see him afterward, you will always remember your first encounter with him and the bad impression he made on you.

On the other hand, if you're introduced to someone who makes a great first impression, you will likely continue to see that person in a positive light. First impressions are powerful and enduring. They are the starting point of social, interpersonal, and professional success.

The burning question is, *How long does it take to make a first impression?*

According to experts, it takes only *four minutes!*

Four Minutes to the Dome

Research has concluded that people form solid, long-lasting opinions of others after only four minutes of interaction. When meeting someone for the first

time, we often know whether that person will become a good friend, lover, or merely an acquaintance—all within a matter of minutes.

Always keep in mind that *the first four minutes is the most important time in making a first impression*. It is during this time that people most stringently assess each other. Research findings indicate that people are most attentive to each other during these first four minutes. Also, people's memories are most vivid of these crucial moments.

When it comes to first impressions, the first couple of minutes are more important than the next couple *hundred*. The impression you make during this short time span may dictate the way a person will think of and act toward you for a long time to come.

Since we only have four minutes to create the impression we want, it is beneficial to know the elements of a good first impression. So here they all are, in no particular order:

Elements of Style

Smile

A simple smile is the most important element of a great first impression. Smiling at the people you meet sets them at ease and makes your first encounter relaxed and pleasant. You're always off to a good start with a friendly smile.

The field of psychology has established that people who smile are perceived as being more attractive, approachable, intelligent, fun-loving, and successful than their nonsmiling counterparts. A genuine smile conveys warmth and charm and lets other people know that you're interested in them and what they have to say.

It's almost funny how many people forget or deliberately neglect this simple, common-sense gesture. There are even some students who don't smile *on purpose!* They think that by *not* smiling they are emanating an "attitude" and impressing everyone—a ploy that usually backfires. In their attempt to be "cool," they end up looking less interesting and less intelligent, and they actually become less desirable to the opposite sex.

Some students don't smile because they allow a prevailing bad mood or personal problem to dictate the way they act toward other people. Other students don't smile because, well, they just don't know any better.

So when you're doin' the ol' *meet-and-greet,* be sure to smile! People like being around social graces, not boring faces. Plus, who wants to get to know an old sourpuss?

Firm Handshake (when appropriate)

We Americans are famous for our custom of shaking hands. It's important to be hip to the convention, because people derive so much meaning from this simple act of touching.

For example, if you grip someone's hand too *tightly,* you may be considered overly aggressive or dominant. A handshake that is too *loose* is often interpreted as a sign of wimpiness or insecurity. Holding on to a person's hand for too long usually implies deep interest, attraction, or a desire to become intimate. Pulling your hand away too quickly, in contrast, often conveys timidity or apprehension.

The perfect handshake is a firm, steady one. Your grip shouldn't be so tight that your hand muscles are strained, and shouldn't be so loose that your hand wiggles like a dead fish. To ensure a good, firm handshake, make sure that the web of your hand (the area between your thumb and index finger) connects with the web of the other person's hand.

An impressive handshake usually lasts for three to five seconds. That's the perfect amount of time to convey warmth, confidence, and interest in the other person.

Adults usually confirm introductions by way of a handshake. But in many college social situations it's not necessary. A handshake is more of a formal *get-to-know-you* ritual. If you are at a wet-and-wild, smoke-in-the-air, beer-on-the-floor, techno-music-blaring party with a beer-tap hat on your head and popcorn all over your clothes . . . you don't have to worry about shaking people's hands.

Good Eye Contact

There is an art to good eye contact. Looking at the people you talk to is a sign of interest and respect. It's also common courtesy. Making a positive first impression means giving someone your undivided attention. It means treating a person like he or she is the only person in the room.

If your eyes are constantly scanning the room, looking up and down, and glancing from left to right to left again, you'll probably create a negative impression. You will be perceived as shy, preoccupied, untrustworthy, or just plain bored—even if you are none of the above. Remember, the perpetual roving eye has no place in a first encounter. Always maintain good eye contact with the people you talk to.

But, alas, eye contact has its limits. People will feel uneasy, even threatened, if you stand before them *staring* into their eyes. You've got to break your gaze occasionally. If you don't, you may be unintentionally projecting an

image of competitiveness, hostility, or inner aggression. Not exactly the way to a person's heart.

The general rule of thumb is to maintain good eye contact but not to stare incessantly. Follow this rule, and you'll (1) convey self-assuredness and poise, (2) display interest in the other person, and (3) all but ensure a comfortable first meeting. Now *that's* the way to a person's heart!

Exchange Names

Don't forget to swap names during every first encounter. The minute you offer your name, you become more than just a friendly, familiar face. You become a friendly, familiar face *with an identity*. If you want to boost your popularity, get some exposure. Let people know who you are.

Cordial Greeting

Tried and true greetings are simple statements like "It's nice meeting you," "It's good to meet you," or "Pleased to meet you."

Try to avoid using clichéd greetings like "How 'ya doin'?" "What's up?" or "How's it going?" Cliché questions only get clichéd answers. You know the drill . . .

"How are you doing?"   →   "Fine."

"What's up?"   →   "Not much."

Clichéd greetings are useless icebreakers that do nothing more than eat up time. Saying "Hi, I'm Jenny. It's nice to meet you" is much better than uttering some cliché alternative like "Yo, what's happenin'?"

If someone greets *you* with a "How are you doing?" you can make an excellent impression by offering a cheerful response such as *"Terrific!"* *"Couldn't be better!"* or *"Great!"*—as opposed to the standard, "Fine," "Not bad," or "Okay, I guess."

Start Up a Positive Conversation

Talk some, listen some. Simple. Have fun shootin' the breeze with a new person! Just remember to bring up *positive* topics. You won't make a positive impression if you bring up negative topics. In other words, no one wants to hear about how crappy the weather is, how much your back aches, how boring the accounting class is, how terrible the dorm food is, or how much you hate your biology professor.

Open up some positive chitchat: where you're from, where the other

person's from, majors, interests, personal experiences. You know, nothing too deep at first, but personal enough to make a good connection.

Always, Always, Always . . . Be Yourself!

A crucial part of making a good first impression is to relax and be yourself. No matter who you're meeting, no matter where you are or how you happen to be dressed that day, *no matter what,* you *never* have to act like something or someone you're not. *Be yourself, and you can be comfortable anywhere.* Or, as Chris Fernandez of Texas A & I declared, "Be yourself, and you'll never be out of place."

A Final Word

The Elements of Style presented in this chapter are not rules or codes of conduct. In other words, you do not *have to* follow them precisely in order to make a great first impression. Everyone has his or her own way of reacting to new situations and to new people, after all.

On the whole, however, Elements of Style represent the seven communicative gestures to which people respond most favorably. Use them in your first encounters, and you'll make great first impressions!

Sources

DeVito, Joseph A. *Human Communication.* 3rd ed. New York: Harper & Row, 1985.
Elsea, Janet G. *First Impression Best Impression.* New York: Fireside, 1984.
King, Norman. *The First Five Minutes.* Englewood Cliffs, N.J.: Prentice-Hall, 1987.
Myers, David G. *Social Psychology.* 2d ed. New York: McGraw-Hill, 1987.

College   © Dan Killeen

▲ It is in college that one finds oneself doing things that one never expected to have been doing; it is a time for experimentation, a time for exploration, and a time for initiation. One must try out, discover, and start new things in order to establish one's own identity. Be it campus activities, social relationships, or academia, the college years are a time of self-establishment and realization.

GARRETT M. GIL DE RUBIO
Dartmouth College

▲ My dad, a total bookworm, recently grilled me on why I was so involved on campus and why I never seemed to be studying. That was my cue to quote Samuel Johnson: "All intellectual improvement arises from leisure." I told him that my grades were coming along better this semester than in semesters past. Plus, I was also getting more out of the college tuition that was coming out of *his* pocket. He never said another word about it.

STEPH ADAMS
University of Louisville

REACHING OUT:

EMBRACING NEW EXPERIENCES, MEETING NEW PEOPLE, AND GETTING INVOLVED ON CAMPUS

The desk is a dangerous place from which to watch the world.

JOHN LE CARRÉ

By reaching out to new experiences and meeting new people during college, we not only learn about whatever we're reaching out to, but we also learn more about *ourselves* in the process. We literally become more *worldly* and more *wise* at the same time—while at the same time making lots of new friends. Now that's a win-win proposition!

▲

Meet As Many New Students As You Can

Students come from all over the country—all over the world, for that matter—to attend college. It's nothing like high school, where everyone is from the same hometown (yawn). College campuses are absolutely brimming with diversity. Be sure to experience some of that diversity.

Think about it this way. There may be *thousands* of fascinating people on your campus. Each one of them knows things you don't. A whole new world of knowledge and friendship is within your reach. All you have to do is make the effort.

If you are feeling a little shy, keep in mind that most other students are just as eager to make new acquaintances as you are. We're all in the same boat here. So go ahead and take the first step. Reach out. Initiate. Don't wait for other people to approach you.

Experiment, Experiment, Experiment

Make it a point to try out new things in college—even some that you have never *dreamed* of doing.

If you've never gone rock climbing or snorkeling, why not give 'em a shot? If you've never been involved in sports, try racquetball or volleyball or karate. If you don't know much about politics, check out a student senate meeting or a political lecture. If you want to meet the cute student at the end of the hall, go introduce yourself. If you've never seen a play or a live debate or a student rally, go see what they are all about. Broaden your horizons through new experiences. In the sage words of Bill Clinton: "Expand yourself." It's one of the most fun and beneficial things you can do as a college student.

Keep an Eye Out and an Ear Open

You can always find out about new events or campus activities by flipping through the school paper or campus catalog, looking at post-ups and flyers in the student union, or visiting with others. Lots of events are circulated through word of mouth. Talk to people and find out how they spend their free time.

Be Spontaneous

Sometimes you won't know about an event until the day of—or even the *hour* of. Allow yourself to make some spur-of-the-moment decisions. If you can spare the time, by all means, go for it.

Be Open-Minded

For any new experience, try not to predict whether you will like it or hate it. Have an open mind. As the bumper sticker says, "Minds are like parachutes. They only work when they're open."

And remember, trying something doesn't mean that you have to totally commit yourself. Just give the new experience a chance. If you enjoy it, great; do it to your heart's content. If it doesn't turn you on, that's fine too; pass on it, and move on to something that does. The point is, you'll never know till you try.

Use Good Judgment

Obviously, we can't do *everything* that is offered to us. Most of us are busy trying to balance our academic responsibilities and social lives with our given time constraints. If we extend ourselves too much during the semester, we may find our grades alongside Drāno.

With all of the new experiences that are available to us, it can be real easy to get wrapped up in the excitement of it all. Reaching out and trying new things is great as long as schoolwork remains high on our list of priorities.

Oh yeah, I almost forgot. There are some new experiences that are *not* worth trying, not even once—even though they may seem intriguing or faddish or cool or whatever (like experimenting with drugs or having unprotected, drunken sex with a virtual stranger—not good!).

Obviously, just because an experience is *new* does not automatically make it good for us. So we always have to use common sense when deciding what we want to try and what we *do not* want to try. I don't want to sound preachy here, so I'll just cut to the chase: *Any illegal, reckless, or otherwise foolish activity is not worth your time—ever!*

Establish a Balance

Our off-campus lives are just as important as our on-campus lives. And things that we learn *outside* and *inside* the classroom are both valuable to us. We just have to keep the proper perspective. *It is best to find a balance between our schoolwork and our extracurricular activities.* It is not a good idea to focus completely on one or the other; if you do, your overall college experience may

suffer. But the decisions are yours; it's totally up to you to determine your own balancing point.

Enjoy It!

Be sure to have some new experiences in your weekly schedule. Always set aside some of your time to indulge in new, purely leisure-time pursuits. It is healthy to make that a normal part of your college experience. Suck the marrow out of life, as they say. You'll be glad you did.

Getting Involved

Being a student gives you the opportunity to pick and choose from a long list of college organizations and clubs. Your campus likely has a vast array of club activities, unions, governments, and special-interest groups. You're the customer; your college is a buffet. Everything is here for YOU. So get involved in whatever you want. After all, you paid for it.

Here are some common choices. Which ones sound good to you?

- Sports / athletic groups
- Student senate / government
- Band / music groups
- Political groups
- Fraternities
- Sororities
- Dance groups
- Fine arts / acting / poetry
- Environmental groups
- Religious groups
- Community service organizations
- Hobby-related clubs
- Role-playing game clubs
- Campus newspaper / radio
- Computer clubs
- Debate / forensics
- Scholastic fraternities
- Travel / camping clubs
- Ethnic clubs
- Yoga / massage / Tai-Chi clubs
- Photography clubs

If you do not currently belong to any campus organization, maybe you should consider joining one!

Why Get Involved?

Whether you are a freshman or a grad student, there is a whole slew of reasons to get involved in campus activities. Here are a few:

1. Build Strong Friendships

Some of the best friends you make during college are those with whom you spend quality time and work closely. That makes sense, right? After all, strong friendships often develop when people share common interests and work toward a common goal. This creates a special bond between people, a certain camaraderie. You will make some great friends, and who knows, you may even make a love connection or two!

2. Develop an Awesome Résumé

We all know that employers look at more than a person's GPA. Companies want to hire organized, well-rounded people who can work well with others. They look favorably upon people who are involved in extracurriculars. Having practical experience *as well as* scholastic knowledge is a definite plus.

By getting involved we can learn leadership skills, team-work skills, social skills, and cooperation—just what employers want in a candidate. This can really benefit us when we enter the job market. And it also helps us create a glowing résumé.

3. Eighty-Six Your Tension

It is a good idea to take breaks from the daily toils of school. Sometimes we just need to get away from it all—you know, take a TIME-OUT from all of the deadlines, homework, test preparation . . . all the pressure. Campus activities serve as wonderful time-outs. Playing ball or painting a picture in an oil-painting group will allow you return to your studies refreshed and rejuvenated.

4. Have a Great Time

Honestly, having fun is a major part of college life. You know what they say: All work and no play . . .

"Will My Grades Suffer?"

Here's a hot tip: *studies indicate that students who are more involved in campus activities actually <u>get better grades</u> than do uninvolved students.*

The studies show that those who are active on campus learn to organize their time better and study more effectively, and they have greater feelings of accomplishment and self-esteem. Active students also report being more satisfied with their schools and happier in their daily lives. Furthermore, these go-getters are usually the ones who secure the better job offers *after* graduation.

Many students think being active in extracurriculars will harm their grades. This isn't necessarily true. Professor Jack Rhoads has counseled college stu-

dents at Northern Illinois University more than twenty years. In a personal interview, he explained:

> Most college students do not spend *all* of their time studying. Students who are not involved in any campus activities just spend their free time elsewhere. And often, that time is devoted to more trivial pursuits like watching TV, playing cards, or hanging out at a local bar. Involvement in school is great because it encourages students to take action—to make the most of their time, and to get the most out of the college experience.

My friend Steve Jones from San Jose State summed up the idea after making the dean's list for the first time.

> My grades improved since I joined Student Senate and the Tae Kwon Do Club. Being active on campus gives a greater sense of purpose to my day, and keeps me focused. I get more done, and I'm more productive. Last year, I wasn't involved in anything. I spent my free time sitting on my ass, glued to an idiot box with a beer in one hand and a remote control in the other. I had no idea how much I was missing out.

"Will I Have Enough Time?"

Most of us have quite a bit of free time in college. The average student spends three hours a day in class. *The rest of the day is ours.* Thank heaven college is not like our high schools used to be. Man alive, we spent seven hours a day in that joint.

It is true that college classes are harder and require more study time. And it is also common for students to have part-time jobs. Regardless, you will still probably be able to fit a club activity or two into your weekly schedule.

For example, most athletic and music clubs meet only a few times per week. Government, religious, ethnic, and social groups normally meet once each week. Some groups only get together once every *other* week. If you have to, do a little creative scheduling, a little activity juggling. As John Heywood said, "Nothing is impossible to a willing heart."

A Potential Road Block

Many students are reluctant to get involved because they fear that organizations will expect them to commit too much time and energy. They worry that

if they miss some meetings or club events, the other members will think of them as uncommitted or lazy.

If you are interested in joining a club, the first thing to do is *call up the group leader or go check it out in person*. Find out how often it meets, how long the meetings last, and what is required of new members.

If the club you are interested in requires too much time, then consider joining a less demanding one. If you want to join a club, but do not know if you will always have time for it, here's a suggestion: *inform the group leaders about it ahead of time*. Be up front with them about your schedule. In most cases they will understand completely.

By handling this roadblock ahead of time, you will relieve yourself of any undue pressure. The organization and its members will understand if you have to miss some meetings or club events. In fact, they will appreciate the time that you *do* have to contribute and won't have any unrealistic expectations of you. So don't worry, no one's going to make you sing "I'm a Little Teapot" and dance around in your underwear as punishment for missing a meeting.

Realize, though, that if you want to hold an office or a leadership position, the club will probably have higher expectations of you. It takes some extra work and time, but many students feel it's worth the effort. It's the old "you get out of it what you put into it" idea.

A Reaching Out Exercise

Those who spend their lives in closets smell of mothballs.

MUGSY PEABODY

Fill in the blanks. Later on in the semester, refer back to this page. How many of them did you pursue? How many are you *still* involved with? How much do you enjoy them?

Can you think of any clubs, organizations, or groups that sound interesting to you? Write down three here:

_____

_____

_____

Can you think of any people that you would really like to meet and get to know? Jot down a couple here:

_____

_____

_____

Can you think of any new hobbies or skills (playing guitar, learning tennis, dancing, weight lifting, etc.) that you would like to learn? Write down three:

_____

_____

_____

Jot down a list of any other random activities that you've always wanted to observe or try, but haven't for whatever reason:

_____

_____

_____

_____

Congratulations! You just completed your first exercise. Now be sure to go out and *take action*. Check out some new experiences, meet some fascinating new people . . . REACH OUT!

Sources

Branden, Nathaniel. *The Art of Self-Discovery*. New York: Bantam Books, 1985.
Chambliss, Arring, Wayne Meisel, and Maura Wolf. *Light One Candle*. White Plains, N.Y.: Peter Pauper, 1991.
Gottesman, Greg. *College Survival*. 2d ed. Englewood Cliffs, N.J.: Prentice Hall, 1992.

Igmee   © **David Estoye**

How to hook up with your fabulous babe of a date

DATING, RELATIONSHIPS, AND SEX

The ideal college experience: five sexual partners, four love interests, three steady relationships, two "I love you" exchanges, one everlasting love.

STACIE NOBLE

Dating, relationships, and sex are pervasive issues on all college campuses and are areas of common ground for us students. However, there are simply no clear-cut answers to such subjective aspects of life. And no chapter, no book, no authority in the world can provide us with universal advice in this regard.

Authors who spout forth advice on these subjects are not only deluding themselves, they are also missing the point. In my research I have found that students essentially want to learn how *other* students feel about these areas of college life, so that they can discover their own truths, based, in part, on that understanding. They want exposure to a wide variety of perspectives on a wide variety of issues, from a wide variety of sources.

That's exactly what this chapter provides. The following pages are comprised of quotes that have been submitted by college students, just like yourself, from campuses all over the United States.

I communicated with my fellow students and collected their quotes either

by face-to-face conversation, through E-mail, through postal mail, or by phone. Through that lengthy process I learned that most contributors did not want to be identified in full. They wanted to remain somewhat anonymous so that they could be free to give their most honest and candid responses. Therefore, actual identities have been withheld to accommodate the wishes of my contributors.

Every student has his or her own opinions about dating, his or her own beliefs about relationships, and his or her own attitudes about sex. This chapter seeks to combine them and present them in a categorical format. But be warned: you may find some of these quotes upsetting and offensive, fallacious and overly generalized. However, they represent a good cross section of the mentalities of college students across the country and thus have been hand picked for this chapter.

▲

Students Speak Out . . . on *DATING*

"Having sex in the 90s is like kissing on the lips was in the 60s. It's normal to have done it by the fourth date." —*Sam P., University of Notre Dame*

"Too many women are finicky about who they go out on dates with. If the guy isn't gorgeous or popular, he gets turned down. I'll give just about any decent guy a chance. Even if he turns out to be a total dud, a good meal and a good movie really isn't such a bad way to spend a Saturday night."
—*Barbara S., Elon College, North Carolina*

"Dating in college isn't anything like dating in high school. You've got more opportunities and fewer limitations. One thing to consider: you are constantly changing in college. You could date a person who seems perfect for you, and three months later find that person to be totally wrong for you. It's amazing how easy it is for college students to grow in different directions."
—*Erica E., West Georgia College*

"*Never* bring a date to a guy's—or women's—night out event. You'll never live it down." —*Wendy B., University of Texas, Austin*

"Who needs a social life when you've found one special person to date and get busy with? Friendships always take a back seat to sex."
—*Jas L., Indiana University of Pennsylvania*

"What makes the college experience fun? Certainly not the professors. Definitely not the homework. The dating scene is what makes college life so live." —*Tammi D., Xavier University, Louisiana*

"I'm a conformity atheist. I believe that the most exciting thing in the world is interracial dating. You can learn so much more about the world by taking in the viewpoint of a lover who comes from a different culture. They say love is blind. It should also be color blind." —*Susan R., University of Missouri*

"College girls crack me up. They are attracted to us because we're energetic, curious, fun to be around. But when it comes to serious dating, they expect us to somehow assume other roles and also be stable, settled, and mature in everything we do. It's like they want us to be Brad Pitt, Kenny G, James Dean, David Letterman, and their sweet old grandpa all wrapped up in one. They like the fact that we're young and free-spirited; they just don't want us to be *too much* of what we are." —*Fred G., Menlo College, California*

"If you date a lot *during* college, you'll know exactly what you want in a marriage *after* college. There's really no down-side to dating."
—*Phillip R., Stanford University*

"A little game playing will keep your dates on their toes. You can't be so totally straightforward with all your intentions and hopes, especially during the first couple dates; if you do and a relationship develops, you will already be a predictable, boring mate. 'Always keep 'em guessing.' That's my motto." —*Andrew S., Roger Williams College, Rhode Island*

"The way to get a lot of dates is just to be nice to everyone you meet. I'll probably be busted by the cliché police for this one, but here goes: 'You can catch more flies with sugar than with vinegar.' "
—*Leigh F., St. Joseph's College of Maine*

Students Speak Out . . . on RELATIONSHIPS

"A strong relationship is not made of grandiose gestures. It is made of small sacrifices." —*Bonnie B., Roanoke College, Virginia*

"Relationships usually do not end because we no longer like the other person. They end more because we no longer like ourselves when we are with that person." —*Jeff G., Colorado College*

"You can tell you're in the right relationship when you feel like the person you've always wanted to be." —*Connie T., St. Francis College, Pennsylvania*

"I once heard John Laroquette say on TV, 'It's funny how the word "wife" rhymes with "life" but means the opposite.' The same could be said of most any committed relationship in college. This isn't the time to just stay with one person until you graduate. Do that, you miss out on the 'stuff' that college is made of." —*Craig P., Rice University*

"Be careful of the people you get serious with. My last girlfriend wanted us to be together 24/7. She would've made it 25/8 if she could. Nothing is more of a turn-off than a person who crowds you."

—*Keith F., Mississippi State University*

"You've got to treat a woman in a way that she is not used to being treated. Fail at this and there's nothing differentiating you from all the millions of other guys out there." —*Roger P., North Dakota State University*

"Don't ever feign compassion. If it doesn't come from the heart, don't try to force it. Never think that your feelings have to develop in the same way or at the same rate as your mate." —*Frank V., St. Ambrose University, Iowa*

"I think every relationship requires a little game playing. You cannot be completely honest with everything or you lose intrigue—and that's part of the sexual tension that keeps a relationship exciting. Therein lies the dilemma. You want to be totally open, but it can be dangerous to wear your heart on your sleeve." —*Stacie N., Vassar College*

"If you want to be wanted, you're normal. If you need to be wanted, you're questionable. If you need to be needed, you're impossible."

—*Bob C., Kansas State University*

"You can tell that a relationship is headed for trouble when you find yourself making constellation patterns from the shiny specks on your ceiling while you have sex." —*Jennifer F., University of Chicago*

"A relationship is only complicated if it's wrong."

—*Judy Y., University of Scranton, Pennsylvania*

"The most difficult kind of relationship is a long distance one. If you don't spend enough time together physically you will grow apart emotionally. And the further away two people are proximity-wise, the harder it is to maintain. My friends and I follow the two-state rule: never have a relationship with somebody who is more than two states away from you."

—*Iva F., Loyola College, Maryland*

"A relationship is like an extended game of poker. There's a little skill involved, a little luck, and a lot of bluffing; plus, you can't really back out once you've started. You have to keep playin' with the hand you've been dealt."

—*Walter B., Northern State University, South Dakota*

"My mom used to tell me that the way a guy treats his mom and the way a gal treats her dad is how they'll treat *you* in a committed relationship. Before you make a commitment to someone, find out how well he or she gets along with his or her parents." —*Sue S., Smith College, Massachusetts*

"Compatibility in couple-hood comes from communication, not sex. A hot body does not a good relationship make."
—*Brenda L., North Central College, Illinois*

"If a relationship isn't good from the get go, get goin'."
—*Reginald E., Lamar College, Texas*

Students Speak Out . . . on SEX

"When you're deciding whether to have sex with someone, you have two things to weigh: (1) how badly you want it, and (2) how much crap you'll have to deal with the next day." —*Brad R., Wichita State University*

"All sex is experienced through an egocentric filter." —*Pam A., Yale*

"To be a godlike lover, all you have to do is think of sex as Einstein thought of his theory of relativity: 'Creativity is more important than knowledge.' "
—*Denise G., Towson State University, Maryland*

"Every interaction between man and woman is sexual on some level."
—*Janice L., UCLA*

"Love should be more than passion and sex should be more than pleasure." —*Maria T., St. Michael's College, Vermont*

"Sex distorts reality." —*Roger P., Dartmouth College*

"A pervert is someone who expresses out loud the same sexual thoughts that most people keep to themselves."
—*Lester S., Southwest Texas State University*

"Sex is an important part of any relationship. If you or your mate is having borgasm orgasms, the relationship is probably doomed."
—*Tim D., Tougaloo College, Mississippi*

" 'Safe sex' is an oxymoron." —*Pablo S., University of Texas, El Paso*

"If you want to land a man, get into sex more. There's no way we can *not* fall in love with women who are as obsessed with sex as we are."
—*Dan S., Lane College, Tennessee*

"When a woman goes after a man she really likes, she sees him as flawless. The first time they have sex is a turning point. If the sex is average or poor, she

will then immediately begin to notice flaws in him. If the sex is phenomenal, the man is utterly revered. . . . He becomes something of a hero in the woman's eyes." —*Dana I., Tulane University*

"Are you crazy? If you're not married you shouldn't even be having sex."
—*David F., Seton Hall University*

"A lot of students hold power with their sexuality when they've lost their self-esteem." —*Patty G., Oregon State University*

"For many students, the idea of someone being attracted to you sexually is new. And it is human nature to explore anything that is new."
—*Kimberly J., Maryville College, Tennessee*

"The point is, guys *can* wait for sex; but they'll wonder if it's worth it to wait too long. Patience is a virtue, but I don't think it is a common one for people at this age." —*Heather C., Mount St. Mary's, Maryland*

"Do what's best for yourself and you will naturally become more appealing to the people you date. My grandmother always used to say, 'You'll never find the perfect mate until you become the person you want to be.' "
—*Ruth A., Pacific University, Oregon*

Students Speak Out . . . on ONE-NIGHT STANDS

"Few students will openly admit that one-night stands are a big reason they came to college. A one-night stand does not necessarily mean having 'intercourse' per se. It can mean having a drunken mash, a little touchy-feely, or just an evening of harmless flirting with a new friend. The possibility of 'one nighters' adds to the excitement of every college experience."
—*Adam P., Oregon Institute of Technology*

"One-night stands take away from the beauty of sex. With every one-night stand you allow, you make the act of sex less special and you make yourself less desirable. But if you're going to do it, at least 'cover the stump before you hump.' Insist on condoms." —*Tammy T. and Gina F., UCLA*

"Every weekend, students walk around with their inebriated smiles and fancy clothes and try to pick each other up. That scene was cool last year when I was still an underclassman. But it all seems so juvenile to me now. I watch people and think, 'My God, was I really like that?' "
—*"Snoop," University of Miami, Florida*

"One-night stands are hazardous to the body and vexatious to the soul. You'll never regret *not* having a one-night stand."
—*Patty U., Lafayette College, Pennsylvania*

"People always preach about how unscrupulous one-night stands are. Most of these people are those who are so damn ugly they can't have 'em even if they wanted to. Thus, their unattractiveness gives them power to moralize. For those, I say 'get off your imaginary high horse and give your conscience a rest.'" —*Phillip E., Ohio State University, Columbus*

"One-night stands have value. You can appreciate a lover more when you *know* you like him or her better than you like others. Many college students don't know what good sex is because they have nothing to compare it to."
—*Lori R., Rockhurst College, Missouri*

"Here's how my brothers and I think about one-night stands: knowing in our minds that we can get laid is just about as good as the actual sex is, without all the bullshit. Getting to the point in an encounter where someone wants us sexually is 90 percent of the excitement. From there, all there is, is the physical fun of a one-nighter, much of which we can get from our right hands and a bottle of Lubriderm." —*John M., University of Central Florida*

"Here's a question that really shows a difference in sexual convention between people from the Baby Boomer era and people from Generation X. In the late 90s, why are more and more 21-year-old women having one-night stands with 18-year-old freshmen men? The answer is simple: Because they can." —*Thom R., North Carolina State University*

Students Speak Out. . . on INFIDELITY

"For most college men, being faithful isn't a matter of having phenomenal morals. Being faithful is more a matter of not having enough golden opportunities to cheat. I'd say that nine out of ten guys will cheat on their girlfriends if they get propositioned by just the right woman in just the right way. I am not trying to be a calamity howler here. I'm just being realistic."
—*Winnie C., University of Nebraska*

"We all make mistakes in our dating experiences—a part of the maturing process. Just because you have made an indiscretion or two doesn't mean you are a moral leper." —*Kelley A., University of Maine*

"It's not easy to forgive infidelity, but if you do, I guarantee that you will have a lot of leverage later in the relationship."
—*Sal S., Oakland City College, California*

"Cheating causes irreversible damage to a relationship. You can't forgive infidelity, because if you do you'll perpetuate the problem. You can't forget infidelity because it's almost impossible to regain trust once you've lost it. You

can only forgo infidelity; that's the only way to keep a relationship strong and beautiful." —*Tonya I., Tulane University*

"La Rochefoucauld wrote, 'One pardons in the degree that one loves.' When you forgive your mate's humanness, you free yourself. You become a paragon of acceptance. With love, cynicism wavers, then fades with time."
—*Sam P., Northern Arizona University*

"Your attitude about infidelity depends on the way you define the word. Every couple should sit down and talk about what they believe constitutes cheating. This is a good exercise because everyone has different ideas of what cheating is." —*Anna J., Merrimack College, Massachusetts*

"If you can't be faithful in a relationship, you shouldn't be in one at all."
—*Oscar B., Olivet College, Michigan*

"Even the most loving of couples are subject to infidelity. After all, a crime of passion is a crime of passion. And we're all guilty of letting our libidos rule our heads at one time or another. That doesn't mean we care any less. It just means we're human." —*Matt G., Mississippi State University*

"Don't do it, and you won't have to worry about it."
—*Gary K., University of Washington*

"You will not be able to trust anybody unless you trust yourself. You create your own paranoia, just like you create your own security."
—*Claire R., Rice University*

Students Speak Out . . . on FIRST DATES

"If you want to ask someone out on a date, just go for it. Don't worry about your approach or choice of words. Just be natural and, most importantly, follow through once you have made up your mind to do it. If you don't try, don't cry." —*Scott N., Baylor University, Texas*

"If first dates make you nervous, arrange them in a group. Any time you go out with a group of people you will probably have a good time. It makes a first date less intimidating and opens up other possibilities. You could end up making some new friends. You could even end up swapping dates."
—*Sandy W., State University of New York, Oswego*

"A rule for every guy: don't spend a lot of money on a first date. It is only a trial period. If you find that you really like the person, then take her out for a more extravagant date the second or third time around. You want to make sure she is going out with you for you, and not for some other reason. Don't

be cheap on a first date, because that makes both of you look bad, but don't go all out either." —*Daniel G., Southwest Texas State University*

"When a woman suggests on a first date that she is interested in you sexually but also says things like, 'You're such a good friend to me'—that's like the ultimate mind game." —*Peter W., Southern Arkansas*

"The best way to get over the anxiety of a first date is to realize that the other person is probably just as nervous as you are. Be mindful of the fact that first dates are where you both set up your personal boundaries. It is a rare first date where two people are totally open and relaxed."
—*Connie P., Wilson College, Pennsylvania*

"I always insist on paying half on first dates. I usually don't know that person very well and I don't want either of us to feel obligated to the other in any way. Some guys think it's a nice gesture, and others freak out over it. But I've made it a personal policy to go Dutch on first dates. That keeps the ball out of his court." —*Pamela O., Pennsylvania State University*

"When you go out with a girl for the first time, make darn sure you stimulate all of her physical senses. She has to like what she sees, what she hears, what she smells, and so on for the entire evening. Appeal to her comprehensively and your overall attractiveness will soar. Cover all the bases of charisma."
—*James S., San Diego State University*

" 'You get what you pay for' applies to everything except generic peanut butter and cheap dates." —*Scott S., University of Denver*

"Always say you'll pick her up at her place. For one thing, most women appreciate it. It also prevents you from looking like an idiot waiting for her if she's late." —*Lisa K., Seton Hall University*

Students Speak Out . . . on EMBARRASSING SITUATIONS

"Screamed out the wrong name during sex."
—*J. P. I., Molloy College, New York*

"Once I farted during foreplay." —*Pat Y., University of Missouri*

"My roommate and three of her friends walked in on my boyfriend and me having sex on the kitchen table."
—*Melinda T., Eastern Michigan University*

"When my mom found a pair of my boyfriend's underwear in my hamper." —*Sheri E., Harvard University*

"I did a seductive dance for my boyfriend and he laughed."

—*Cassie B., North Carolina State University*

"I accidentally knocked my purse off my desk in the middle of sociology class and a condom fell out, in full view of about ten people, including the prof." —*Lan T., San Francisco State University*

"On a blind date, I got a boner while I was slow dancing with my partner and she noticed." —*Travis O., San Diego State University*

"I brought this girl to my apartment and, like a fool, I checked my answering machine while she was in the room. One of the messages was from a girl that I had a one-night stand with the week before; she bitched me out for never calling her like I said I would." —*Frank T., University of Nebraska*

"For Valentine's Day, I was so busy planning a nice dinner and gifts at a fancy restaurant that I forgot to bring my damn wallet."

—*Jason C., University of Washington*

"Last year I went to my boyfriend's house to meet his parents for the first time. Right before dinner, I had to go to the bathroom bad (number 2) and then the toilet clogged on me. There was no plunger and I had to call my boyfriend into the bathroom because the toilet was overflowing."

—*Gayle P., Smith College, Massachusetts*

"My R.A. caught me masturbating in the hall bathroom."

—*David H., Indiana State University*

"A date and I were flipping through my old photo album and there was a picture of me and my date's best friend kissing at a winter formal."

—*Cheryl D., University of Utah*

Students Speak Out . . . on CONDOMS

"We hardly ever see the word 'sex' anymore without seeing the word 'condom' next to it. Everywhere we go it's condoms this and condoms that. 'Condomize,' 'condomwise,' 'condomplate,' 'condomsense'—these are all stupid buzz words and I am getting sick of all the 'condom-awareness.' It's like, hey media, we get the picture." —*Tony B., California State University, Chico*

"A lot of us men want sex purely for physical reasons. Doing it with a tight latex wrapping just isn't as pleasurable and isn't nearly as fulfilling from a physical standpoint. I guess that's one reason we hate using them."

—*"Doc," Seton Hall University*

"Why is it that when men carry condoms in their wallets they are considered responsible, but when women carry condoms in their purses they are considered predatory?"   —*Beth G., Plymouth State College, New Hampshire*

"Having sex without a condom is like sky-diving without a parachute."
—*Bill N., Alaska Pacific University*

"Sex is best when you feel emotionally secure and physically safe. Condoms help provide coverage, so to speak, in those respects. They give you peace of mind so that you can let loose and have fantastic sex. Make memories, not babies."   —*Tina F., University of Massachusetts, Amherst*

"Stopping in the middle of an intimate moment to roll on a condom disrupts the passion, sure. But I never let that stop me from doing the right thing. Any rationalization to the tune of 'not wanting to ruin the mood' is nothing more than a half-baked cop-out."   —*Walter G., University of Idaho*

"You can actually get creative with condom usage. There are condom stores out there that sell all sorts of different kinds: flavored, glow in the dark, ribbed, french ticklers. If you have to use them anyway, you may as well make the experience an enjoyable one."   —*Karl B., College of William and Mary*

"A guy who suggests that he put on a condom before sex—instead of waiting for the woman to bring it up—is a major turn-on. Most women don't want to let go of a lover who is both responsible and sensitive."
—*Nancy F., Michigan State University*

Students Speak Out . . . on ORAL SEX

"Some unsolicited womanly advice: never give a man oral sex too soon in a relationship. He'll either want it all the time or he'll expect it more than you may want to give it."   —*Dana T., Smith College, Massachusetts*

"Oral sex spurs intercourse. If you can get a woman to have oral sex with you, you can probably get her to go all the way."   —*Steve H., Texas A&M*

"Several guys I dated would go down on me assuming that a good screw was soon to come. Many of them were disappointed. Just because a woman wants oral sex doesn't mean she wants it all."   —*Jill R., Menlo College, California*

"I don't want to 'speak out' on oral sex. That's some nasty shit."
—*Pete S., Pomona College, California*

"I love performing oral sex on my lovers because I like knowing that I am giving them pleasure, and that they can just lay back and enjoy me. I am in total control of the final outcome!"

—*Britt S., University of Montevallo, Alabama*

"If the idea of oral sex intrigues you, but you don't have a taste for cunnilingus or fellatio, well, there are always 1–900 numbers."

—*Joe B., Georgetown University*

"For most women, no matter how much you want it, you could never verbally ask for it. It's too embarrassing. All you can do is imply that you want it through body language." —*Missy F., Samford University, Alabama*

"Sometimes you gotta take what you can get. I'd rather have oral sex than no sex at all." —*George L., Seattle University*

"Getting oral sex is the definitive power trip for a guy. Giving it is no big deal at all." —*Frederick G., University of Iowa*

"Oral sex . . . what can I say? I love it!" —*Mary N., University of Richmond*

"If you're worried about technique, don't hesitate to check out a porno or two. Oral sex is a skill just like any other. Why not learn from the best?"

—*Christene K., University of Rhode Island*

Students Speak Out . . . on DIFFERENCES BETWEEN MEN AND WOMEN

"In relationships, women pull, men push."

—*Justin C., Stonehill College, Massachusetts*

"They say it is impossible to make peace with the opposite sex. I couldn't disagree more. It's not that we're against each other, it's just that we're out for ourselves." —*Leslie J., Long Island University, Brooklyn*

"A man's looks can grow on a woman, but a woman's looks can't grow on a man." —*Peter S., Pratt Institute, New York*

"I think that women are more analytical at the post-relationship stage. They reflect on what went wrong and try to come to some sort of understanding. Guys, on the other hand, do whatever they can to forget about the relationship directly after a breakup. They probably feel the same pain, but they deal with it differently." —*Andrea Y., University of Minnesota*

"Men are great. Women are greater." —*Joan B., Georgia College*

"Women tend to be attracted to men's total packages; they carefully consider personality, brains, looks, and everything else in their assessments of men. Men can be attracted to just one aspect of a woman and fall for her; this is demonstrated beautifully every time a man labels himself as a 'boob dude,' an 'ass man,' a 'lip lover,' or a 'thigh guy.' I guess most males are just one-dimensional by nature." —*Jill E., Southeastern Louisiana University*

"Men are incapacitated by their emotions because they don't express them freely. Women are freer to express their emotions but are not as free to express themselves sexually. Oh, what I'd give for a week of nationwide role reversal." —*Kat P., Brandeis University*

"A woman's greatest fear is that the man she is dating wants her only for her body. A man's greatest fear is that the woman he's dating wants him for much more than his body." —*Thomas K., Long Island University, Southampton*

"Women are sensitively shrewd. Men are shrewdly sensitive."
—*Anne B., Rutgers University, New Brunswick*

"Here's a woman: 'If the relationship is good, then I'll think about sex.' Here's a man: 'If the sex is good, then I'll think about a relationship.' "
—*Barry L., Spalding University, Kentucky*

"If a guy cooks, it's sexy. If a woman doesn't, it's a defect."
—*Steven G., University of Rochester*

"When a man meets the perfect woman, he's always head over heels. When a woman meets the perfect man, she's always skeptical."
—*Heather W., Illinois Wesleyan University*

Students Speak Out . . . on FLIRTING

"Flirting is a medium where the unsaid is understood."
—*Stacie C., Vassar College*

"Looking at a person with 'bedroom eyes' is *the* flirting technique—as you hold eye contact with your soon-to-be-lover, keep your eyelids open just a tad bit wider than usual, hold your gaze just a tad bit longer than usual, and, when you blink, blink just a tad bit slower than usual. Do that enough and trust me, they'll line up like jetliners at an air terminal."
—*Nadine G., California State, Fresno*

"A wink is a loaded invitation."
—*Matt I., Susquehanna University, Pennsylvania*

"Let me start out by saying that there is a big difference between a handsome guy and a charming guy. A handsome guy is someone you notice. A charming guy is someone who notices you. If you can find both in one person, that's your cue to flirt." —*Katherine W., Oglethorpe University, Georgia*

"Flirting ability is a by-product of self-confidence."
—*Emma R., University of Nevada, Reno*

"Flirt and flatter all you want, but one thing I know for sure: no woman is truly convinced of her own beauty." —*Pat B., St. Mary's of Maryland*

"To flirt you must know how far you can go without hurting the other party. I have seen many people genuinely fall for others because they were playing flirt games, only to take a hard fall later."
—*Chris D., Aquinas College, Michigan*

"You can flirt successfully with any woman by remembering the following phrase: 'Beautiful women like to be told they're intelligent and intelligent women like to be told they're beautiful.' "
—*Dan G., Quinnipiac College, Connecticut*

"The recipe for flirting: one part looks, two parts eye-contact, three parts attitude; add a dash of humor, a splash of wit . . . set timer and bring to boil." —*Dorothy P., University of Tampa*

Students Speak Out . . . on THE COLLEGE PARTY SCENE

"Frat parties are fun to go to, but they are always based on 'who can get who in how long.' They're big sausage-fests where guys sword fight over women and drink 'till they drop. It's immature at times, but I have to admit, college night-life revolves around them—and for good reason, especially if you're good looking." —*Kelley P., Pennsylvania State University*

"Most guys I know have to have some alcohol before they will even think about approaching a girl at a party. It's like they are looking for courage in a shot glass." —*Jan H., North Dakota University*

"It happens at every party. By midnight, I get beer-goggles. By one in the morning, my beer-goggles have an extra-good-looking filter. Nobody is ugly at two in the morning." —*Kenny F., University of Washington*

"She could be the best-looking girl at the party, but I'd never take her seriously if she comes on to me too strong. When a girl is easy, it's like I get cheated out

of the challenge. And when there's no challenge, there will be no sustaining interest." —*Will H., Yale University*

"Why go to parties? Free advertising!"
—*Timothy F., Mercer University, Georgia*

"I stopped going to parties after someone close to me was 'acquaintance raped' at one. It sounds clichéd, but watch out, it can happen to you."
—*Melissa N., Loyola College, Maryland*

"The last party I went to was a dream: I drank free beer, I danced for hours, guys treated me like a queen, and I ended up meeting a terrific person before I went home. Having fun and making a love connection at a party is a numbers game. But to play, you have to attend."
—*Carol P., Western Washington University*

"The way a lot of guys behave around each other at parties can be described with one word: masturbatory. Honestly, we get off on stroking our own egos. We brag about our own stories and conquests over a couple beers, feel pretty damn fulfilled afterwards, and then, after we've had enough, want to go right to sleep." —*Larry E., Stetson University, Florida*

"Some basic party guidelines for college women: always wear a watch, never wear your best shoes, don't bring a purse, go to the bathroom in pairs, be nice to everyone (even ugly guys), resist the urge to take off your clothes, keep some breath mints in your pocket, dance a lot, flirt a little, wear scented underwear, and never underestimate the power of a revealed bra strap."
—*Charlotte M., Villanova University*

"I always clean my room before I go out partying . . . you never know."
—*Bret M., University of Missouri*

"Going to a college party is a little like being a mosquito in a nudist colony. You know what you have to do but you don't know where to begin."
—*"Golie," University of South Carolina*

Students Speak Out . . . on DATE RAPE

"Date rape is too broadly defined. Read the fine print of that statute and you will find that any person can be accused of date rape. The laws are unfair to both genders." —*"Goose," Norfolk State University*

"I'll never forget an open discussion we had on date rape in a large lecture hall. One guy gave his opinion to the class. He actually stood up and said,

'Date rape laws get abused by a bunch of whiny-ass femi-nazis who don't want to be called sluts.' I later found out that he had been accused of date rape twice, but was never indicted. That was quite an eye-opener to the college dating scene." —*Janet B., University of Miami, Florida*

"What if a woman says 'yes' until after penetration, and then suddenly says, 'no'? If that's rape, then I'm a rapist."

—*Wayne F., University of California, Irvine*

"Before I got to college, I heard that one out of every four college women get raped, mostly by acquaintances. I thought it could never happen to me, but it did . . . I was an eighteen year old virgin and I trusted him to stop when I told him to . . . after it was over, I cried for hours in the bathroom. With the bathtub faucet on I watched my virginity wash down the drain. There's no experience that is more demoralizing than being sexually abused by someone you trusted as a friend. But I want my suffering to be of value to others. If it ever happens to you, take my advice and call the Rape Crisis Hotline at 1-800-656-4673. This number not only saved my sanity, it also helped me get justice on that pitiful bastard." —*Anonymous, University of Texas, Austin*

"Society rewards hypermasculinity in men. Screw society. The definition of a real man is 'control.' " —*Ned R., Youngstown State University*

"Date rape isn't about sex. It's about power. And I've learned from experience that the least powerful of men are the most insistent."

—*Jane W., Russell Sage College, New York*

"A general P.S. to all the date rape discussions out there—it *is* possible for a woman to rape a man. I just hate how people treat date rape as a one-sided, only-men-are-at-fault type of issue."

—*Gregory D., Manchester College, Indiana*

"You can do everything the dating handbook tells you to do: 'Don't go there,' 'Don't wear that,' 'Don't say this,' 'Don't smile like that'—but you can't always control another person. You just have to use intuition before deciding who you want to go out with." —*Jill B., Hampshire College*

Students Speak Out . . . on SEXUALLY TRANSMITTED DISEASES

"College is a breeding ground for STDs. Everyone should get checked up at least once a year. When you have sex with someone, you also have sex with everyone that person has had sex with. You never know who has what. It's pretty disgusting when you think about it."

—*Larry G., Quincy College, Illinois*

"The worst mistake you can make regarding sexually transmitted diseases is to think, 'It won't happen to me.' The younger you are, the more invulnerable you tend to think you are. News flash, people: nobody's invulnerable. I'm living proof of the words I write. But I'm not going to make the same mistake twice."   —*Faith G., Cambridge University, England*

"The fear of AIDS and other diseases has forced people to be more selective with their sexual partners and exercise more discretion in their sexual activities—which is the way it should be in the first place. It's interesting that such a horrible fear can have a positive consequence."

—*Harry A., Carnegie Mellon University, Pennsylvania*

"To stay safe from STDs, college women have to take on a vegetarian role, if you know what I mean . . ."   —*Pam L., Harvard University*

"I can't talk about anything aside of AIDS. I have been lucky enough to not encounter any other STD. I do want to express my feelings on safe sex: you can't understand AIDS until you have watched your friends and lovers die for no reason. To watch men and women in their prime disabled and destroyed by the unknown—it scares me."   —*James P., University of Miami*

"I did not get AIDS because I'm gay. I got AIDS because I had unprotected sex. There's a difference. And if you're going to be sexually active, you have to be clear on that difference."

—*Mitch B., California State University, Long Beach*

"I've read that 40–50 percent of people carry the virus for genital warts and don't even know it. What makes STDs dangerous—beyond the obvious—is that they can be so easily passed on from person to person . . . many of them are asymptomatic. You can't see physical proof of certain diseases even though you may have been carrying them around for years. Should safe sex be mandatory? I say 'hell yes.' "   —*Karen O., Rice University*

Students Speak Out . . . on HOMOSEXUALITY

"College is the time to experiment with your sexuality. Do what's taboo."
—*Matt C., Northeastern University*

"I think the gay community expects a little too much from the rest of society. Homosexuals don't merely want to be tolerated; they want to be embraced. And, even in the 90's, that's just not an easy thing to do."
—*Trish L., James Madison University, Virginia*

"I just discovered that my pot-luck roommate is a homosexual. Big deal."
—*Lauri G., Princeton University*

"I found college to be the very best time to come out. I had many accepting friends and the availability of gay male groups plus counseling made meeting other gay and bisexual men more accessible."

—*John C., University of Washington*

"I feel that one of the biggest problems in the gay dating scene—or the straight scene for that matter—is the idea of looks. I have always found a man's personality the reason for a long term relationship. Honeys, there ain't no such thing as ugly when the lights go down!"

—*Gary E., Temple University*

"College is a time for all of us to experience life, yes. But more importantly to experience ourselves. Homosexuality, as well as heterosexuality, is a part of every single person. To be the most successful in your chosen path you must have 100 percent of yourself." —*Janet G., St. John's University, New York*

"Speaking from a gay perspective, I have a hard time with injustice. When people act as if I am somehow less of a man, less of a Christian, less of a person in any way because of my sexual orientation, I cannot help but get upset—even though I know that their prejudice should not be my problem. It just gets my goat when homosexuals are discriminated against because of people's homophobias, bigotry, or because of a label."

—*Jason B., Southern Oregon State College*

"Sting sang, 'We share the same biology, regardless of ideology.' Those are certainly words to live by. A lot of straight people treat homosexuals like they are of an entirely different species. People should spend more time rejoicing in their similarities and spend less time debating over their differences."

—*Eileen K., Murray State University*

"There are still people out there who think AIDS is a gay disease. Education is the only cure for ignorance." —*Yolanda S., University of Dallas*

"One thing that we have over heterosexuals is that we never have to worry about unplanned pregnancy." —*Lynne W., Indiana University, Bloomington*

"The sense that you don't have to conform is the most liberating feeling in the world. Societal rules that straight people follow blindly have little impact on the gay community. We don't feel that we 'have to' do things like straight people do. You know the litany: get married, raise a family, save for a child's future, etc. This gives us more freedom to learn new skills and talents, devote ourselves to more worthy causes, and basically experience more of what life has to offer. This is a luxury that I cherish—one that most straight people will never know." —*Matt G., University of Illinois, Urbana/Champaign*

Students Speak Out . . . on *BREAKING UP*

"Breaking up with someone should be done like taking a Band-Aid off your skin. It's best to do it quick—ZIP!—and get it over with. For heaven's sake, be fair to the both of you and don't drag it out."
—*Lee S., University of Scranton, Pennsylvania*

"A good way to break up with your mate is to act stupid, obnoxious, and disinterested. Create problems and make the other person want to break up with you. A lot of people have a problem with being dumped; it's a pride thing. A breakup can be easier in the long run if you give that power to the other person." —*Jeff M., University of Notre Dame*

"If you want to break up with somebody, do it tactfully, no matter how badly you want out. Don't feel that you can be a jerk about it just because you're not going to be with that person anymore. You have to remember that the world isn't flat, it's round, and what goes around comes around."
—*Valerie O., Spelman College, Georgia*

"Avoid staying in a relationship because you are waiting for the other person to change. This hoping-and-coping strategy doesn't work. As clearly as night follows day and a Greek guy a Greek gal, a breakup follows incompatibility. Don't put off the inevitable." —*Rebecca S., University of Oklahoma*

"Some useful advice: Don't tell your friends that you are going to break up with someone before you do it. If you change your mind about it, you'll have to explain yourself to everyone and you'll look as whipped as whipped can be." —*Robin R., University of North Florida*

"If you want to break up with a guy—call him five times a day and start bringing him flowers regularly." —*April E., Wake Forest University*

"The best way to handle a breakup is to focus on the possibilities of the future. Realize that there is a life beyond the relationship. Go out and enjoy your freedom. You won't have it forever." —*John J., Dartmouth College*

"Be quick, be honest, be armed." —*Bud I., University of Nebraska*

"After a breakup, stay away from movie theaters, restaurants, and putt-putt golf courses. Keep the radio off and don't watch soap-operas. Who are we kidding? The world was made for couples."
—*Bob A., College of the Southwest, New Mexico*

" 'I love you but I'm not in love with you' is the best thing to say when you're breaking up with someone. You want to be firm, but you don't want to make

the person feel insignificant. Be gentle. Never cut something that can be untied." —*Tracy E., Vanderbilt University*

"I couldn't stop crying when it happened. By the time he dumped me I had distanced myself from my friends so much that they didn't even bother to console me. If I had to do it all over again, I wouldn't forget about my friends." —*Linda K., Whitman College, Washington*

"Whatever you do, don't try to soften the blow by saying, 'we're better off being just friends,' or 'I still want us to remain friends.' Those corny 80s phrases don't float with people from Generation X. To have a clean break, you have to be straightforward, sometimes to the point of being crass. Say what you mean and own what you say." —*Lauren F., Yale University*

"Get out, get angry, get even, and get over it."
—*Tom P., Marlboro College, Vermont*

"Chalk it up to experience and move on. Every breakup is a learning experience and you become wiser by going through it. Don't expect yourself to know everything about relationships too soon. You can't put an older head on younger shoulders." —*Alexander G., University of Tulsa*

"Just had a breakup? Welcome back to the world of masturbation."
—*Mike H., Colorado College*

Students Speak Out . . . on THE CHEESIEST PICKUP LINES THEY'VE EVER HEARD

"How shall I get in touch with you tomorrow, should I call you or nudge you?" —*David S., Millsaps College, Mississippi*

"Baby, you must be a magician because when I look at you, everyone else disappears." —*Allison P., Adams State College, Colorado*

"Your eyes are the same color as my Porsche."
—*Stephen J., Harvard University*

" 'Hey, are your legs tired?'
'No. Why?'
'You've been running around in my mind all day long.' "
—*Robert T., King's College, Pennsylvania*

"If I could have just one wish, I'd change the alphabet and put 'U' and 'I' together." —*Denise M., University of Vermont*

"(Wave person over with pinky finger)

'Yes? Did you want something?'

'No, I just wanted to see if I could make you come with my pinky.' "

—M. E. F, University of Illinois

"Wow, I didn't think angels could fly so low."

—Christi B., Jacksonville State University, Alabama

"I just inherited 12 million dollars. Can I buy you a drink?"

—Elizabeth C., Southern Oregon State College

" 'Is there a thief in your family?'

'No.'

'Well, somebody stole all the stars from the sky and put them in your eyes.' "   —Gil M., Rice University

"Hi, my name's Scott. You can tell me yours once you catch your breath."   —Scott N., Santa Clara University

"You're so sweet, I get a toothache just looking at you."

—Larry N., National-Louis University, Illinois

"You can kiss heaven goodbye, because it's got to be a sin to look that good."   —Vivian A., Georgia State University

"Milk does a body good, but damn, girl, how much milk you drinkin'?!"

—Terri M., Oklahoma State University

College   © Dan Killeen

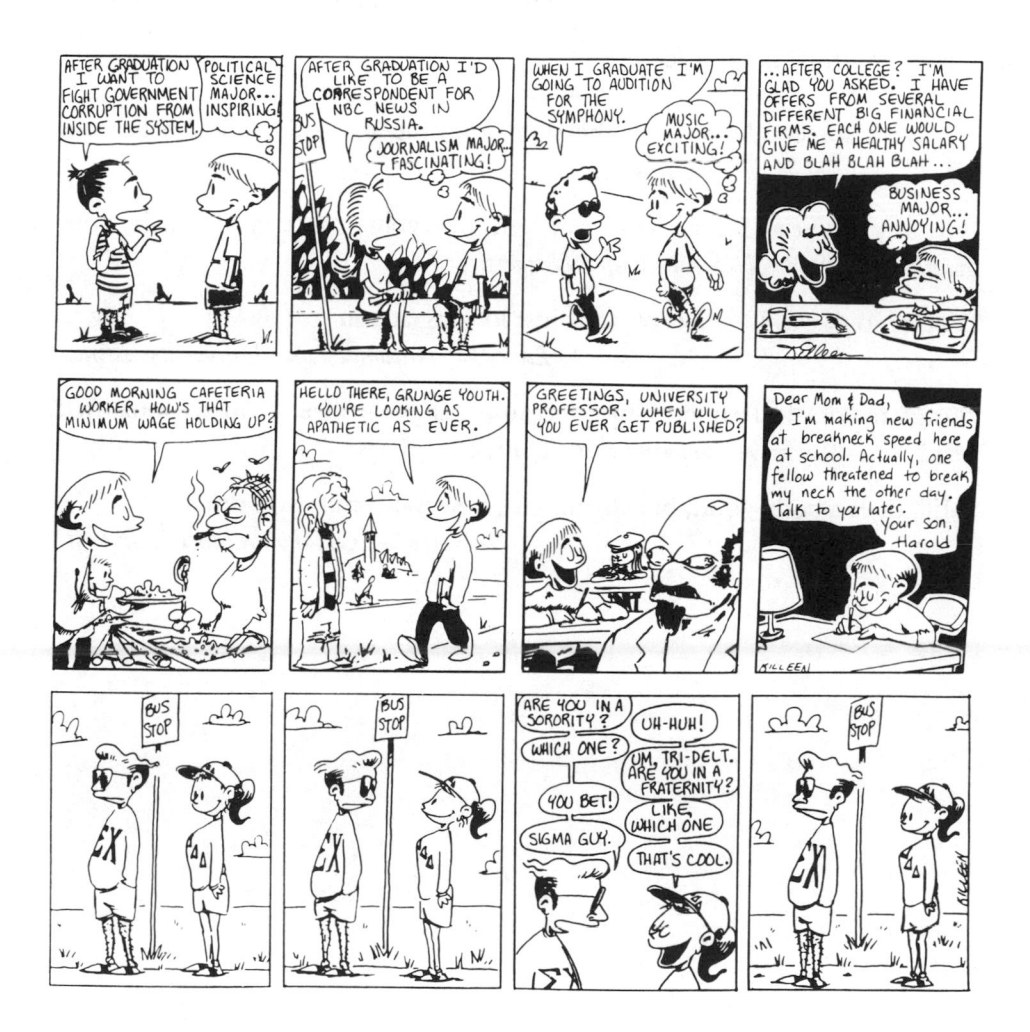

▲ The best friendships you will ever form happen after dark in hallways, through conversations about sex, life, love, and good times.

ELIZABETH SIMMONS
University of Richmond

▲ Superficial chit-chat is often required to start up a conversation. But to keep it going, there has to be a genuine interest in the person you're talking to.

BRIAN LEE
University of California, Davis

EIGHT TRAITS OF
EXPERT CONVERSATIONALISTS

Many a friendship is lost for lack of speaking.

ARISTOTLE

College life is a series of interpersonal relationships—relationships with friends, family members, classmates, teachers, love interests, and other acquaintances. Perhaps the only thing that all relationships have in common is that they are built on the same foundation: conversation.

Through the simple act of talking and listening to people, we enrich our lives and give them true meaning. At the same time, we satisfy what's called our *relationship imperative*—which is the powerfully innate desire that human beings have to build relationships with others. Conversation is the one and only way to really get to know other people and to let other people really get to know us.

All of this talk about conversation leads directly to an interesting point on the subject. There is a myth floating around out there alleging that "conversationalists are born, not made"—that certain students are destined to be social activists and interpersonal dynamos, while others are doomed to be social passivists and interpersonal dullards.

I'm here to debunk that myth. Being an expert conversationalist is not, I repeat *not,* an inborn trait. There's no conversation gene in your DNA. We are all born with abilities to hold stimulating, meaningful, and mutually rewarding conversations with whomever we choose. It's all a matter of learning, or being reminded of, a few basic communication skills and applying them directly to our conversations.

This chapter covers the dynamics of conversation in college. It presents eight important traits that expert conversationalists share. No matter how interpersonally adept you are, these traits will help you polish and refine your communication skills—which will add more punch to all of your rap sessions.

▲

Trait 1: Express Admiration and Give Honest Praise

Psychologist William James once said, "The deepest principle in human nature is the craving to be appreciated." How true. There isn't a person alive who doesn't enjoy being noticed, encouraged, or admired in some way. *If you outwardly show appreciation for the people you talk to, you will be well-liked by virtually everyone you come into contact with.*

Sincere compliments are excellent expressions of appreciation. They not only make people feel great about themselves, but they also add optimism to otherwise humdrum days. So spread some cheer! Be that rare someone who takes the time to notice other people's good qualities. This is a sure-fire way to keep the lines of communication open between you and anyone you choose to spend time with. After all, everyone loves being with people who make them feel good.

> *Blessed are they who have the gift of making friends, for it is one of God's best gifts. It involves many things, but, above all, the power of going out of one's self, and appreciating whatever is noble and loving in another.*
>
> *THOMAS HUGHES*

During conversation, always feel free to mention what you like or admire about the person you're speaking with: a fashionable article of clothing; a fresh outlook on life; a unique personality; a commendable achievement, whatever it may be. Be encouraging. Be complimentary. But most importantly . . .

Be Sincere

Sincerity is essential, especially in the realm of interpersonal relations. People can sense when a compliment is artificial, just as they can tell when one is genuine.

There is a world of difference between honest appreciation and mere flattery. A compliment is a sincere form of admiration. Idle flattery, on the other hand, is a phony ploy used in an attempt to get someone to like you. If you use flattery, your compliments may end up sounding like "lines" or "come ons"—both of which are major turnoffs. If you do not feel completely genuine in paying someone a compliment, it's best not to give one at all. Insincerity shows through like blinking neon.

Luckily, almost everyone has *something* that is praiseworthy. If you look for the good in people, you will surely find it. And once you do . . .

Be Specific

Compliments are most warmly received when they are specific. For example, instead of simply saying "You look nice," elaborate. Tell the person *exactly how* he or she looks nice. Be expressive in your compliments: "Sarah, you look great in that outfit! Blue is definitely a perfect color on you."

Trait 2: Ask Questions to Stimulate Conversation

The essence of making conversation is to show interest in and to involve the other person.

"How can this best be done?" you ask.

Well, questions are the answer.

The key to promoting free-flowing conversation is to ask the other person questions. Sounds easy enough, I know. But it's not always that simple. If it were, we would never have to yawn through drab conversations or boring small talk about the weather or politics.

There is a lot more to asking questions than many students realize. They must be posed prudently in order to stimulate conversation. If you ask the wrong kinds of questions, you will discourage dialogue rather than encourage it.

There are basically two kinds of questions you can ask: *limited-response questions* and *open-response questions*.

Limited-Response Questions

Limited-response questions are just like the fill-in-the-blank and multiple choice questions that we see on our exams in school. They require specific, single-statement answers such as "yes," "eleven," "fine," "George Washington," and "Bud Light."

Conversations tend to drag when too many limited-response questions are asked in succession. Since these questions require only short answers, they allow the speaker no room to elaborate. And they often lead to conversational dead ends.

To illustrate, consider the case of Fred and Wilma, who have just been introduced at a school year kick-off party.

Curtains, please . . .

Fred: Hey there! I'm Fred. It's nice to meet you.
Wilma: Nice to meet you, too. My name is Wilma.
Fred: Fun party, don't you think?
Wilma: Yes.
Fred: Yeah, it's great. So what year are you in school?
Wilma: I'm a freshman. I just moved here a few weeks ago, actually.
Fred: Do you like this college?
Wilma: Very much.
Fred: Have you decided on a major?
Wilma: No, not yet.
Fred: Oh. Well, where are you from?
Wilma: Dallas, Texas.
Fred: So you're a Texan, huh? That's a pretty cool place to live, isn't it?
Wilma: Yeah. Uh, I'd better go catch up with my friends. See you later . . .

We've all been in the awkward situation of trying to find *something* to talk about with another person. And as the example illustrates, it's not easy to make a connection with someone when our questions extract only one- or two-word responses.

You can ensure that this situation never happens to you by keeping in mind that free-flowing conversations are a result of asking questions that encourage *extended* responses. Talk-show hosts are masters of this art. You will notice that in conversation they always pose plenty of . . .

Open-Response Questions

Open-response questions promote stimulating conversation because they request extended replies and explanations. They encourage the other person to

really open up and get involved in the dialogue. This is precisely why expert communicators use them so routinely in their conversations.

Asking open-response questions is useful because it

- Encourages people to share their feelings, opinions, and personal experiences with each other
- Gives people freedom to express themselves
- Makes people feel special, interesting, and important
- Creates a bond between people
- Allows both parties to relax, enjoy themselves, and learn more about each other

Now then, let's jump back to the example. Fred could have initiated a meaningful, worthwhile conversation with Wilma simply by asking her some good, open-response questions such as:

"What are some things about college life that you like better than high school?"

"Tell me, what are some of your biggest interests?"

"How did you decide to come to this university?"

"What do you think of the night life 'round here?"

"What do you think will be the hardest part about your first year of college?"

"How did you feel about moving away from home?"

Fred and Wilma could have enjoyed an entire evening of captivating conversation. But instead, they met, exchanged a few pleasantries, parted company, and that was that: a potential friendship or relationship lost by default.

Fred may have walked away thinking, "She wasn't very responsive to me. She's probably just stuck up." And Wilma may have thought, "He was nice and all, but I felt like I was being grilled by a minor-league Perry Mason." It's sad but true: bad conversations are social saboteurs.

Unfortunately, uncomfortable situations like Fred and Wilma's play themselves out over and over again on campuses all over America. Students meet or get together to talk, but their conversations are lackluster, awkward, or just plain boring.

The Good News

The good news is, you can add zeal to any conversation simply by adding more open-response questions to your dialogue. The key is to use the informa-

tion you get from your limited-response questions to help you form stimulating open-response questions.

For example, if you ask an out-of-towner, "Where are you from?" and he replies, "Dallas, Texas," you can follow up with a more open question such as "Really! I haven't met many people from Texas before. *In what ways are Texans different from the people you've met around here?*"

Asking people open-response questions places them in the limelight. It motivates them to speak freely about themselves, their experiences, and their interests. Your conversational partners will be delighted with your interest in them and will willingly open up to you . . . provided, that is, that your questions aren't *too* personal or intrusive.

You'll also find that when you encourage people to talk about themselves, they become more interested in *you*. Chances are, they will reciprocate by asking you questions about *yourself, your* experiences, and *your* opinions. Symmetrically, each person learns more about the other, and a friendship deepens effortlessly.

Trait 3: Listen Actively

A good conversationalist is a good listener. In many cases it's more important to listen than it is to talk. Maybe that's why we have two ears, but only one mouth.

Good listeners enjoy tremendous social and interpersonal success. We are all naturally drawn to people who are attentive to us and who make us feel valued and understood. We confide in good listeners and love spending time in their company.

But active listening means more than keeping your mouth shut. *It requires that you listen in such a way that others feel heard.* Not only do you have to pay close attention to what others are saying, you also have to *show* them that you are listening actively, through nonverbal means.

Nonverbal communication plays a vital role in expressing attentiveness during conversation. In his book *Making Contact,* Arthur Wassmer recommends using the acronym SOFTEN to help you remember these essential nonverbal signals:

Smile—Help create a comfortable, optimistic atmosphere in which the person can open up.

Open posture—Refrain from closed postures such as having your arms folded across your chest.

Forward lean—Incline your body, or at least your head, toward the other person.

Touch—Literally touch the other person every so often.

Eye contact—Give the other person your full attention by looking him or her in the eye.

Nod—Provide encouraging, understanding responses while the other person speaks.

These signals confirm your interest in the other person. They send the message that you are interested in what the speaker has to say, and they prompt him or her to share deeper thoughts and feelings with you. You can improve your conversations and, ultimately, your personal relationships simply by becoming a better listener!

Trait 4: Build Intimacy through Self-Disclosure

Research shows that more than 80 percent of people identify expressive, open, intimate talk as an important element in friendship. When people share their feelings, ambitions, concerns, and opinions with each other, a magical bond is formed—one that creates trust and caring and draws people closer together. If you think about it, many of your closest friendships were formed through self-disclosure.

An integral part of being a good conversationalist is the willingness to disclose various aspects of yourself to others. After all, you can't expect people to care about you if they don't know you. And you can't expect people to trust you if you do not display your trust in them by disclosing yourself to them.

This isn't to say that you should casually reveal all of your deepest secrets and most sacred thoughts; there *is* something to be said for keeping a little mystery and intrigue alive in any relationship. But if you do not reveal anything about yourself, you'll quickly become less of a fascination and more of a frustration.

If you act like your whole life is a closed book, you're gonna get shelved.

MIAH KIM, *Pratt Institute, New York*

Certain topics are likely to build closeness and intimacy between college students. Here are some of the most popular ones:
- Relationships
- Life goals and ambitions

- Family and personal upbringing
- Sex and intimacy
- Majors and future career possibilities
- Friendships
- High school experiences
- Recreation and hobbies
- Humorous experiences
- Personal successes and failures
- Attitudes on marriage
- Personal values and lifestyles
- Religious views
- Fantasies
- Tastes and personal preferences
- Hangups, pet peeves
- Dating experiences

A great way to promote free-flowing conversations is to disclose something about yourself *first*. If you begin asking people personal questions from out of the blue, you may catch them off guard and put them on the defensive. But if you break the ice and go first, they'll be much more willing to express themselves.

Trait 5: Draw on a Wide Range of Topics

It's important to keep abreast of current events, especially if you spend a lot of time in the company of others. If someone brings up a significant nationwide event, it won't become you to go, "Huh? Uh, what in the world are you talking about??"

Take some time to read through your campus newspaper, check out the local news, or watch some CNN. It takes less than half an hour to get completely caught up on the major events in the world. This will allow you to cultivate a wide range of topics during conversation. Plus, it'll keep you astute, well-informed, sharp as a tack.

Trait 6: Control Those Fillers

Ok, um, next let's like, y'know, talk about those, uh, er, annoying conversational fillers. They can seriously, like, y'know, detract from the, uh, quality of

your, um, conversations. You can see how fillers can be distracting, even irritating to the listener. Your effectiveness as a conversationalist hinges not only on what you say, but also how you say it.

Back in high school, I had a chemistry teacher who saturated his lectures with "Y'know," "Y'see," "Like," and "Okay now." He would use each of these fillers forty to fifty times every hour! I know. I counted. It was all I could do to stay awake in those classes.

Even though *what he had to say* was relevant and important, *the way he said it* was so nail-bitingly irritating that no one in class was able to pay attention to the content of his lectures. And no one learned a darned thing about chemistry.

Luckily for us, conversational fillers can be easily controlled. They are usually used to fill in dead space during speech. But it is never necessary to occupy gaps of silence with words that have no meaning. *The trick is to substitute filler words with pauses.* And don't worry, pauses won't make you sound dim-witted or slow. Quite the opposite, in fact.

Pauses can add emphasis to your sentences and can help accentuate the points you make. So when you feel a filler word coming on, pause for a second—take a breath, mentally skip over the filler, and then continue talking.

Try this as an experiment sometime this week: tape record yourself talking on the phone. I know it sounds totally nutty, but give it a go, just once. A little self-assessment, say the communications experts, can be extremely enlightening and tremendously useful.

It is important to hear yourself as others hear you, particularly when it comes to those annoying little fillers. Problem is, filler words are normally *unconscious* utterances. We rarely, if ever, realize how often they seep through our lips. And since it's impossible to control something that we are not aware of, the record-a-conversation experiment can really come in handy. It'll provide you with awareness; and as the old saying goes, *awareness is a hell of a guide*.

Trait 7: Have a Sense of Humor

A good sense of humor is a cornerstone of popularity. Numerous questionnaires have been developed to answer questions such as What do you think are important characteristics in a friend? and What qualities do you find most attractive in a mate? Invariably, *a sense of humor* ranks at the top of these lists.

College students who are humorous, uplifting, and fun to be around are adored by their peers. Humor creates smiles. It generates laughter. It smooths over the rough spots of life and improves people's moods instantly.

So produce those uplifting chuckles during your conversations. Offer a good joke, tell an amusing story, bring up a funny topic . . . and be responsive to other people's expressions of humor. If you learn to use humor effectively in conversation, you will quickly become a source of happiness and joy for others—and people will be drawn to you like you wouldn't believe.

Trait 8: Ask Fun, Intriguing, or Thought-Provoking Questions

You can add loads of intrigue to your conversations by posing some I've-never-been-asked-that-before questions. Socially and interpersonally, it favors you to be a fun conversationalist. If the mood is right, and both you and your conversational partner are open and comfortable with each other, toss out some offbeat, absolutely silly, positively unique questions, such as those below:

"IF THERE WAS A BOOK WRITTEN ABOUT YOUR LIFE, WHAT WOULD ITS TITLE BE?"

"IF YOU COULD DESCRIBE YOUR SEX LIFE WITH AN ADVERTISING SLOGAN, WHICH ONE WOULD YOU USE?"

"IF YOU WERE A TOY, WHAT DO YOU THINK YOU'D BE AND WHY?"

"IF YOU WERE CHOSEN TO STAR IN A MOVIE, WHAT KIND OF MOVIE WOULD IT BE, AND WHAT KIND OF ROLE WOULD YOU PLAY?"

"IF YOU WERE A PARTICULAR FOOD, WHAT WOULD YOU BE AND WHY?"

"WHAT DO YOU THINK YOUR FUTURE WIFE OR HUSBAND WILL BE LIKE?"

"IF YOU COULD CHOOSE ANOTHER MAJOR, WHAT WOULD IT BE?"

"WHAT'S THE CRAZIEST THING YOU'VE EVER DONE ON A DATE?"

"WHAT DO YOU FIND MOST ATTRACTIVE IN ANOTHER PERSON?"

"HAS ANYONE EVER PULLED A PRANK ON YOU IN PUBLIC? WHAT WAS IT?"

"IF A GENIE MAGICALLY APPEARED RIGHT NOW AND GRANTED YOU THREE WISHES, WHAT WOULD YOU ASK FOR?"

"WHAT DO YOU THINK YOU'LL BE DOING FIVE YEARS FROM NOW?"

"IF YOU COULD LIVE ANYWHERE IN THE WORLD, WHERE WOULD YOU CHOOSE AND WHY?"

"IF YOU COULD SOLVE ONE WORLD PROBLEM, WHICH ONE WOULD IT BE AND WHY?"

"HAVE YOU EVER HAD A 'DATE FROM HELL'? WHAT HAPPENED?"

Mirrors of the Soul

When you look into a mirror, what do you see? A reflection of yourself, right? Okay, that's simple enough. If you ever want to see what you look like, all you have to do is walk into a bathroom, turn on the lights, and take a look-see.

But what if you want to see an aspect of yourself that isn't visible? What if you want to see a reflection of your attitude? Your demeanor? Your character? Your personality?

These things cannot be seen in any reflection in any mirror. But they *can* be seen . . . through other people.

The way others act in your presence may say a lot about you. Do people smile and laugh when you're around? Or do they act indifferent or aloof? Are people polite and friendly toward you? Or are they smart-alecky and sarcastic? To a large degree, *you know yourself to the extent that you are known.*

Human nature dictates that what you send out to other people gets returned to you in kind. There are a few exceptions to the rule, of course. For instance, there are some people who are crude to everyone, no matter how nicely they are treated. But like I said, they are exceptions, not the rule.

In the context of interpersonal relations your attitudes and behaviors will be mirrored back at you. For example:

- If you are friendly and considerate to people, they will be friendly and considerate to you.

- If you are rude to people, they will be rude to you.
- If you smile at people, they will smile back at you.
- If you frown at people, they will frown back at you.
- If you are guarded and judgmental toward people, they will be guarded and judgmental toward you.
- If you are kind to people, they will be kind to you.

Great, we're on a roll. Since this concept is so important, let's beat it into the ground and do a couple more. Fill these out yourself:

- If you are sarcastic toward people, they will be _____ toward you.
- If you are supportive of people, they will be _____ of you.
- If you act like a jerk toward people, they will act like _____ to toward you.
- If you listen attentively to people, they will _____ to you.
- If you point out the good in people, they will _____ in you.

Get the picture? *You don't need to look into a mirror to see a reflection of yourself.* Uh oh, I'm feeling a poetic groove coming on. Here's my attempt at being lyrical:

I'M A MIRROR, ACCURATE AND TRUE.
YOUR ATTITUDE REFLECTS OFF OF ME
TO REVEAL THE REAL YOU.

Well okay, so that'll never win a Pulitzer . . . but you get the idea.

Mirrors of the Soul is an incredibly simple idea to understand, but it could very well be the most powerful concept in the realm of social and interpersonal relations. When you carry a philosophy that rings true for most everyone, you develop a certain sensitivity toward people—a worldliness that is sure to shine through in your personality.

Manners are the shadows of virtues . . . If we strive to become, then, what we strive to appear, manners may often be rendered useful guides to the performance of our duties.

SYDNEY SMITH

The Ten Commandments of Conversation

Do to others as you would have them do to you.

THE HOLY BIBLE

COMMANDMENT I:	THOU SHALT NOT INTERRUPT OTHERS
COMMANDMENT II:	THOU SHALT NOT BE INSINCERE
COMMANDMENT III:	THOU SHALT NOT BE SELF-ENGROSSED
COMMANDMENT IV:	THOU SHALT NOT USE EXCESSIVE RIDICULE OR SARCASM
COMMANDMENT V:	THOU SHALT NOT BE INEXPRESSIVE OR INSENSITIVE
COMMANDMENT VI:	THOU SHALT NOT ACT LIKE A KNOW-IT-ALL
COMMANDMENT VII:	THOU SHALT NOT MONOPOLIZE THE CONVERSATION
COMMANDMENT VIII:	THOU SHALT NOT GIVE UNSOLIC-ITED ADVICE
COMMANDMENT IX:	THOU SHALT NOT INSULT, OFFEND, OR CRITICIZE UNDULY
COMMANDMENT X:	THOU SHALT NOT BE JUDGMENTAL

Sources

Donaldson, Les. *Conversational Magic*. West Nyack, N.Y.: Parker, 1981.

Garner, Alan. *Conversationally Speaking*. New York: McGraw-Hill, 1988.

Glass, Lillian. *Talk to Win*. New York: Perigee Books, 1987.

Hiltner, Pearl N. *Vignettes*. Coshocton, Ohio: Shaw-Barton, 1983.

Myers, David G. *Social Psychology*, 2d ed. New York: McGraw-Hill, 1987.

Van Fleet, James K. *Conversational Power*. Englewood Cliffs, N.J.: Prentice-Hall, 1984.

Making the Grade © Bob Berry

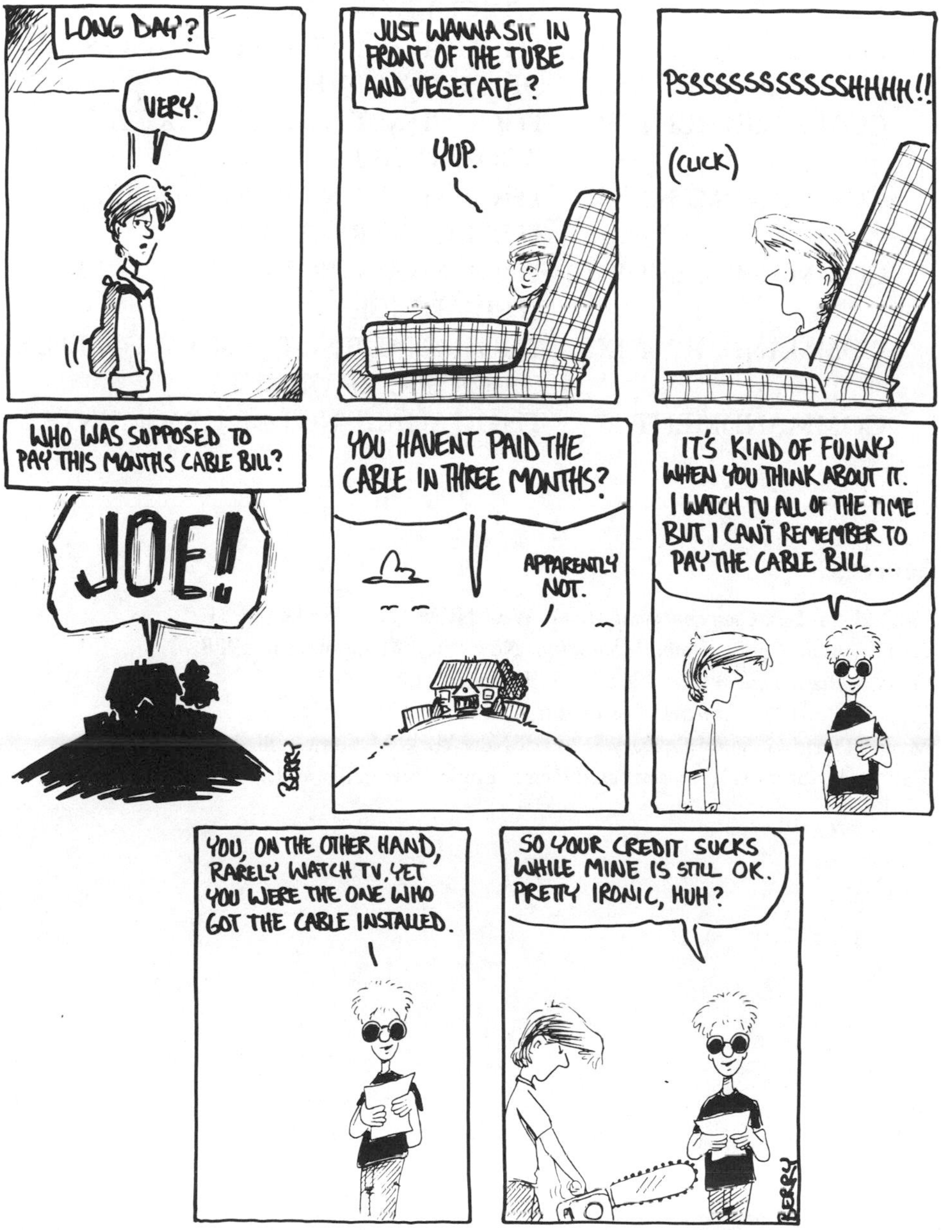

ROOMMATE DYNAMICS

What's mine is yours, and what is yours is mine.

SHAKESPEARE

College represents a time when people with different social and economic backgrounds, races, religions, and interests all have opportunities to live en masse—opportunities that most of us have never had before and will probably never have again in such a finite span of time.

Each of us brings to college his or her own set of values and living standards. Sharing dorm rooms, apartments, or houses with other students allows us to observe different customs and living habits; it teaches us how to communicate better, how to more fully understand ourselves and others, how to compromise, and basically, how to grow as individuals.

But this aspect of college life, however exciting, introduces many potential problems. Sharing a limited space with a roommate isn't always easy. And it's true what college advisors always say to incoming freshmen: *The relationships you have with your roommates have a lot of bearing on how balanced your personal and social lives are, and even on the grades you make.*

This chapter outlines several ways for you to get along with your college roommates and make the most of your living arrangements. The suggestions

presented here are intended to help you create permanent friendships from temporary roommate relationships.

But the road between *now* and *then* is a long one to travel. So let's shake a leg and take the first step . . .

▲

Lay Out the Ground Rules Together

As soon as humanly possible (ideally on the day you both move in), sit down with your roommate and take some time to agree on the house rules. *This is the single most important thing you can do to set the stage for a smooth living arrangement.* The exercise usually takes about an hour or so, so grab a couple drinks and some snacks, and hash out a game plan.

Go through the following checklist together. Make sure that each one understands the views of the other with regard to each item on the list. Be completely up-front, candid, and truthful with your roommate during this initial powwow. Doing so will help foster a relationship that is based on reciprocated understanding and courtesy. You can even take notes to have a written record of your agreements.

_____ Daily class schedules

_____ Philosophies on privacy and personal space

_____ Philosophies on personal belongings (clothes, jewelry)

_____ Philosophies on quiet time or study time (when you need it, when you don't)

_____ Philosophies on having overnight guests (friends, lovers)

_____ Philosophies on having alcohol and drugs in the room

_____ Philosophies on having parties and social events in the room

_____ Philosophies on having friends over

_____ Philosophies on borrowing and using each other's durable goods (dictionary, hair dryer, compact disks, silverware)

_____ Philosophies on borrowing and using each other's consumable goods (shampoos, perfumes, notebook paper, pencils)

_____ Philosophies on food (individual vs. sharing)

_____ Philosophies on having pets

_____ Who should be in charge of paying which bills (phone, electric, gas, water, cable)

_____ Who should be in charge of which household chores (dusting, taking out the trash, cleaning the bathrooms, vacuuming)

_____ How clean the place should be kept on a daily basis

_____ Use of appliances (TV, stereo, phone)

_____ Pet peeves

_____ How to pay for miscellaneous expenses (cracked light fixtures, plumbing, carpet cleaning)

_____ How to arrange the furniture

_____ How to decorate the place

_____ Past roommate experiences

Although it may be more comfortable at the time to brush off the possibility of any future problems and just "hope that things work out" or assume an attitude of "let's just see how things go," it is far better to take some preventive medicine and establish the house rules verbally—and as early as possible.

If, after this exercise, you both realize that you simply don't see eye to eye on the most important factors on the list, don't be afraid to bail out early. There's nothing wrong with agreeing to disagree; sometimes it is best to just go your separate ways. The short-term pain of establishing a new living arrangement could save you both from an entire semester or year of agony.

And Now, On to Finances

For any roommate agreement that deals with a significant amount of money, I recommend that you put everything in writing. Phone, electricity, and other utilities are generally registered under one person's name. If you and your roommate are sharing utility services, it is safer to have a written agreement specifying that certain payments be made by certain dates. This will serve as a financial shield for both of you.

Roommate written agreements can be very simple and short. They usually look something like:

I, Allison Bass, hereby agree to have my share of the rent paid by the twenty-third of each month .... _____

I, Pam Rogers, hereby agree to have my share of the rent paid by the twenty-third of each month .... _____

I, Allison Bass, hereby agree to have my part of the phone bill figured and paid by the third of each month .... _____

I, Pam Rogers, hereby agree to have my part of the phone bill figured and paid by the third of each month .... _____

I, Allison Bass, hereby agree to have the electricity bill paid by the twelfth of each month .... _____

I, Pam Rogers, hereby agree to have the water bill paid by the ninth of each month .... _____

_____   _____
          (roommate 1)   *(date)*

_____   _____
          (roommate 2)   *(witness)*

Grab your roommie and fill out your own . . .

Roommate Financial Agreement

initials

I, _____ , hereby agree to have my share of the rent paid in full by _____ .... _____

I, _____ , hereby agree to have my share of the rent paid in full by _____ .... _____

I, _____ , hereby agree to have my part of the phone bill figured and paid in full by _____ .... _____

I, _____ , hereby agree to have my part of the phone bill figured and paid in full by _____ .... _____

I, _____ , hereby agree to have the electricity bill paid in full by _____ .... _____

I, _____ , hereby agree to have the water bill paid in full by _____ .... _____

I, _____ , hereby agree to have the gas bill paid in full
by _____ .... _____

I, _____ , hereby agree to have the trash bill paid in full
by _____ .... _____

I, _____ , hereby agree to have the cable bill paid in full
by _____ .... _____

I, _____ , hereby agree to have the _____ bill paid
in full by _____ .... _____

I, _____ , hereby agree to have the _____ bill paid
in full by _____ .... _____

_____   _____
(roommate 1)   (date)

_____   _____
(roommate 2)   (witness)

You may be thinking, "Is this really necessary?" Well, technically, no, it isn't. The financial agreement sheet is neither a standard obligatory form nor a legal document. If you prefer, you can be totally nonchalant about the financial aspect of your living arrangement.

But think about it this way: if any bill payments are late, not only will someone be charged extra for late fees, but someone's credit rating will also take a sharp nosedive—a breeding ground for interpersonal conflict. Even if you and your roommate fully trust one another, it never hurts to take some smart precautions.

> *If there is any aspect of living together that you should be nit-picky about, it's* making sure that payments are made promptly. *Even the best of friendships can come to an abrupt end when someone gets wronged financially.*
>
> BRIAN SMITH, *Brown University*

A Decent Proposal

Think about your telephone situation. Do you and your roommate share the same phone line? If you do, do you get monthly migraines every time you try to split up the phone bill, arguing over strange, unaccounted-for long-distance calls?

These are common problems for college roommates. If you think your phone situation is, or could be, problematic, here's a decent proposal from me to you: *get only basic service (no in-house long distance function) for your phone line, and get two separate calling cards*. Each of you will be billed separately for your long-distance services, which will eliminate the guesswork from your monthly statements.

Conflict Resolution

The ways you and your roommate handle conflict will ultimately determine whether or not you maintain a happy home. Roommate conflicts range from little pet peeves ("Put the cap back on the tube of toothpaste!") to full-blown personality clashes ("You're such an organized neat-freak that I don't feel like I can even relax in my own apartment!").

To an extent, having disagreements is a natural and inevitable part of any living situation. Our aim here is to learn how to manage conflict constructively and find amicable solutions to problems. Trying to prevent or eliminate conflict completely is unrealistic and impossible; if you have any brothers or sisters, surely you're hip to this fact.

Should you ever have a bone to pick with your college roommate, the best way to handle the situation is to communicate your grievance immediately via the DESC formula:

Describe:	Calmly and objectively describe the bothersome behavior to your roommate; use "When you . . ." statements.
Express:	Let him or her know how the behavior negatively affects you and how you feel about it; use "I . . ." and "I feel . . ." statements.
Specify:	Openly communicate the ways you would like to see the behavior change; use "I would appreciate . . ." "I would prefer . . ." or "I would like . . ." statements.
Consequences:	State a positive consequence for making the requested change, a negative consequence for not making the change, or both; use "If . . . then . . ." statements. (Stating positive consequences is the most effective way of encouraging the desired change; state negative consequences only when absolutely necessary.)

Here is an example of a student using the DESC formula to resolve an "early bird vs. night owl" conflict with his roommate:

(Describe) When you play your music loud in the morning while I'm still asleep. (Express) I wake up tired and upset and end up feeling grumpy and resentful throughout the day. (Specify) I'd really appreciate it if you'd use headphones or listen to your music softly while I'm sleeping. (Consequence, positive) If you do, I'll make an extra effort to keep things quiet for you late at night when *you're* trying to sleep. (Consequence, negative) If you don't, then I'll be less inclined to be considerate late at night.

Notice the difference between this statement and one made without the necessary DESC components:

God, you're so inconsiderate! You had your stereo cranked *again* this morning and I had a big test today! How would you like it if *I* woke *you* up every morning?! (leaves and slams the door)

Keep in mind that the basic message behind these two statements is exactly the same. But the ways the messages are conveyed are completely different— and you can bet the outcomes of the conversations were completely different as well. Using the DESC formula helps both parties by creating a win-win situation.

It is also important to choose your words carefully as you express your gripes. In her book *Smart Talk,* Roberta Roesch says, "A large part of getting your verbal messages across depends on selecting words and phrases that help, rather than handicap, your efforts to obtain the responses you want." With that in mind, check out the following examples . . .

When you are voicing a complaint, be sure to criticize the *behavior,* and not the person.

"When you don't put away your dirty dishes, it leaves an unsightly clutter around the place, and I'm usually the one who cleans it up."

rather than:

"You're a lazy, irresponsible slob."

If you have to repeatedly complain to your roommate about the same behavior, take on a more assertive posture—but as always, stay even-tempered. ⟶

> "Jason, I've asked you four times to put away your dirty dishes after you use them, and you still don't. If there is a problem, would you tell me what it is?"
>
> rather than:
>
> "This is the fifth time I've had to tell you to put away your dirty dishes! What, do you need your mommy to come by and pick up after you like a little kid?"

> When you begin to experience a communication breakdown with your roommate, try to get him or her to see your point of view.
>
> "How do you think I feel when my friends come over for dinner and your dirty dishes are still on the table?"
>
> rather than:
>
> "I'm sick and tired of picking up after your sloppy ass."

If all else fails, consider getting an unbiased opinion from a mediator. Many a conflict has been resolved amicably by bringing in a neutral third party.

Okay now, let's say your roommate approaches *you* with a gripe. How should you handle it? First and foremost, be open-minded and listen objectively. When your roommate voices a complaint, he or she may be very upset at the time—which means the complaint could sound crass, exaggerated, even derogatory. Keep a cool head, and most important, *focus on the content of the gripe instead of the emotion behind it.*

What exactly does that mean?

Well, you know what it's like when you're upset with someone: the things you say in the heat of the moment are often raw ("You're totally inconsiderate!") and undiplomatic ("You're driving me crazy!"). If you focus only on the emotions you see and the words you hear, you may become defensive and spiteful—which could lead to finger pointing and eventually a full-blown argument. But if you focus on the content of the gripe, you'll keep your cool and will be in a better position to understand your roommate's frustrations.

So remember to be objective and not too reactionary if and when your roommate approaches you with a complaint. Underneath all the emotion and inflated words, there could be a legitimate gripe—one that you weren't even aware of. If so, take action to resolve the problem; if not, explain how his or her criticism is inaccurate.

And just to make sure that you understand the complaint fully, *repeat back to your roommate what he or she is saying in your own words*. You could start out with, "Let me see if I understand you correctly. What you're saying is that . . ."

Let's illustrate this point with our previous example:

Roommate ...."*God, you're so inconsiderate! You had your stereo cranked again* this morning, and I had a big test today! How would you like it if *I* woke *you* up every morning?! "

You ...."Let me see if I understand you correctly. What you're saying is that you'd like for me to keep the music low while you are sleeping? "

Roommate ...."Yeah, or use headphones. It really pisses me off when I have to wake up to the sounds of electric guitars, screaming voices, and cymbal crashes."

You ...."Okay, I'll make an effort to keep it quiet for you in the morning if you make an effort to keep it quiet for me late at night."

Roommate ...."Alright, it's a deal."

This technique will keep the conversation rational, while promoting mutual understanding and empathy.

What to Consider When You Choose a Roommate

The underlying principle behind most successful roommate relationships is "birds of a feather flock together." Choosing to room with someone who shares many of your personality traits and daily habits is generally a smart move. If you choose to room with someone who is your opposite in terms of personality and daily habits, you will probably experience more than your fair share of interpersonal conflict.

In evaluating a potential roommate, give serious consideration to the following factors. Make sure they are in line with—or at least acceptable to—your way of living:

- Is he/she a smoker or a nonsmoker?
- Is he/she more of a morning person (early bird) or more of an evening person (night owl)?
- Is he/she more clean and organized or more untidy and disorganized?
- Is he/she more sociable and outgoing (a party animal) or more nonsociable and introverted (a homebody)?

- Is he/she more empathetic toward others or more self-centered?
- How seriously does he/she take studying and schoolwork?
- How often will he/she have friends, boyfriends, or girlfriends over?
- How responsible is he/she financially?
- How often and how long will he/she be using the phone?
- What kind of music does he/she listen to? How loud is it?
- Does he/she respect other people's privacy and personal belongings?
- Does he/she keep confidences?
- Does he/she follow through on promises?

Get a Message Board

An excellent way to boost communication and prevent misunderstandings is to buy a large message board and put it up in a conspicuous place. Message boards are great for writing down phone messages, personal messages, necessary errands, miscellaneous reminders, and also for letting each other know that a visitor dropped by. Best of all, these boards are cheap, easy to clean, and reusable throughout the year. Many students report that messages left on pieces of paper such as Post-it notes get misplaced or lost far too often.

In Sum

There are no fancy tricks or novel strategies for maintaining a happy college home. It's all a matter of applying the concepts of courtesy and good old-fashioned common sense—a *do-to-others-as-you-would-have-them-do-to-you* philosophy regarding your living arrangement. The best way to keep any relationship in check is to periodically walk a mile in each other's shoes.

Your college roommates are people you will always remember. So make your living relationships as special as you can. Cherish your roommates—keep their confidences, support them in their times of need, compromise when you have to . . . and you will have strong friendships and great memories that can last you a lifetime.

How Do You Handle Conflict?

Indicate how often you rely on each of the following tactics by circling the number that you feel is most appropriate.

	Rarely				Always
1. I argue my case with my roommate to show the merits of my position.	1	2	3	4	5
2. I negotiate with my roommate so that a compromise can be reached.	1	2	3	4	5
3. I try to satisfy the expectations of my roommate.	1	2	3	4	5
4. I try to investigate an issue with my roommate to find a solution acceptable to us.	1	2	3	4	5
5. I am firm in pursuing my side of the issue.	1	2	3	4	5
6. I attempt to avoid being "put on the spot" and try to keep my conflict with my roommate to myself.	1	2	3	4	5
7. I hold on to my solution to a problem.	1	2	3	4	5
8. I use "give and take" so that a compromise can be made.	1	2	3	4	5
9. I exchange accurate information with my roommate to solve a problem together.	1	2	3	4	5
10. I avoid open discussion of my differences with my roommate.	1	2	3	4	5
11. I accommodate the wishes of my roommate.	1	2	3	4	5
12. I try to bring all our concerns out in the open so that the issues can be resolved in the best possible way.	1	2	3	4	5
13. I propose a middle ground for breaking deadlocks.	1	2	3	4	5
14. I go along with the suggestions of my roommate.	1	2	3	4	5
15. I try to keep my disagreements with my roommate to myself in order to avoid hard feelings.	1	2	3	4	5

To determine your primary conflict-handling style, place the number 1 through 5 that represents your score for each statement next to the number for that statement. Then total up the columns.

Competing	Collaborating	Avoiding	Accommodating	Compromising
1. _____	4. _____	6. _____	3. _____	2. _____
5. _____	9. _____	10. _____	11. _____	8. _____
7. _____	12. _____	15. _____	14. _____	13. _____
_____	_____	_____	_____	_____

Totals

Your primary conflict-handling style is the category with the highest total. Your fall-back style is the category with the second highest total. (This is an abbreviated version of a thirty-five-item instrument described by M. A. Rahim in "A Measure of Styles of Handling Interpersonal Conflict," *Academy of Management Journal,* June 1983, pp. 368–76.)

Sources

Bower, Sharon A., and Gordon H. Bower. *Asserting Yourself.* Reading, Mass.: Addison-Wesley, 1991.

Greenberg, Jerrold S. *Comprehensive Stress Management,* 2d ed. Dubuque: William. C. Brown, 1987.

Myers, David G. *Social Psychology,* 2d ed. New York: McGraw-Hill, 1987.

Roesch, Roberta. *Smart Talk.* New York: AMACOM, 1989.

College   © Dan Killeen

▲ Leadership in college doesn't wait for you to jump on the bandwagon; it expects you to pull it.

OSCAR YUAN
Stanford University

▲ If you have a big bone, any dog will follow you down the road. Carry a dead mouse, and cats will follow too. If you keep the dog from eating the cat and the cat from running away, then you can call yourself a leader.

SCOTT M. BURNS
Dartmouth College

▲ Leadership is an outward expression of confidence and comradery as much as it is knowledge of a certain group or situation; sometimes you have to look the part in order to play the part. All in all, the best leader is not the person who blazes a trail for other people to follow, but someone who provides others with the tools to find their own trails.

BETSY PENNEBAKER
Williams College

BECOMING A
LEADER AMONG LEADERS

Eagles don't flock—you have to find them one at a time.

ROSS PEROT

As college students, we are the future leaders of society. But among the fourteen million college students in America is an elite group: the leaders of the leaders—the students who *really* want to make a difference.

Do *you*?

If so, this chapter is for you. But let me say right off the bat that *true leadership is based on expertise relative to a given situation.* For example, being a leader of a sorority will require that you learn everything there is to learn about that house, the factors influencing it, the people involved in it, and the projects it undertakes. Obtaining that expertise is, of course, up to you.

What this chapter will equip you with, however, is no-nonsense suggestions for developing a leaderlike presence—a charisma, along with the necessary expertise, that will take you to the top and keep you there. That charisma can be represented by what I call *The Three V's of Leadership:* Visual Charisma (traits you can see), Vocal Charisma (traits you can hear), and Visceral Charisma (traits you can sense).

Developing these traits will help you land college leadership positions. Gaining some practical, hands-on experience as a leader is important for all of us, for all sectors of our lives. Employers in particular tend to favor applicants who have assumed leadership roles during college and who can exhibit leaderlike qualities in a variety of environments; managers tend to promote and give pay raises to those who prove themselves as leaders.

Surprisingly, your effectiveness and credibility as a communicator is established in a somewhat predictable manner. In his research, communications expert Albert Mehrabian has found that the total impact of a message breaks down as follows:

BODY MOVEMENTS (posture, expressions, gestures) 55%
VOCAL QUALITY (rate, volume, pitch, inflection) 38%
VOCAL CONTENT (the actual words being used) *7%*
100%

We will cover each of these factors separately; if you so choose, try to improve on each as much as possible. All that I ask is that you keep these statistics in mind as you read about the charismatic traits that make up effective leaders.

▲

Visual Charisma: Traits You Can See

Good Posture

Over the years, we have all heard our parents' incessant reminders about posture. "Stand up straight," they would nag. "Don't slouch."

But did we listen?

No, not really.

That's probably because they did not explain the real benefits of a strong posture. The truth is that the majority of Americans have poor posture—which directly contributes to a whole raft of physical problems such as:

LOW ENERGY: Bad posture collapses the chest by bringing the shoulders forward; this restricts lung expansion, limits oxygen intake, and hampers blood circulation.

BACK PAIN: An improper posture throws off your center of gravity, applying much more pressure to the spine and lower back.

HEADACHES: Slouching with your head forward (past the shoulders) puts an unnecessary and continuous strain of about fifteen pounds on the neck muscles.

A *proper* posture, however, prevents and relieves back problems and headaches, immediately increases energy levels, enhances vocal quality, and gives you a more powerful, leaderlike presence. You can literally add two inches to your height and lose two inches around your midsection simply by standing up straight from a slouching position.

Aside from these physical effects, there are also a number of psychological factors involved—especially where leadership is concerned. *Along with eyes and hair, your posture is one of the first three things that people notice about you.* The way you stand conveys a great deal about your attitude, confidence level, and personality—a universal law that can work either for you or against you.

When you slouch, for instance, you send the message that you are lethargic, depressed, or have low self-esteem. But when you stand tall and carry yourself well, you will be perceived as a dynamic, competent leader. As the saying goes, "If you have enough confidence in yourself to stand up straight, others will have confidence in you as well." Or, for the more negatively minded: "If you don't have enough confidence in yourself to stand up straight, others won't have much confidence in you either."

Take a look at the profile of your body in a full-length mirror. Relax (your stance should not be stiff or militarylike), and stand with your . . .

- feet shoulder-width apart
- weight distributed evenly between both legs
- knees bent slightly
- eyes and head level
- chin parallel with the ground
- arms straight down at your sides
- rib cage lifted slightly off of your pelvis
- stomach moderately tucked in
- buttocks tightened and tucked (straightens your spine)

With the proper posture you should be able to see in your profile an imaginary straight line that runs from (1) the top of your head (2) to your ear (3) to the center of your shoulder (4) to the center of your hip and (5) down to your ankle.

Remember that good posture is a principal trait of a leader. By standing straight and walking tall, you can command a powerful physical presence in any situation, exude confidence and energy wherever you go, and establish yourself as a leader.

Controlled Gestures and Movements

With regard to leaderlike gestures and movements, it is as beneficial to know what *not* to do as it is to know what to do. Below is a list of behavioral traits that are associated with unassertive nonleader types. Being in control of these minor, seemingly trivial quirks will have a positive impact on your physical presence.

- Blinking your eyes rapidly
- Swallowing or clearing your throat frequently
- Not maintaining eye contact with others
- Crossing your arms across your chest during conversation
- Scratching your head or rubbing your neck frequently
- Touching your hair excessively
- Holding a tight-lipped expression
- Constantly fiddling with jewelry or adjusting clothing
- Shifting your weight from one foot to the other while standing
- Any random jerky or fidgety movement

Leaders generally move in a slower, more self-assured and purposeful fashion. Everything that a leader does physically *looks* intentional. For instance, watch any world leader—such as Bill Clinton or the Prince of Wales—on television sometime; there will always appear to be a distinct purpose behind every action, no matter how routine or insignificant it may seem.

> *Regardless of what's going on, you've got to look like you know exactly what you're doing and why you're doing it.*
>
> DAVID HIBLE, *Cornell University*

Nodding your head in agreement, sitting down in a chair, taking off a pair of glasses, flipping through pages of a magazine, walking down a flight of stairs, or *anything else* can be done either in a slower, controlled manner or in a discomposed, abrupt-looking manner. How you move is your call, of course. But if you would like for people to distinguish you as a leader, slow and controlled movements are definitely the way to go.

Power Walk

Another very noticeable trait of leaders is, believe it or not, their style of walking. Leaders tend to take longer, confident strides as they walk, not quick, frenetic little steps. This gives the impression that they know exactly what they are doing and where they want to go. To exude more confidence visually, take

a good look at your walking pace. If you discover that your steps are too short or rushed, slow down a bit and take slightly longer strides.

Dress for Success

As much as leaders are able to *stand out,* they are also able to *fit in.* A good way to connect with the people you want to lead is to wear clothes that embody the style of that group. After all, as a leader you are essentially representing a given group of people. And since image plays a major role to that end, it pays to dress the part. Remember, there is a big difference between mindlessly conforming to an imaginary dress code and thoughtfully choosing a style that will enhance your charisma and credibility.

Vocal Charisma: Traits You Can Hear

Speak at an Appropriate Tempo

The tempo or rate at which you speak reveals much about your moods and emotions and influences the impact that your words have on others. Leaders are usually in positions where they have to be objective and controlled in their dealings with others—which explains their inclination to speak at slower tempos. Talking at a slightly slower rate has three major benefits: (1) it allows you to enunciate your words better, (2) it makes you seem more credible, and (3) it keeps the spotlight on you for longer periods of time.

Keep in mind, though, that along with standard vocal traits such as volume, pitch, and inflection, *your speaking rate should be adjusted according to the leadership style you want to project.* For example, if your aim is to inspire, motivate, or persuade, a faster rate of speech would be more effective. If your aim is to explain, reassure, answer questions, or instruct, then a slower rate may be more appropriate.

Why is this so?

Voice has a physiological effect on people, which makes it a powerful tool for influencing others. Research shows that speaking rapidly and loudly will increase a listener's heartbeat and adrenaline flow, while speaking slowly and calmly will usually have the opposite effect.

One of the most engaging qualities of a leader is the ability to adjust the rate at which he or she speaks to fit the situation at hand and the people being addressed. So before taking on any leadership role that requires a lot of speaking, consciously think about the kind of effect you want to have on your listeners; then adjust your voice—rate, volume, and pitch—appropriately.

Use Examples, Anecdotes, and Stories

Leaders are effective storytellers. They are able to command attention from others in part because they use plenty of anecdotes and personal experiences in their conversations and speeches. As a leader you should use stories to colorize and add character to the points on which you speak.

> *The best leaders . . . almost without exception and at every level, are master users of stories and symbols.*
>
> TOM PETERS

If you can tell a good story or give a related example which really hits home with other people, your message will be all the more effective. *The Book of Virtues* by William J. Bennett is an excellent source of moral stories and anecdotes. If you are ever in a leadership position where you have to address or promote such issues as self-discipline, responsibility, or perseverance, this book will give you literally dozens of stories to choose from.

Power Talk

The words you use in communicating a message determine the power of that message. Use the wrong words, and even the best-intended message will be disregarded. Use the right words, and you'll project the image of a competent speaker and a dynamic leader, and your message will be taken to heart.

Many leaders use similar types of phrases when they communicate with others. Their choice of words always seems to encourage and motivate their listeners and make them feel important and valued. This forms person-to-person bonds that last.

Below is a long list of phrases that energize, involve, and inspire people. Use these phrases—or variations of them—as you communicate with others:

"Let's work on it together." "I take full responsibility . . ." "I'm willing to compromise." "I'm proud of you." "I appreciate your . . ." "I value your judgment." "I'd love to get your opinion on . . ." "What do you think is the best way to handle this?" "You can count on me." "You can do it." "If you ever want to talk, you can contact me anytime." "I'll take care of it." "I'd be glad to help." "Trust me." "I'll stand by you." "I'd be honored." "I'm all ears." "I can relate to . . ." "I see what you're saying." "I can assure you that . . ." "I have faith in your abilities." "We'll solve the problem together." "You'll do great." "I'm here to help." "I appreciate your help." "From personal experience, I've learned that . . ." "You've got some excellent ideas." "Don't give up." "I hope we can all agree that . . ." "I'm

confident that we'll come to an understanding." "I respect you for . . ." "We'll make it work." "Let's forge ahead." "Let's work it out." "How do you think we can do better at this task?" "I'll do my best." "What are your thoughts on . . .?" "If anyone can handle this task, it's you." "Your feedback would be very helpful to me." "Let's do the best we can." "You're very important to me." "You are a valuable part of this group."

Visceral Charisma: Traits You Can Sense

Have a Distinct, Definable Mission

In his classic book *On Becoming a Leader* Dr. Warren Bennis points out, "The first basic ingredient of leadership is a guiding vision." Being a leader among leaders entails a definable, clear-cut mission or vision of the future—one that you wholeheartedly believe in and constantly strive toward, one that is your passion.

Whether your leadership vision is to spearhead a group project for an organizational behavior class, help establish a new on-campus club, or fulfill the duties of a Greek pledge educator, a strong and ongoing sense of purpose is what will create the enthusiasm necessary to get the job done successfully and elicit plenty of support for yourself along the way.

As philosophical as this concept may seem, it has a very practical application: *the key to leadership is to use your mission as a point of reference from which you base all of your actions.* Your mission should serve as something of a mental compass, pointing you in the right direction whenever you have actions to take or decisions to make.

Practice Altruistic Egoism

Altruistic egoism is a term credited to stress management expert Dr. Hans Selye. Essentially, the idea here is that if we go out of our way to help others, we will win their respect, "earn their love," and elicit their continual support. This is what's often called the *what-goes-around-comes-around* approach to leadership. Simply put, we have to give in order to get. The trick is to be magnanimous and courageous enough to give first—which is precisely what separates leaders from the rest of the pack.

> *You can get anything in life you want if you will just help enough other people get what they want.*
>
> ZIG ZIGLAR

According to Dr. Selye, we can help others (altruistic) and at the same time satisfy our own "innate self-centered natures" (egoism). Constantly keeping this dual-focused perspective in mind is what creates a rewarding, leaderlike lifestyle during college. As a general rule *investments of generosity are always reimbursed with respect and support*. To leaders, this is one rule that's carved in granite.

Set the Stage, Then Set 'Em Free

The basic function of a leader is to provide direction and guidance for the less experienced or less capable. That's fine, at least from a short-term perspective. But a relationship that continues to be based on *dependence* lacks power in the long run.

Your charisma as a leader will reach new heights when you empower others to make their own decisions *based on what you've taught them*. Herewith, another secret to college leadership: share with others valuable lessons you've learned, display your trust in them, and then set them free to make their own choices and take responsibility for their own decisions. This will teach others to lead themselves while, theoretically, following you at the same time.

> *Give a man a fish, and he will be fed for a day;*
> *Take a man fishing, and he will be fed for a week;*
> *Teach a man to fish, and he will be fed for a lifetime.*

> **CHINESE PROVERB**

Keep in Mind the Visceral Top Ten List

Another important aspect of being a leader is knowing which characteristics others associate with effective leadership. Santa Clara University and Tom Peters Group/Learning Systems conducted a survey of 5,200 senior managers and asked them to describe the leadership traits that they most admired. The results, as listed below, were published in *Management Review* magazine:

1. Honest
2. Competent
3. Forward-looking
4. Inspiring
5. Intelligent
6. Fair-minded
7. Broad-minded
8. Courageous
9. Straightforward
10. Imaginative

Right now, take a couple of minutes to think about where you stand with respect to each of these traits. Consider each characteristic individually. How much do they define your character? Could you use improving in any of these

areas? Improve on these traits as much as possible, and actively look for situations in which you can outwardly exhibit them.

Group Dynamics and Teamwork

It's going to happen.

Sooner or later, you—yes you—are going to find yourself in charge of a group of fellow students. You may be accountable for leading a small group with a small agenda, such as a microbiology study/project group. Or you may be directing a larger group with a more extensive agenda, such as a task force responsible for a philanthropic event for your college.

Whatever, it's going to happen. You can count on it.

"Synergy" is the word for what happens when people in a group work together toward a common goal; their effect will be greater than the summation of the group members' individual efforts. In other words, promoting teamwork in a group somehow increases its effectiveness. In generic terms, *the whole is greater than the sum of its parts*. We should always use this concept as a guidepost for our leadership decisions.

Below is a list of suggestions that, when followed, will create positive synergy in your group:

Lead by Example.   Albert Schweitzer once said, "Example is not the main thing in influencing others, it is the *only* thing." *As a leader, you will set the tone for the group by your actions*. Remember that group members generally take their behavioral cues from the person in charge—in this case, YOU. If you display high energy and passion for the group's mission, chances are your exemplary conduct will inspire others to follow suit.

A good rule to remember as you lead a group is to periodically ask yourself, "What kind of message are my actions sending?" This will keep the *lead by example* suggestion in focus.

Treat Each Member as an Invaluable Part of the Group.   No matter how small a role one of your group members may be playing, treat that person as you would your right-hand man or woman. All members should be treated with equal respect, even if, on the surface, their duties or functions may seem to vary in weight. Every contribution is valuable, which makes every contributor an invaluable part of the group. For example, who's to say that in the end a dishwasher's job is any less important than that of a chef?

The only exception to this rule is when a member refuses to contribute

anything worthwhile to the group. In that case, speak with the person in private and try to find the root of his or her problem. If a solution can't be reached, talk it over with the other group members and consider giving that person the boot. Part of being an effective group leader is sending the message, in no uncertain terms, that indolence is unjust and won't be tolerated.

Define the Group's Goals.   Together with all the members of your group, take a half hour or so and create a mission statement that specifies what is needed to fulfill your group's purpose. This statement doesn't have to be long, but it does have to be clear, something like: "To successfully organize our philanthropic athletic event, we have to submit our plan by September fifth, and stay within a budget of fifteen hundred dollars. Our first course of action is to . . ." To get the best output from your group, all members have to be totally clear on why they're doing what they're doing.

Convey Your Messages in the First Person Plural.   Using "I . . ." "You . . ." "He . . ." and "She . . ." statements is generally an ineffective way of creating a sense of teamwork among group members. Your main duty as a group leader is to synergize your people by constantly instilling within them the awareness that "we're all in this together."

Frequently use the first person plural ("We . . ." and "Let's . . ." statements) when you communicate with your group. This will foster a strong sense of camaraderie among members and bond them to you. Remember, it is always easier to lead a group of teammates who are working together for a common cause than to supervise individuals who are working separately for their own purposes.

Involve Your Members in the Decision-Making Process.   Just as you should speak in the first person plural, you should also make decisions in the same way. The *my-way-or-the-highway* style of leadership fizzled out in the eighties, when people realized how ineffective it was for promoting effective group dynamics. When there are major decisions to be made, fill your group members in on all the important variables. Get their input and involve them as much as possible.

Delegate, Delegate, Delegate.   Sharing responsibility is an important aspect of leadership, yet many leaders have difficulty delegating. They think that it reflects badly upon themselves to ask others for help. So they end up biting the bullet and working far harder than they need to.

Delegating responsibility gives you more room to run the show. It also encourages group participation, which brings out the potential in each individual member. Here are three ways to delegate: (1) during group meetings, ask

for volunteers, (2) go ahead and appoint a specific task to each member, and (3) recommend that the group brainstorm and figure out task assignments for its individual members.

Acknowledge and Compliment Hard Work. If one of your group members has shown outstanding commitment for the group's mission, be sure to offer praise to that person in front of the entire group (but do it tactfully; no pretentious backslapping, please). Outwardly recognizing people for their efforts is an excellent way to promote similar behavior from other group members. This will help keep your group moving in the right direction.

Share the Credit, Take the Blame. The most effective and charismatic leaders are those who are willing to stick their necks out for their group members. Interestingly, this often entails personally taking the blame when things go wrong and not personally accepting any credit when things go right. Ah, the life of a leader . . .

> *If anything goes bad, I did it. If anything goes semi-good, then we did it. If anything goes real good, than you did it. That's all it takes to get people to win football games for you.*
>
> PAUL "BEAR" BRYANT

Get to Know Each Member on a Personal Level. The relationship you have with each group member doesn't have to be entirely work-related or task-oriented. By taking an interest in your members' personal lives, you will bond with them both on a group level *and* on a personal level.

Your Leadership Style

Think of the one person with whom you work least well. He or she may be a current coworker or someone you've worked with in the past. This person may not be the person you dislike the most, just the person with whom you had the most difficulty getting a job done. For each of the sixteen components listed below, describe that person by placing an X in the appropriate space.

Pleasant	___	___	___	___	___	___	___	___	Unpleasant
	8	7	6	5	4	3	2	1	

Friendly	___	___	___	___	___	___	___	___	Unfriendly
	8	7	6	5	4	3	2	1	

Rejecting	__	__	__	__	__	__	__	__	Accepting
	1	2	3	4	5	6	7	8	
Helpful	__	__	__	__	__	__	__	__	Frustrating
	8	7	6	5	4	3	2	1	
Unenthusiastic	__	__	__	__	__	__	__	__	Enthusiastic
	1	2	3	4	5	6	7	8	
Tense	__	__	__	__	__	__	__	__	Relaxed
	1	2	3	4	5	6	7	8	
Distant	__	__	__	__	__	__	__	__	Close
	1	2	3	4	5	6	7	8	
Cold	__	__	__	__	__	__	__	__	Warm
	1	2	3	4	5	6	7	8	
Cooperative	__	__	__	__	__	__	__	__	Uncooperative
	8	7	6	5	4	3	2	1	
Supportive	__	__	__	__	__	__	__	__	Hostile
	8	7	6	5	4	3	2	1	
Boring	__	__	__	__	__	__	__	__	Interesting
	1	2	3	4	5	6	7	8	
Quarrelsome	__	__	__	__	__	__	__	__	Harmonious
	1	2	3	4	5	6	7	8	
Self-assured	__	__	__	__	__	__	__	__	Hesitant
	8	7	6	5	4	3	2	1	
Efficient	__	__	__	__	__	__	__	__	Inefficient
	8	7	6	5	4	3	2	1	
Gloomy	__	__	__	__	__	__	__	__	Cheerful
	1	2	3	4	5	6	7	8	
Open	__	__	__	__	__	__	__	__	Guarded
	8	7	6	5	4	3	2	1	

What Your Score Means

Your LPC (Least Preferred Coworker) score measures your leadership style. To determine your LPC score, add up the points (1 through 8) for each of the sixteen items. If your LPC score is 64 or above, you are a *high* LPC person or *relationship*-motivated. If your score is 57 or below, you are a *low* LPC person or *task*-motivated. If your score falls between 57 and 64, you will need to come to your own conclusions regarding the category you belong in.

According to Fiedler, knowing your LPC score can allow you to find a situational match, and therefore it can help you to be a more effective leader.[1]

Note

1. Stephen P. Robbins. *Organizational Behavior: Concepts, Controversies, and Applications*. 6th ed. (Englewood Cliffs, N.J.: Prentice-Hall, 1993).

Sources

The Bathroom Book. Salt Lake City: Compact Classics, 1992.

Benton, Debra A. *Lions Don't Need to Roar*. New York: Warner Books, 1992.

Bethel, Sheila M. *Making a Difference*. New York: Berkley Books, 1990.

Brill, David. "Straight and Narrower." *Men's Health Magazine*. December 1994, 48–50.

Manz, Charles C., and Henry P. Sims, Jr. *Super-Leadership*. New York: Berkley Books, 1990.

McKay, Matthew, Martha Davis, and Patrick Fanning. *How to Communicate*. New York: MJF Books, 1983.

Secrets of Executive Success. Emmaus, Pa.: Rodale Press, 1991.

Robbins, Stephen P. *Organizational Behavior*. 6th ed. Englewood Cliffs, N.J.: Prentice-Hall, 1993.

Ziglar, Zig. *Zig Ziglar's Secrets of Closing the Sale*. New York: Fleming H. Revell, 1984.

Making the Grade   © Bob Berry

HOW TO
REMEMBER PEOPLE'S NAMES

Remember that a person's name is to that person the sweetest and most important sound in any language.

DALE CARNEGIE

One of the most embarrassing social situations to be in is to be approached by someone who remembers *your* name, but you can't remember his or her name. This has happened to all of us, and our usual response is to stumble with our words and try to make light of the awkward situation: "Wow, I've had so much beer that I can't even remember my own name. . . what's your name again?" The worst response possible—also very common—is to call someone by the wrong name.

With all of the people that we meet during our college years, it can be pretty difficult to keep track of everyone's name. We usually do not have much of a problem recognizing people's faces, but remembering individual names is quite another story.

Excuses aside, remembering people's names is a vital social skill. Even if you can remember everything about a person you have met in the past, if you cannot remember his or her name, you sustain a severe social handicap and may never gain that person's favor. A key to popularity is being able to make

every person you have met feel special and worthy of your recall. The maxim is true: *by remembering people, you become more memorable.*

This chapter will show you how to fuse people's names with their faces and keep their names locked away in your memory bank. Choose the techniques that work for you, practice them regularly, and you'll become a master at remembering names.

▲

Techniques for Remembering Names

The Stay-on-Your-Toes Technique

Samuel Johnson once said, "The true art of memory is the art of attention." For memory purposes, we have to consciously make mental notes of names after we hear them. The problem is, it's very difficult to pay attention to people's names while we are being introduced, especially for the first time.

Why is that?

As mentioned in the previous chapter, communications expert Albert Mehrabian has found that, statistically speaking, we focus on others in the following manner: about 55 percent of our attention is spent noticing people's body language—facial expressions, posture, and so on. Secondly, we focus about 38 percent of our attention on people's vocal quality—volume, rate, pitch, inflection, and so on. And lastly, we focus a mere 7 percent of our attention on the actual words a person uses.

That is the primary reason why we have such a hard time remembering names. We are so busy noticing the way people respond to us through their body language and vocal tones that we all but disregard the actual words they use. At the same time, we are also concentrating on ourselves—how we look, act, and speak in the presence of others. This does not leave much mental room for us to concentrate on people's names. To illustrate this point, think back to how many times you have forgotten a person's name just minutes after hearing it.

To pick up the slack attention-wise, simply remind yourself to be extra attentive when someone tells you his or her name. Make it a point to focus your attention on the name first. And if that doesn't work, move on to the next technique.

The Repeat Technique

Once someone tells you his or her name, look directly at the person and repeat back the name immediately, "Good to meet you, *Elizabeth*." Don't just say, "Hi there." The process of verbalizing a person's name as you look at his or her face is often enough to ingrain it in your memory.

The Name-to-Name Technique

A memorization method that works for many people is to form a name-to-name link with each person you meet. This is a terrific method; its only limitation is that it can only be used with common names.

The technique works like this: you link together a characteristic of a person whom you *don't* know with a characteristic of another person—with the same name—whom you *do* know. For example, let's say you meet a guy named Tom. Simply choose one feature about him that reminds you of a Tom you already know. If the Tom you have just met has a sturdy jaw and dark brown hair, you can link his name to another Tom who shares similar characteristics, such as Tom Cruise.

Or imagine that you meet a friendly, energetic woman named Nancy, whose outgoing personality reminds you of a Nancy you knew back in high school. Bingo—you've just formed a name-to-name link that will prompt your memory for that name. If you meet a student named Phil, think about another Phil you know and look for any characteristics—physical or other-wise—that they have in common. Form those links; remember those names.

The Catch-Phrase Technique

Here's a silly but effective memorization method for you to try out: attach rhymes and catchy, descriptive, and fitting words to people's names. For example, "Sassy Cassie," "Slick Rick," "Smilin' Susan," "Daring Daniel," "Way-Cool Walter," or "Blonde-haired Barbara."

The Exaggerate-a-Trait Technique

This technique is effective, because it allows you to make use of your imagination as you memorize people's names. *The first step is simply to pick one noticeable physical feature of the person whose name you want to remember—a long nose, a double chin, a frizzy hairdo, round glasses, big ears, or any other notable feature— and exaggerate and magnify it in your mind's eye.*

For example, if you meet a guy named Bill who has a long nose, you could

imagine a massive twelve-inch-long nose jutting out of his face. If you meet a woman named Jen who has big ears, you might imagine two huge, leathery elephant ears growing out of the sides of her head. And if you meet a guy named Frank who has shiny white teeth, you could magnify that aspect of his face and imagine him with a mouth full of huge, razor-sharp, piranhalike teeth. Really let your imagination go on this first step.

The second step is to mentally form a visual image from the person's name. For the name "Bill," for instance, you can imagine a dollar bill. "John" can prompt you to think of, you guessed it, a toilet. "Mike" can remind you of a microphone. Some others include:

Jen → gem
Ann → Raggedy Ann doll
Steve → sleeve
Matt → welcome mat
Brian → brain
Katie → kitty
Chris → Christmas tree
Frank → frankfurter
Harry → hair
Jack → Jack-in-the-box
Mark → X marks the spot
Jim → Slim Jim
Dennis → tennis racket
Hank → handkerchief
Sandy → sand
Bob → bobcat
Jeannie → genie

The third and final step is to use your imagination to form a mental link between the exaggerated feature and the visual image of the person's name. Let's put this technique into practice and say that you have just been introduced to Bill—the guy with the long nose. How can you lock his name into your memory bank?

First, exaggerate the length of his nose in your mind's eye. Second, imagine a dollar *bill*. And third, link the two visual images together: picture him trying to balance a stack of hundred-dollar bills on his twelve-inch-long nose. Use as much action, movement, and color as possible in your mental pictures; this will increase your ability to retain the image in your memory.

Let's do another. Say that you have just been introduced to Jen, who you notice has big ears. Step one: exaggerate the size of her ears—make them monstrous, elephant-size ears. Step two: imagine a *gem*. Step three: use your imagination to fuse the two images together, using action. Maybe you could

imagine her putting on a pair of gigantic ruby-red gemstone earrings on the lobes of her gigantic elephant ears.

Getting the hang of it?

Great, let's do one more. Imagine that you meet a guy named Frank who has straight, bright teeth. Step one: exaggerate the size of his teeth in your mind—give him a huge piranha mouth. Step two: picture a *frankfurter*. Step three: "link 'em up," perhaps by imagining him wildly chomping on a big frankfurter with his piranha-like teeth.

Remember that the sillier and crazier the images you create, the more they will stick out in your mind—and the easier the names will be to remember. Make your visual links as outrageous and action-packed as you can!

From this point on, whenever you see Bill or Jen or Frank, you will recall the mental images you created. Their outstanding features will serve as retrieval cues to help you recollect their names.

Keep in mind that this technique will probably seem a bit awkward, time consuming, and foreign for you at first. That's completely normal. But once you apply it a few times, it will become easier and more natural to use. You will soon be surprised at how quickly you can create two mental images and link them together in your mind.

The Syllable-Breakdown Technique

This technique is best used for first and last names that do not lend themselves easily to visual images. While names like Belle Byrd and Cliff Goldfield are fairly easy to associate with visual images, names like Antoinette Anderson and Douglas Hamilton are abstract and two-dimensional—and not easy to form pictures from.

That's a problem, but the syllable-breakdown technique is a terrific problem solver. It works like this: First, break down the name into its syllabic parts. Second, verbally repeat each syllable; concentrate on the sound of each syllable, not the spelling. Finally, use your imagination to come up with a coinciding visual image through a similar-sounding word or words.

Below is a list of examples:

Kendall = ken-dall → Ken doll
Perry = per-ry → pear tree
Martin = mar-tin → martian
Renshaw = ren-shaw → wrench and saw
Bigelow = big-e-low → big fellow
McIntyre = mac-in-tyre → a Big Mac in a tire
Nicole = ni-cole → nickel
Weber = web-er → web on a bar

Tucker = tuck-er → trucker
Debbie = deb-bie → dead bee
Wallace = wall-ace → wall of ice

Try some of your own:

Ginny = gin-ny → _____

Harrison = har-ri-son → _____

Siegel = sie-gel → _____

Fleming = flem-ing → _____

Melanie = mel-a-nie → _____

VanMeter = van-me-ter → _____

Baldwin = bald-win → _____

Fernandez = fer-nan-dez → _____

Once you form a mental image from the name, link it to the person through the exaggerate-a-trait technique, and voilà—you'll have the name committed to memory.

This method requires a little more thought and effort, but it is a long-term memorization technique and can be of tremendous benefit to you socially and interpersonally. Use this technique, along with one or more of the others, and remembering names will never be a problem again!

Sources

Carnegie, Dale. *How to Win Friends and Influence People*. New York: Pocket Books, 1982.
Herold, Mort. *You'll Never Forget a Name Again!* Chicago: Contemporary Books, 1992.
Lorayne, Harry, and Jerry Lucas. *The Memory Book*. New York: Dorset Press, 1974.
McKay, Matthew, Martha Davis, and Patrick Fanning. *How to Communicate*. New York: MJF Books, 1983.
Trudeau, Kevin. *MegaMemory*. Niles, Ill.: Nightingale-Conant, 1991.

The Good Life   © David Phipps

HOW TO GIVE
DYNAMIC PRESENTATIONS

The human brain is a wonderful thing. It operates from the moment you're born until the first time you get up to make a speech.

HOWARD GOSHORN

Question: *What do you think is the number one fear in America?* A fear of heights? Nope. A fear of snakes? Uh-uh. How about a fear of deep water? Or hairy insects? Or financial problems? Or even death?

Sorry, none of the above.

As noted by the *Book of Lists,* the number one fear of Americans is a fear of public speaking. And as much as we may hate speaking in front of groups and try to avoid it, most—if not all—of us will have to go through the experience several times before we graduate.

Granted, giving speeches is not something that we college students are required to do very often. But let's not underestimate the importance of this social skill. Being a dynamic speaker can benefit us on a number of fronts: academically, socially, interpersonally, and professionally. Without a doubt public speaking is one skill that can take us far—provided that we take some time to enhance it.

Fortunately for us, the elements of a dynamic presentation can be easily learned. This chapter will provide you with twenty ingredients for a dynamic speech. With the suggestions detailed in the following pages, you will be able to develop the skill and confidence to speak well in front of any audience.

▲

Elements of a Dynamic Presentation

1. Know Your Purpose

Preparing a dynamic presentation requires that you *begin with the end in mind*. You need to establish in your own mind the effect that you want your speech to have on your listeners. This means—before doing anything else—that you secure a clear, forthright answer to the question, "What is my specific purpose in giving this speech?" For example, is your primary goal to inform, persuade, direct, console, entertain, or motivate?

Although you may want to incorporate a combination of these objectives into your speech, focus your attention on the main one. Remember, if the purpose of your speech is not clear to you, it won't be clear to your audience either. And there's nothing more frustrating—from a listener's viewpoint—than wondering when a speaker is going to "get to the point."

2. Know Your Audience

In order for your presentation to be most effective, it has to be tailor-made for the people in your audience. For instance, a speech that would be well received in a fraternity house may not go over very well with members of a Bible study group.

Give serious consideration to the following aspects of your audience *before* you prepare your speech: age, gender, ethnicity, tastes, attitudes, and educational level, as well as the size of the group. Look for trends or patterns in your audience so that you can get an overall idea of what would turn them on and what would turn them off.

Once you analyze your audience, you will be in a better position to handpick the examples, illustrations, stories, jokes, audio or visual aids, quotes, and statistics that would be most appropriate for that group of people. In any presentation you need to make your listeners feel that they are being spoken *to,* not spoken *at.*

3. Organize Your Speech

As a general rule dynamic presentations are organized in a straightforward, even predictable fashion. Some popular organizational formats include

- Sequential/chronological order
- Categorical/topical order
- Pros and cons
- Point and counterpoint
- Question and answer
- Problem and solution
- Compare and contrast
- Cause and effect

Choose an organizational format that fits the purpose of your presentation and stick with it; this will help make your speech smooth and seamless throughout your delivery. If the direction of the presentation is easy to follow, you will keep the attention of your listeners and prevent yourself from going off on tangents.

As for organization structure, the best advice I've ever heard comes from author Leon Fletcher, a public speaking expert of over twenty-five years. In his book *How to Speak like a Pro,* he outlines the following "all-purpose, all-speech, format":

   I. Introduction
      A. Attention getter
      B. Preview
  II. Discussion
      A. Main points
      B. Arranged logically
      C. Supported with data
 III. Conclusion
      A. Review
      B. Memorable statement

Fletcher recommends that we *allocate about 15 percent of our time introducing ourselves and our presentations, 75 percent of our time discussing and going over the main points of the speech, and 10 percent of our time in conclusion (reiterating the main points that were made).* This seems to follow that old, time-tested, schoolhouse wisdom: "(1) Tell 'em what you're gonna tell 'em, (2) tell 'em, and (3) tell 'em what you told 'em."

4. Practice Your Speech

Practice is the best way to ensure a dynamic speech. *If at all possible, rehearse your speech in a place similar to the one where you will be giving it.* For example, if you have been assigned to give a presentation in front of your philosophy class, make a few dry runs in an empty classroom.

As you simulate the conditions of the actual speech, you prepare yourself mentally and boost your confidence. This way, you will not feel totally out of your element when you finally *do* get up in front of your audience.

Another great way to practice is to tape-record yourself making your presentation; if you can get your hands on a camcorder, that's even better. Becoming a dynamic speaker necessitates a little self-evaluation. You need to— at least one or two times—hear your speech as others will hear it.

A word of caution: don't judge yourself too harshly as you listen to or watch a recording of yourself; as the expression goes, *you are your own worst critic.* Many of the nit-picky imperfections you see and hear in yourself will not be noticed by others. Be objective in your observations, but not overly critical.

5. Get a Second Opinion

Have a friend, classmate, or roommate listen to your speech. Other people can be a wonderful source of feedback. They may be able to give you some good suggestions and help you refine your speech before you actually deliver it in front of an audience.

6. Chill Out

You have to be in control of your anxieties in order to deliver a sensational speech. One of the best ways to control stage fright is simply to understand that it follows a pattern.

Feelings of anxiety are highest right before you get up to speak and during the first minute of your speech. Your heart rate may actually double during this time. But after that initial sixty seconds, your heart rate will decrease, your anxieties will ease off, and your overall physiology will begin to reestablish its balance. So when you feel those powerful surges of anxiety right before you get up to speak, remind yourself that they are normal and that the worst will soon be over—then forge ahead with your presentation.

7. Grab Your Audience's Attention Right Off the Bat

Just as television commercials and news headlines do, you should grab your audience's attention right at the beginning of the presentation. Never start a speech by saying something bland like, "My name is Joe Smith and my speech is on divorce."

In lieu of a dull opening, say something that will shock your audience and make them take notice. Have a shtick: *"Did you know that 80 percent of couples*

who get engaged during college end up divorcing within 5 years? Good afternoon, my name is Joe Smith, and today I would like to talk about the ever-popular topic of divorce in America."

Terrific attention getters include:

- Relevant quote
- Rhetorical question
- Shocking statistic or fact
- Interesting and relevant personal experience
- Strong opinion
- Joke relevant to the topic
- Striking visual aid

8. Breathe Properly

Contrary to common belief, *proper breathing originates from the diaphragm, not the chest.* As you deliver your speech, you should not be breathing in such a way that your chest expands and contracts or that your shoulders rise and lower. Take steady and controlled diaphragmatic breaths throughout.

Also, breathe in through your nose rather than through your mouth; this will prevent you from getting dry mouth. Professional speakers and opera singers breathe in this fashion to create rich, resonant sounds with their voices. You should as well.

9. Speak Clearly

A clear, resounding voice is a well-received one. But a strange thing often happens before we get up to deliver a speech: *out of sheer nervousness, our throats and vocal chords get tight and our mouths get dry*—an anomaly often called "the cotton-mouth effect." To protect and retain your vocal quality, it is a good idea to keep the following two techniques in mind.

The first is called the *MY-ME-NO-NU-GA* technique: simply say "MY-ME-NO-NU-GA" aloud, slowly and deliberately (under your breath if you need to) five to ten times before you get up to speak; this exercise will help loosen up the muscles in and around your vocal chords and will open up your vocal tract. Second, suck on a couple of lemon drops before your presentation; they will help lubricate your throat and keep it moist during your speech.

10. Animate Your Voice

Speaking in a boring, monotone voice will sabotage any effect—aside from pure boredom—that you may want to have on your listeners. Even if your speech is appropriate for your audience, well organized, perfectly timed, and impeccable content-wise, you'll send your listeners to the land of Forty Winks if you deliver it with a drab, colorless voice.

The key to dynamic speaking is being able to animate your voice strategically throughout your presentation. Here are two bona fide public speaking pointers:

First, *vocally accentuate key words*. This is a crucial detail from your listeners' standpoint. You can literally change the entire meaning of a sentence simply by emphasizing certain words over others. Let's do a quick run-through:

"Okay fine, I won't talk to him anymore."
(a straightforward statement, which can be taken at face value.)

"Okay *FINE,* I won't talk to him anymore!"
(insinuates that you won't talk to him anymore, but that you are angry and disinclined to cooperate.)

"Okay fine, *I* won't talk to him anymore."
(implies that *you* may not talk to him anymore, but that someone else might.)

"Okay fine, I *WON'T* talk to him anymore."
(suggests that you are definite in your promise not to talk to him anymore.)

"Okay fine, I won't *TALK* to him anymore."
(connotes that you won't necessarily talk to him anymore, but that you may communicate with him through another means.)

"Okay fine, I won't talk to *HIM* anymore."
(implies that you won't talk to that particular person anymore, but that you may talk freely to someone else.)

"Okay fine, I won't talk to him *ANYMORE!*"
(suggests that you are promising never to talk to that person ever again.)

Second, *prolong key phrases and sentences*. You should always vary your rate of speaking throughout your presentation. A few times during each presentation, there should be occasions when you "draw out" your speech. When you get to the heart of a major message, speak just a bit slower and louder for emphasis, and insert some split-second pauses between words. Let your audience know rhythmically that this . . . is . . . a . . . *major* . . . point . . . you are making now.

11. Watch Your Language

Here are a few language habits to avoid: *First, avoid passive language; use the active voice as much as possible in your presentation*. For example, a passive

statement such as "The issue of attendance was discussed by our group" is not nearly as powerful as its active counterpart, "Our group discussed the attendance issue."

Second, avoid using too many colloquialisms—especially when credibility is valued over popularity. Using standard English will generally be your best bet. "Moving right along, I am now going to talk about an issue that many feel is very important on our campus . . ." sounds more credible and professional than "Movin' on, I wanna rap 'bout somethin' that should be front page news in these halls of ivy . . ."

Third, avoid complicated language. To appeal to the lowest common denominator of understanding, always speak in a language that can be easily understood by everyone. Every sentence of your speech should be simple and concise ("After our student senate meeting yesterday, we realized that we have been inflexible with our policies.") instead of complicated and jargon-laden ("Subsequent to yesterday's student senate meeting, we deduced that we have been unwittingly obtuse in persisting with our idiosyncratic emphasis on several questionably subversive doctrines.").

12. Use Note Cards When Necessary

Note cards can be very helpful to you during any presentation. With a set of 3 x 5 cards at your disposal, you will be able to refer quickly and easily to your notes, should you ever lose your place or train of thought. Note cards also allow you to keep your hands somewhat occupied in a legitimate way.

As you prepare your note cards, be sure that you do not write out your entire speech on them. Cramming too much information on your cards will tempt you to merely read from them and neglect making eye contact with your audience. So instead, just write key words, phrases, and sentences on your cards; they will serve as superb mental cues for you as you deliver your speech.

13. Make Eye Contact with Your Audience

Although you are speaking to the audience as a whole, you want to connect with as many people on an individual basis as you can. That requires plenty of direct eye contact. As you deliver your presentation, periodically look at people in every section of the room. Don't just look at an area on the back wall, look downward at the ground, or stare at your notes.

Also, *be sure to rotate your entire head as you scan the room*. Too many students make the mistake of looking at people around the room with their eyes only, while keeping their heads stationary. This makes them seem shifty, stiff, and uncomfortable, which lessens their perceived credibility as speakers. You will not appear to be a dynamic speaker if you look at people cockeyed.

14. Use Your Whole Body, Face and All

For the vast majority of speeches, it is recommended that you smile intermittently and use your whole body to accentuate your main points. If you can, step away from the podium during some transitory stages in your presentation; move toward one area of the room, then shift over to another. Motion is an important part of keeping an audience's attention; you don't want to come across as a talking statue.

The amount of gesturing you do will depend on the purpose of your presentation. *Generally, the more serious the tone of your speech, the less physically active you should be in your delivery.* For instance, it probably wouldn't be a good idea to be a grinning, arm-waving, finger-pointing, bouncy speaker if you are delivering a eulogy to a room full of mourners.

Finally, avoid keeping your hands in your pockets or behind your back, as that gives the impression of insecurity. And never have your arms folded in front of your chest; your aim is to establish rapport with your audience, not distance yourself from it. If you don't know what else to do with your hands, just keep them relaxed, down at your sides.

15. Interject Some Humor

At some point in your speech, draw on a funny personal experience, rattle off a short joke or pun, or show your audience an amusing visual aid. Most presentations benefit from an appropriate use of humor. Everyone likes to be entertained, and if you can make your audience laugh—or at least chuckle or smile—your speech will be more appealing and memorable.

Just make sure that any humor you use in your presentation is tasteful and relevant to the issue on which you speak. Also, avoid telling random jokes in an attempt to "loosen up your crowd," and do not go overboard with jokes and puns. Your goal is to be a dynamic speaker, not a stand-up comic.

16. Speak Extemporaneously

A speech can be delivered in a number of ways: you can recite it word for word entirely from memory (a bad idea), you can read it to the audience straight from your notes (an even worse idea), you can get up and "wing it," (no, no, please no), or you can take the advice of professional speakers worldwide and deliver it extemporaneously.

Delivering a speech extemporaneously means that you memorize your opening and closing statements, the main points of your speech, the correct sequence of these main points, and all key words and phrases. This is the most widely favored method of public speaking. It requires thorough, but not outrageous, preparation on your part and remunerates you with great flexibility and control.

17. Wrap It up Professionally

Conclude your speech as professional speakers do—by providing your audience with a strong sense of closure. Avoid making weak conclusions such as, "Well, I guess that's about it. Any questions?"

Instead, wrap up your speech with authority; your conclusion should be simple, powerful, and to the point, for example: "In conclusion, (memorable closing statement). I believe I still have a few minutes left, so I'll be happy to answer any questions at this time."

18. Handle the Q & A

Sometimes at the end of your presentation you will have to field questions from the audience. The question-and-answer period can be particularly stressful, because your credibility, knowledge, and professionalism may all be under scrutiny during that time.

Obviously, the best way to handle any Q & A is to know your subject inside and out. But there are some other tricks of the trade that can give you an edge as well.

If someone asks you a question that you cannot answer, don't be afraid to say so. It is far better to honestly admit, "I don't have the answer to that, but I can get it and let you know," than to try to pull an answer out of the air: "Well, um, you know, it's like . . . okay, here's the situation . . ."

If you don't understand a question fully, ask the person to rephrase it. Many people ask vague questions, and you may not respond smoothly if you try to tackle it immediately. A good technique is to repeat the question to the person to make sure you understand it correctly: "Let me see if I understand your question: what you're asking is . . ."

Finally, as you answer someone's question, concentrate on that person only. Pretend that you are having a person-to-person conversation with him or her and temporarily block out the rest of the audience as you listen and respond. This makes the Q & A session much less intimidating, because you are focusing on one person at a time—which makes you less cognizant of all the other staring faces in the room.

19. Get Feedback on Your Presentation

Be sure to ask people to give you feedback on your speech after you deliver it. Any presentation will give you an important opportunity to learn and grow, because the experience is such an intense one. You can learn more from five minutes of talking in front of an audience than you can from five hours of talking to people one-on-one. But part of that learning should come from

members of the audience who can objectively point out what you did well and how you can improve on your next speech.

20. Reward Yourself

After you deliver a speech, go out and celebrate! Remember, the experience itself taught you more than you probably realize; and that's definitely cause for celebration.

Dynamic Presentation Checklist

There is no such thing as making the miracle happen spontaneously and on the spot. You've got to work.

MARTINA ARROYO

Before taking the stage, make sure that you have answered "yes" to every point (except no. 13) on this checklist:

1. Have you defined the precise purpose of your speech? .... Y / N

2. Have you analyzed your audience? .... Y / N

3. Have you organized your speech according to Leon Fletcher's all-purpose format? .... Y / N

4. Have you tape-recorded and evaluated yourself practicing your speech? .... Y / N

5. Have you practiced your speech in a place similar to the one where you will be giving it? .... Y / N

6. Have you obtained a second opinion on your speech? .... Y / N

7. Does your speech have an attention-getter in its intro? .... Y / N

8. Have you included any humor in your speech? .... Y / N

9. Have you memorized your opening and closing statements? .... Y / N

10. Have you memorized the main points, the correct sequence of these main points, and all key words and phrases? .... Y / N

11. Does your conclusion contain a memorable closing statement? .... Y / N

12. Have you practiced your breathing? .... Y / N

13. Did you get feedback on your presentation? .... Y / N

Sources

The Bathroom Book II. Salt Lake City: Compact Classics, 1993.

Bower, Sharon A., and Gordon H. Bower. *Asserting Yourself.* Reading, Mass.: Addison-Wesley, 1991.

Fletcher, Leon. *How to Speak Like a Pro.* New York: Ballantine Books, 1983.

Glass, Lillian. *Say It . . . Right.* New York: Perigree Books, 1992.

Leeds, Dorothy. *PowerSpeak.* New York: Berkley Books, 1991.

Part **3**

▲

▲

▲

▲

Academic Success

Chicken Bird © Ron DiCesare

ACTIVE LISTENING

Listen not just with your ears. Listen with your mind, your heart, your entire being.

STEPHANIE ELDRIDGE

Active listening is an essential skill for academic success. To get good grades, you have to be able to listen, I mean *really listen,* to what's being said (and inferred) in the classroom.

I know what you're thinking: "Yeah, yeah. I've heard that before. Tell me something I *don't* know."

Well, okay. Here goes.

Did you know that there are two different ways of listening to a teacher? There's *active listening,* which is the very best, yet least common, form of listening (promotes high GPAs). And there's the plain old, run-of-the-mill *passive listening,* which most students are accustomed to (perpetuates average GPAs).

In this chapter, we'll bring to light the differences between active and passive listening. We'll also discover eight listening techniques that we can incorporate into our daily classroom experiences. The intent here, of course, is to arm ourselves with the skills necessary to score high on exams and assign-

ments and to make great grades—while spending the *least amount* of study time possible.

But first, here is a brief quiz to estimate YOUR effectiveness as a listener. Place a Y beside those statements that ring true for you. The more Ys you have, the more passive a listener you are, and the more you can benefit from this chapter.

▲

"How Well Do I Listen in Class?" A Listening Checklist

1. _____ Do you scrutinize personal characteristics or mannerisms of your teachers (examples: the way they dress, walk, talk, or style their hair)?

2. _____ Do you frequently catch yourself daydreaming in class?

3. _____ Do you habitually fake paying attention?

4. _____ Do you look at notes that you have written on past lectures and think, "None of this looks familiar"?

5. _____ Do you spend class time drawing pictures, doodling, or writing notes (unrelated to the class) or letters?

6. _____ Do you let minor distractions (a cough, a sneeze, a door closing, a person walking in late) break your flow of concentration?

7. _____ Do you let personal feelings about certain teachers affect the way you listen in class (example: sitting in class thinking, "I hate this guy. He was such a jerk when I went in to talk to him during his office hours.")?

8. _____ Do you often find that you have *no idea* what will be asked on upcoming exams?

9. _____ Have you ever been called on in class to answer a question without even realizing it? ("Who, ME?!")

10. _____ Do you often feel like you've sat through entire lectures without learning anything new or useful?

SCORE =   /10

HOW HIGH DID YOU SCORE? If seven or more of these questions made you nod your head emphatically, you are probably not a good bet for a high GPA right now. But don't fret! A few basic changes in your listening habits will do wonders for the ol' report card.

Active Listening vs. Passive Listening

Passive listening is a mechanical and effortless form of listening. Passive listening merely serves as proof that our ears function properly. It happens naturally whenever we sit in a classroom more or less awake, and doesn't require any special effort on our part.

Passive listeners *hear* the spoken words of the teacher and perhaps can differentiate between the major and minor points of the lecture. But that's all. These students have a *ho-hum attitude* during class and rarely, if ever, get enthusiastic about the material presented to them.

Active listening is totally different. It requires that students concentrate on *the content of the lecture*—not on the lecturer himself, and not on any random distractions going on in the room or in their minds.

Active listeners do more than focus on facts, figures, and ideas. They actively associate the material presented in class with their own experiences. They are able to absorb the content of every lecture and convert what they have heard into something meaningful, something useful, for themselves.

Active listeners pay special attention in class because they realize that learning from lectures is not the same as learning from books. For example, if you're studying a textbook, you can reread whatever you need as often as you like, until you fully understand the material. *In the classroom, you get only one chance to understand the information presented to you.*

If you listen actively in class, scholastic learning will become a personal, enjoyable experience—not a boring, mundane one.

Active Listening Can Boost
Your Effectiveness Fourfold

That's right. If you listen actively in class, you can be *four times* more productive than you would by listening passively.

How is this possible?

Research shows that people *think* about four times faster than they can *speak*. Students who listen passively concentrate just enough to keep up with the speaker. In other words, they apply about one-fourth of their mental capacity to the content of the lecture. The remaining three-fourths of their mental capacity is spent daydreaming, fantasizing, or pondering personal problems.

Active listeners apply a full four-fourths of their minds to each lecture and are four times more effective. They are attentive, absorbed in the lecture, and,

believe it or not, enthusiastic during class. Furthermore, they learn a lot more and have an easier time preparing for and taking exams than do passive listeners.

By incorporating a few active listening techniques, you will benefit in the following ways:

- Class time will go by much faster.
- You'll develop a healthy, productive attitude about class.
- You'll increase your memory and retention for the material.
- You'll relieve yourself of undue study time and effort.
- You'll strengthen your mind and increase its capacity.
- You'll always know what to study, come test time.

So what do you say? Do you want to start learning how to become more of an active listener or what?

Eight Tips for Active Listening

Tip 1: Get a Head Start
Before each class, take a look at your syllabus and find the upcoming topic of discussion. *Always do your reading assignments ahead of time*. This will prepare your mind for every lecture.

Once you have read the subject matter, it will be a breeze to become involved in the lecture. You'll recall the major points from your reading. You'll anticipate what the teacher is going to bring up next. And you'll predict the questions and discussions that follow. In short, you will be listening more actively than if you just walked into the class cold turkey.

Tip 2: Appreciate the Speaker
Being a college teacher isn't an easy job. In order to present a one-hour lecture, a teacher has to spend three, five, even ten or more hours in preparation. Researching, selecting, organizing, rehearsing, making handouts . . . our teachers do it all for us. All we have to do is sit back and soak it in.

So empathize a little with your teachers. Cut 'em some slack. After all, they're not just a bunch of lip-flappin' academics whose sole mission is to pester us with assignments and torture us with exams and quizzes. They are well-trained educators who want to share with us subjects they find extremely interesting. They will hand you a wealth of knowledge, if you let them.

Furthermore, you have forked over a lot of green in tuition fees. Be sure to get your money's worth.

Tip 3: Destroy All Mental Blocks

You have to avoid common pitfalls in order to be an effective listener. A sure-fire way to avoid these pitfalls is simply *being aware of them*. Look over the listening checklist (above) one more time. These ten questions illustrate some common listening barriers confronted by college students.

Be mindful of these pitfalls, and do not allow them to throw you off base. Be a stubborn listener!

Tip 4: Identify the Central Theme

Ask yourself, "What's the main point of this lecture?" Find out what central idea the teacher is trying to get across. Is he or she discussing the differences between protons and electrons? Civil turmoil in the Middle East? Mating habits of seals?

Once you find the main purpose, hold on to it. *Consciously keep it in mind throughout the entire lecture.* This way, you will be able to see how the rest of the class (examples, discussion, supporting evidence, graphs) fits together with the central theme.

Tip 5: Discern Your Teacher's Teaching Style

Notice the ways in which your teacher builds on the central theme of the lecture. What kinds of examples are used to support the main points? Are they personal experiences? Research studies? Problems from the textbook? Or other kinds of supporting evidence?

Also, *pay attention to the way your teacher organizes his or her presentations.* Are the lectures structured around *cause-and-effect* relationships? Or do they follow a *chronological order*? Are *compare-and-contrast* methods being used? Or are the lectures based more on *pros and cons*? Does the teacher promote *open-ended discussions* in class? Or does he or she prefer to teach *straight from the textbook*?

It is beneficial to know how your teacher thinks. If a teacher has a specific way of structuring daily lectures, it's likely that he or she will structure exams and grade assignments along similar lines. After all, the way a teacher organizes lecture material often reflects the way he or she organizes his/her thoughts.

Try to gain a basic understanding of how your teacher thinks, how he or she organizes the material. Once you do, you will know from which angle to approach your daily assignments and term papers and will have a better idea of what to expect on exams.

Also, keep in mind that different teachers have different teaching styles. For each class you will have to adjust your study methods. For example, if one teacher encourages lots of in-class participation, while another lectures straight out of a textbook, the way you study for exams should differ substantially.

Tip 6: Sit in the Front Row

It is important to choose your seat wisely. This little tip is much more significant than you may realize. Study after study shows a direct correlation between a student's academic performance and his or her seat location. *The optimal place to sit is in the middle section of the front row*. If you sit in this area, you won't be bothered by all the distractions going on in the room. Instead, you will zero in on the teacher and the content of the lecture.

Sitting in the front row also enables you to see and hear more clearly. This is especially useful if you have a teacher who writes on the blackboard, uses overhead transparencies, speaks in a soft tone, or is difficult to understand. If you sit in the middle or the back of the room, not only will you be more easily distracted, but you'll have a harder time seeing and hearing what's going on as well. Finally, *avoid sitting next to good friends or people you're physically attracted to*. Directly or indirectly, they may divert your attention away from the lecture.

All well and good . . . but there is more. Try this one on for size: once you have a clear view of the teacher, you'll be able to notice little nuances in his or her behavior that might clue you in on important points and possible test questions.

For example, I once had a professor who always (consciously or unconsciously) gave subtle hints when she was driving home a major point. She would either wink, nod, raise her eyebrow, enunciate more carefully, or repeat herself. Every time I noticed one of these clues, I paid special attention to what she was saying *at that moment*. And sure enough, those very points always appeared on the next exam. I got an easy A simply because I could tell which points she thought were important. *Such little nuances can only be noticed if you're sitting in front*.

Dr. Dae H. Chang of Wichita State University holds a high regard for students who sit in the front row. He explains, "I consider students who sit in the front to be more diligent. They impress upon me a commitment, an eagerness to learn—and I respect that. If these students have border-line grades at the end of the semester, I tend to give them the higher one. It's my way of rewarding them for their attentiveness."

So why in the world *wouldn't* a student sit in the front row?

Many students don't like being accountable. They think that if they hide somewhere in the back of the room, they won't have to be as prepared for class; they can daydream and fantasize to their heart's content without ever being noticed by the teacher; or they can write notes, chitchat, blow bubbles, or doze off.

Other students fear that if they sit in front, they will get called on to answer questions they may or may not be prepared to answer. No one likes to be put on the spot in front of the entire class, after all.

But it may surprise you to find that teachers do *not* usually call on students who sit in the front row, especially if the class is held in a lecture hall. Teachers tend to call on students whom they see at eye level. If you are sitting in the front row, you are well below the teacher's eye level. This means you probably won't be singled out to answer all your teacher's most wicked questions . . . but you will be noticed (through your teacher's peripheral vision), your face will be recognized, and you will be perceived as a good student.

So make it a habit to sit in the front row every day. When you do, you will find yourself involved in a productive chain of events. You will prepare yourself more *before class,* concentrate more *during class,* and understand the material more *after class*.

And the end result?

Great grades and a lot of knowledge. What more could you ask for?

Tip 7: Participate

Many teachers factor class participation into your final course grade. Sometimes a good 10–15 percent of your entire grade will be based on participation alone. That's a difference of one, even two letter grades.

So be sure to raise your hand and speak up in class. Make your interest in the subject known. Ask for clarification by the teacher when you need it. Pose intelligent questions. Share some knowledge. Make pertinent comments. But, whatever you do, <u>don't overdo it</u>.

Many academicians and college advisors suggest that you follow the "2 Q/C Rule"—meaning, you should offer at least 2 Questions or Comments in every class, every day. They say top students do this and that you must do the same in order to get good grades.

Extensive talks with college professors and straight-A students reaffirmed my own experiences on this matter. It is not necessary to follow any excessive rules for in-class participation. In fact, *too much* participation can result in negative consequences.

For example, if you religiously follow the 2 Q/C Rule, you may find yourself spending valuable class time pondering, manufacturing questions just for the sake of asking them. This may sidetrack your attention away from the lecture. You may be focusing more on *what you're going to say* and *how you're going to say it*—and focusing less on the content of the lecture. Remember what our fathers told us, "Speak only if you have something to say."

In most cases, one question or comment per class, perhaps one question or comment every *other* class (even less in some classes) is more than enough to display interest and involvement and to earn high participation points. You don't have to be a brown-nosing teacher's pet to get a good participation grade.

The rule of thumb is: *The smaller and more discussion-based a class is, the*

more you should participate. The larger, lecture-based classes normally won't require as much. Still, you should always participate, regardless of how the class is structured. If speaking up in class doesn't come easily for you, chapter 5, "Expanding Your Comfort Zone," may be of great help.

Tip 8: Take Effective Notes
This is a big one. So big, in fact, that the next chapter has been devoted entirely to this topic. Be sure to check it out—it will tell you all you need to know about effective note taking.

Sources

Green, Gordon W. *Getting Straight A's.* Secaucus, N.J.: Lyle Stuart, 1985.
Gross, Ronald. *Peak Learning.* Los Angeles: Jeremy P. Tarcher, 1991.
Pauk, Walter. *How to Study in College.* 3d ed. Boston: Houghton Mifflin, 1984.
Robinson, Adam. *What Smart Students Know.* New York: Crown, 1993.
Starke, Mary C. *Strategies for College Success.* 2d ed. Englewood-Cliffs, N.J.: Prentice-Hall, 1993.

College   © Dan Killeen

EFFECTIVE NOTE TAKING

It is the disease of not listening,
the malady of not marking,
that I am troubled withal.

SHAKESPEARE

Every college student—male or female, young or old, brilliant or ordinary—spends an exorbitant amount of time *taking notes*. Throughout your educational career you may spend well over two thousand hours engaging in this pen-to-pad activity.

The importance of effective note taking cannot be overemphasized. Teachers cover the most important material in class and usually develop their tests based on that material. If you have a good set of notes at your fingertips, exam preparation will be a breeze.

Class notes are a valuable study tool. They serve as the nucleus for good grades. We all know that, yet it's amazing how few college students ever receive any training in this all-important area. There is an optimal way to take notes—a simple, straightforward method that many students know *nothing* about.

And how about YOU? Does your note-taking technique need to be strengthened?

To be an effective note taker you must have some semblance of a game plan. That's what this chapter will provide for you—a series of proven strategies you can use immediately to sharpen your note-taking skills and improve your grades.

As you develop your skills, you will take your in-class experiences to a new level. You'll develop superior listening habits and will become more productive in your classes. You'll become an expert at discerning and writing down essential facts. And you'll be much better prepared for exams. These new skills should have a positive effect on your GPA and on the quality of your overall education.

▲

A Matter of Memory

The simple act of writing down information can boost your memory for the material by upwards of 200 percent!

Studies indicate that you will remember over three-quarters of the information if you write it down. If you don't, you will only remember much less than half, even less than a quarter. That's a huge difference.

Plus, if you write down the important material, you will always have a permanent record of the lecture, which you can refer to at any time. A good set of notes protects you from the inevitable process of forgetting.

Put Skeletons in Your Notebook

The field of anatomy teaches us that the human skeleton comprises between 5 and 15 percent of total body weight. The same premise can be applied to your class notes.

The purpose of note taking is to recreate (in written form) the fundamental structure, the basic outline, the skeleton of each lecture.

Generally, an effective set of notes will represent 5–15 percent of the professor's spoken words. It is usually best to stay within this statistical range.

You see, writing down entire lectures word for word is an ineffective way to take notes. Following this strategy will only net you a mile-high pile of monologue. By the same token, a batch of skimpy, insufficient notes has even less value than the paper it was printed on. Effective note taking is as much an art as it is a skill.

Your notes need to be *succinct* while being *thorough, concise* while being *comprehensive*. Each set of notes should represent a skeleton outline of the lecture. All of your teacher's main ideas need to be recorded for later study. When you take notes, use an outline format. This means that all main topics should be followed by indented subgroups. Outline format follows this form:

I. FIRST MAIN TOPIC
    A. First Subtopic
        1. examples and details

II. SECOND MAIN TOPIC
    A. Second Subtopic
        1. examples and details

. . . and so on . . .

This skeleton-producing technique helps to create effective notes. Following this format, you should more easily develop a thorough understanding of the entire lecture.

So take notes effectively by filling your notebook with skeletons.

Now then, let's move on to the eight proven strategies for effective note taking . . .

Effective Note-Taking Strategies

Tip 1: Preread the Day's Assignment
The most effective notes are taken when you already have a basic understanding of the day's lecture material. That's why it is so important to familiarize yourself with the material *before* class. Follow your syllabus and read ahead; be a step ahead of the other students. You will have an easier time following the progression of each lecture, which will boost your level of understanding for the lesson.

Tip 2: Get Back to the Basics
To be a good note-taker you have to be fully prepared for each class. Bring all essential supplies with you every day, without fail—pen, pencil, textbook(s),

highlighter, notebook, three-ring binder, calculator, paper, ruler, glasses . . . whatever you need to be productive during class.

Other basics: (1) *HAVE A SEPARATE COLOR-CODED NOTEBOOK FOR EACH CLASS*; in each, write down your name, address, and phone number. (2) *WRITE LEGIBLY,* so you won't have to copy your notes later on. (3) *REFRAIN FROM DOODLING,* as it inhibits active listening. (4) *NEVER TAPE-RECORD LECTURES* (a terrible waste of time); you can always take notes correctly the first time around.

Tip 3: Classify Each Set of Notes

At the top of your first page of notes, write the following:

A. COURSE NUMBER
B. DATE
C. TOPIC OF LECTURE
D. PAGE NUMBER

Successive pages should be numbered and dated. This strategy safeguards you from disorganization.

Tip 4: Use Plenty of Space

Do not try to cram an entire lecture onto a single sheet of paper. Notebook paper is inexpensive and recyclable, so you don't have to be stingy with it.

Allot generous amounts of space in your notes. Skip spaces to display changes of topic. Use indentions to give your notes structure. Leave blanks for any words, examples, or details you may have missed or misunderstood (can always be filled in later on, after class). Leave wide margins to write down ideas, make changes, summarize major points, and/or keep a key of abbreviations used during each lecture.

Tip 5: Know When to Take Dictation

Certain segments of a lecture must be written down verbatim. *Record all enumerated items, rules, definitions, lists, and step processes word for word*; if you paraphrase this information, you may inadvertently change the meaning. Also, record everything your teacher writes or draws on the board. These items commonly show up on exams.

Tip 6: Use Abbreviations, Symbols, and Acronyms

Hey, can you think of an instructor who speaks really *quickly?* You know, someone who rattles off vital information at machine-gun speed. Someone who gives you a nasty case of writer's cramp at every lecture.

Taking thorough notes for such teachers can be a major chore. When

lectures are delivered quickly, we tend to write down notes quickly. And the faster we write, the messier our handwriting becomes.

But the problem is, when we try to scribble down every word our teachers spew forth, our notes end up looking like Charlie Brown chicken scratch and become utterly undecipherable. At the same time we add unnecessary bulk to our notes, waste valuable class time, and really learn what it means to *hate going to class*. The best way to combat this problem is to develop your own system for note taking. Abbreviations, symbols, and acronyms can be used to condense the quantity of your notes, while preserving readability. Remember what we established earlier: *our class notes are to be as concise as possible while still being thorough*.

So . . .

- ABBREVIATE COMMONLY USED WORDS. "Because," "with," and "without" can be replaced with "b/c," "w/," and "w/o," respectively.
- USE SYMBOLS IN LIEU OF WORDS. It's much easier to jot down a ">" than to write "is larger than"; "•" is quicker to write than "this is an important point."
- USE ACRONYMS FOR COMMON PHRASES. It's much easier to jot down "OD" or "SEC" than to write "Organizational Development" or "Securities Exchange Commission."

All right, now let's take a moment to put all this in perspective. Imagine that your teacher says,

"Okay class, this is an important event to remember. In the year 1988, more than sixty people were tragically killed when three Italian jets collided at a West German air show."

Instead of frantically writing down every word, you could condense it to:

"* In 1988, > 60 people killed when 3 Ital. jets collided @ a W. Ger. air show."

See the difference? This simple strategy allows you to capture the entire meaning of a 141–letter sentence using only 56 letters/symbols—a *massive* time and energy savings for you.

Let's do another. Now imagine that your teacher says:

"Okay class, this is an important point to remember. In the year 1989, Lieutenant Colonel Oliver North was indicted for his crimes in the Iran-

Contra scandal, and received a three-year prison sentence plus a one-hundred-fifty-thousand-dollar fine."

Try this one yourself. Grab a pencil and condense the sentence as best you can:

_____

_____

_____

Well? How did you do? Did it look something like this?

"* In 1989, Lt. Col. O. North indicted in Iran-Contra, recv'd 3-yr sentence + $150,000 fine."

If your first attempt at this strategy wasn't right on the button, don't sweat it. Effective note taking is a _skill_—and, just like any other skill, it improves with practice.

Apply this strategy to every lecture, and you will become an expert note taker before you know it. Your class notes will be clear, precise, and highly effective—which, in turn, will make exam preparation and rereading much easier for you. Plus, your recall will also be vastly improved, because your mind won't have to waste time mulling through unnecessary words.

Don't underestimate the value of this strategy. It is worth learning, especially considering the _hundreds of hours_ you spend each semester taking notes. If U use Abs, Ss, & Acs in your class notes, U'll C an ↑ in your GPA B4 2 long, QTII!

Tip 7: Review Your Notes Immediately after Class

Our memory for new lecture material fades rapidly. According to the Ebbinghaus Retention Curve, _we forget about half of new information after only twenty minutes_. And after one month's time, an astounding 78 percent of what we learned is forgotten, lost, gone with the wind.

These findings are significant. Statistically speaking, over 60 percent of all the forgetting that we do in an entire month transpires after within twenty minutes. Boy, talk about a crucial time in a student's memory. Those twenty little minutes right after class are golden.

The good news is, you can use this time to your advantage by simply reviewing your notes directly after each lecture. So DO IT! Make it a habit. _Instead of forgetting such massive amounts of information during those crucial_

minutes, you will actually strengthen your memory for the material. Come test time, you'll be sittin' pretty. Trust me.

But an immediate note review does more than enhance your memory. It also helps you clarify your notes. You see, it is easy to clear up questionable concepts and scribblings while the lecture is still fresh in your mind. But if you don't review your notes for weeks on end, you will have a hard time deciphering sections that were sloppily written or conceptually hazy.

This cannot be overemphasized: *always reread and edit your notes promptly after class.* Take some time to rewrite any scribbled words or sentences, underline possible test questions, fill in any incomplete thoughts, and reflect on the instructor's main ideas. Ensure that the lecture makes sense in your own mind.

It happens all the time—college students who implement this strategy achieve high GPAs. This is why many straight-A students recommend *not* scheduling classes back to back. Instead, schedule at least a half hour between classes. This will allow you to review your class notes at the most optimal of times.

Tip 8: Listen Actively

Dante once said, "He listens well, who takes notes." What was true in his time still applies today.

Active listening and effective note taking go hand in hand. You need to be adept at both in order to achieve academic excellence. If you skipped over chapter 18, go back and read it.

Useful Abbreviations, Symbols, and Acronyms

acctg	accounting	hist	history
vs.	against	* / imprt	important
&	and	↑	increasing, up
A	answer	∞	infinity
anthro	anthropology	info	information
archr	architecture	intro	introduction
assoc	association	→	leads to
@	at	<	less than
auto	automatic, automobile	LA	liberal arts
av	average	ling	linguistics
bkgd	background	mgt	management
b/c	because	mktg	marketing
b/o	because of	max	maximum
b/t	between	min	minimum

bio	biology	mill	million
bus	business	—	minus, negative
chem	chemistry	misc	miscellaneous
coms	communications	≠	not equal, different
compsci	computer science	#	number
cont	continued	org	organization
↓	decreasing, down	%	percent
def	definition	PE	physical education
D	demand	+	plus, positive, and
dept	department	polisci	political science
econ	economics	prb	problem
educ	education	prof	professor
eng	engineering	Q	question
=	equal, the same	?	question, uncertainty
est	estimate	S	supply
e.g.	example	∴	therefore
ff	following	2	two, to, too
4	four, for	U	university
←	from, prior to	H_2O	water
geogr	geography	w/	with
govt	government	w/o	without

Sources

Ellis, Dave. *Becoming a Master Student*. 6th ed. Boston: Houghton Mifflin, 1993.

Green, Gordon W. *Getting Straight A's*. Secaucus, N.J.: Lyle Stuart, 1985.

Pauk, Walter. *How to Study in College*. 3d ed. Boston: Houghton-Mifflin, 1984.

Robinson, Adam. *What Smart Students Know*. New York: Crown, 1993.

Starke, Mary C. *Strategies for College Success*. 2d ed. Englewood Cliffs, N.J.: Prentice-Hall, 1993.

Chicken Bird   © Ron DiCesare

GETTING IN THE MOOD:
HOW TO PSYCH YOURSELF UP FOR
EFFECTIVE STUDY SESSIONS

The readiness is all.

SHAKESPEARE

In order to get the most out of an activity, you have to be in the mood to do it. Think about it. *For any activity—watching a sad movie, eating French food, dancing, or making love—if you're not in the mood, you probably won't get much out of the experience.*

The same concept applies to studying. The only difference is, unlike most other activities, studying is something that you *have to do,* whether you are in the mood to do it or not . . . assuming, of course, that you hope to graduate someday!

Cognitive experts have found that your mood and your ability to learn are closely intertwined. Mood and emotion also have a profound effect on levels of concentration and memory. For example, if you have been up all last night talking with your roommate about dating and relationship issues, studying for tomorrow's sociology exam can be a gut-wrenchingly agonizing ordeal.

It is important to put yourself in a resourceful state of mind before your study sessions. Doing so will enable you to absorb more information in less time.

Fortunately, the process of getting in the mood (er, for *studying,* that is) is a lot easier than you may think.

This chapter will show you how to prime yourself for effective study sessions. It offers four practical methods for psyching yourself up and getting into a focused mindset. Try one or more of these simple methods next time you sit down to study. Use the ones that work for you and see what a difference they can make.

Remember: well begun is half done.

Let's begin.

▲

Four Ways to Get in the Mood

1. Clear Your Mind Through Relaxation

Studying is easy if you begin with a clear mind. If you don't, you may become easily sidetracked.

Here's how to clear your mind for effective study:

- FIND A QUIET PLACE TO STUDY.
- MAKE SURE YOU WILL NOT BE INTERRUPTED FOR THE DURATION OF THE STUDY SESSION (turn on your answering machine, turn off the phone ringer, tell your roommates not to disturb you, etc.).
- GET COMFORTABLE IN YOUR CHAIR; SIT NATURALLY (do not fold your arms across your chest or cross your legs; keep all of your joints bent slightly to maximize blood flow and oxygen circulation).
- CLOSE YOUR EYES.
- TELL YOURSELF, "It's time to study now. I will not daydream or think about any problems. I will deal with them *after* I study."
- BREATHE SLOWLY AND DEEPLY (inhale through the nose for 8–12 seconds, exhale out of the mouth for 8–12 seconds).
- FOCUS ONLY ON YOUR BREATHING (when distracting thoughts enter your head, eliminate them by refocusing your attention onto your breathing pattern).
- CONTINUE FOR 3–10 MINUTES.
- SLOWLY OPEN YOUR EYES.
- HIT THE BOOKS!

2. Boost Your Concentration

Students often have a hard time concentrating on their studies. I met a guy named Jack at Georgia State University who told me, "When I'm studying, I'm thinking about partying. And when I'm partying, I'm thinking that I should be back home studying. So when I'm studying, I'm not really studying and when I'm partying, I'm not really partying! My body's in one place, my mind is in another."

I introduced a simple technique to Jack—one that has worked for many other students like him—one that has helped him develop a greater concentration and focus. The technique is called TRATAK, which has its origin in Yoga.

TRATAK was developed centuries ago as a way for people to concentrate for a longer duration, with more intensity. And it has been used by people all over the globe ever since. Yoga practitioners use it. Zen and martial arts masters use it. Spiritual masters use it. You can too. Here's how:

First: CHOOSE A SIMPLE OBJECT TO FOCUS ON (such as a candle flame, pencil, or even your finger).

Second: STEADILY GAZE UPON THE OBJECT; FOCUS ALL OF YOUR ATTENTION ON IT. THINK OF NOTHING ELSE. THEN . . .

Third: CLOSE YOUR EYES AND VISUALIZE THAT OBJECT IN YOUR MIND'S EYE. CONCENTRATE AND TRY TO VISUALIZE EVERY MINUTE DETAIL OF THE OBJECT.

Fourth: REPEAT 3–5 TIMES.

TRATAK helps steady your mind and will prevent it from wandering. If you use this technique regularly, eventually your mind will be conditioned to concentrate whenever you sit down to study—just as your stomach has been conditioned to expect food at certain times of the day.

3. Think Positively

Thinking about a prior academic success or past achievement is an excellent way to get yourself in the mood for studying. If you have an old test or project that received an A, keep it handy so you can refer to it whenever you want.

Looking at your past achievements is inspirational. It encourages you to maintain a high standard for yourself and gives you an "I did it before, I can do it again" air of confidence.

4. Focus on Inspiring Words

Sometimes a little boost from an outside source can motivate us to study harder than we would on our own. Learning perspectives and ideas from respected people often provides a good source of motivation.

The following section consists of quotes from world leaders, philosophers, and top achievers who have reached the pinnacles of success in their lives. Before you begin studying, read one or two of their quotes. They will help put you in a resourceful frame of mind. You can even choose your favorite quote and pin it up on your wall or write it on the inside cover of your notebook, where you can see it often.

Quotes for Motivation, Inspiration, and Concentration

If you only care enough for a result, you will almost certainly attain it.
—*William James*

Success doesn't come to you . . . you go to it.   —*Marva Collins*

Always do your best. What you plant now, you will harvest later.
—*Og Mandino*

Let us train our minds to desire what the situation demands.   *Seneca*

Learning is a matter of attitude, not aptitude.   —*Georgi Lozanov*

The lure of the distant and the difficult is deceptive. The great opportunity is where you are.   —*John Burroughs*

What made me a champion? My father's coaching, training, and persistent encouragement paved the way. But it was something more: I was consistent over a long period of time because I never looked back, never dwelled on my defeats. I always looked ahead.   —*Chris Evert*

From a little spark may burst a mighty flame.   —*Dante*

He who considers too much will perform little.   —*Schiller*

The great pleasure in life is doing what people say you cannot do.
—*Walter Bagehot*

The great end of life is not knowledge but action.   —*Thomas H. Huxley*

There is no substitute for hard work.   —*Thomas Edison*

We can do anything we want to do if we stick to it long enough.
—*Helen Keller*

O! this learning, what a thing it is.   —*William Shakespeare*

Always bear in mind that your own resolution to succeed is more important than any other one thing.   —*Abraham Lincoln*

Desire creates the power.   —*Raymond Holliwell*

Our aspirations are our possibilities.   —*Robert Browning*

In the middle of difficulty lies opportunity.   —*Albert Einstein*

Destiny is not a matter of chance; it is a matter of choice. It is not something to be waited for; but, rather something to be achieved.
—*William Jennings Bryan*

All great achievements require time.   —*David J. Schwartz*

Most people give up just when they're about to achieve success. They quit on the one yard line. They give up at the last minute of the game one foot from a winning touchdown.   —*Ross Perot*

It is the constant and determined effort that breaks down all resistance, sweeps away all obstacles.   —*Claude M. Bristol*

He conquers who endures.   —*Persius*

Hit the ball over the fence and you can take your time going around the bases.   —*John Raper*

Some men have thousands of reasons why they cannot do what they want to, when all they need is one reason why they can.   —*Willis R. Whitney*

Success on any major scale requires you to accept responsibility. . . . In the final analysis, the one quality that all successful people have . . . is the ability to take on responsibility.   —*Michael Korda*

Hold yourself responsible for a higher standard than anybody else expects of you. Never excuse yourself.   —*Henry W. Beecher*

Nothing happens by itself. . . . It all will come your way, once you understand that you have to make it come your way, by your own exertions.   —*Ben Stein*

As human beings, we are endowed with freedom of choice, and we cannot shuffle off our responsibility upon the shoulders of God or nature. We must shoulder it ourselves. It is up to us.   —*Arnold J. Toynbee*

Mental skills get rusty from disuse. Learning of any kind cleans off rust, and restores the gears to fuller functioning.   —*Dennis Thompson*

There is a learner within you, able and confident, waiting to function freely, usefully, and joyfully.   —*Marilyn Ferguson*

The strongest principle of growth lies in human choice.   *—George Eliot*

Don't compromise yourself. You are all you've got.   *—Janis Joplin*

Compete against yourself, not others.   *—Peggy Fleming*

Sources

Carruth, Gorton, and Eugene Ehrlich. *American Quotations*. New York: Wings Books, 1992.

Padus, Emrika. *The Complete Guide to Your Emotions and Your Health*. Emmaus, Pa.: Rodale Press, 1992.

Igmee   © **David Estoye**

What if it were illegal to learn anything until you were 21?

CLASSROOMS WOULD HAVE BOUNCERS

PEOPLE WOULD BRAG....

CRAMMING WOULD TAKE ON A NEW MEANING

STUDYING GAMES

LIBRARY CRAWLS

HARD COURSES WOULD NEED SOME CHASER

OPTIMAL STUDYING

In a world that is constantly changing . . . the most important skill to acquire now is learning how to learn.

JOHN NAISBITT

Academic success depends on how well we study, not how much we study. This chapter was not written in the typical "you should study as much as you possibly can, and here's why . . ." way. Instead, it was created under the premise that *if we study smart, we don't necessarily have to study hard.*

A number of factors influence our effectiveness in school, such as innate learning ability, attitude, and drive. These are important qualities, no doubt about it. But overall, study habits are the most important foundation for good grades.

Even the most eager, hard-working student can make poor grades if he or she doesn't have a good set of study habits. In fact, students who study more than forty hours per week actually make *worse grades* than students who study less than forty hours per week. *The difference in our grades is made by the quality of our study sessions, not by the length, and not by the frequency.*

With the optimal study strategies described in this chapter, you can master your subjects and elevate your grades significantly—even if you are not a

particularly gifted student. And if you *are* a particularly gifted student, this chapter will help you become even better.

You are about to learn six strategies for optimal studying. Some of the ideas may be familiar to you, while others will be totally new and unique. The information presented here is based on decades of academic research, interviews with top students and professors around the country, and, of course, tons of personal experience.

So here they are. Let the grade-raising begin . . .

▲

Optimal Study Is a Matter of Willingness: Do You Have the Will to Do?

Not long ago I was determined to get straight A's. I had missed the mark by quite a bit the previous semester, but that didn't matter. I wanted straight A's, and that was that. Call it stubbornness. Call it good old-fashioned American idealism. But mine was the profile of a student who expected to get a 4.0 and was willing to do whatever it took to reach it.

And reach it I did.

That was my first 4.0 GPA in college, following a long line of 3.5's, 3.0's, even 2.5's. The moment I saw my report card, I stood motionless before the mailbox, grinning maniacally at those precious little digits and wondering what made the difference this time 'round. I mean, I had *always* wanted a high GPA, and I had always studied hard for my classes. For a good long while I wondered why the results of this semester were so much better than all of the others. Then it hit me.

Willingness. That was the key. It was my willingness to study that took me all the way to the top.

I had set a specific goal for myself and resolved to see it through, no matter what. If it meant studying until 3:00 A.M. every other night, I was willing; if it meant sacrificing some fun nights on the town in order to study, I was willing; if it meant hiring a tutor to help me get my toughest subject down pat, I was willing.

Instead of taking the attitude of "I *have to* study" (as I had done in prior semesters), I adopted one of "I am *willing* to study." I changed all of my "I have to's" to "I am willing to's." "I have to read forty pages of Geology" became "I am *willing* to read forty pages of Geology to reach my goal"; "I have to memorize ten Econ curves" became "I am *willing* to memorize ten Econ curves to reach my goal."

It was amazing how such a small shift in attitude created such a huge improvement in my studies and in my grades. I found that an hour of studying with a willful mind was worth more than three hours of forced, involuntary studying. And as a result I earned a perfect GPA and had a good time doing it.

The moral of the story: *all we really need to succeed academically is a will to do*. The will creates the way. Or, more to the point, the will creates the A.

You can develop a powerful will to do simply by focusing more on yourself—*your* goals, *your* standards, *your* intellect, *your* future . . . and less on everything else. Is this being egocentric? Yeah, maybe it is. But intrinsic motivation is what rears optimal study and success; so it pays to be true to it. In the wise words of author Steven R. Covey, "Your attitude determines your altitude."

Optimal Study Is a Matter of Timing: Are You an Early Bird or a Night Owl?

Each of us has a "peak time" during our day—a time when we feel most productive, most alert, most able to concentrate.

Some students are *early birds*—they can hop out of bed right at the crack of dawn refreshed and energetic, ready to conquer the world. They are highly productive in the mornings and early afternoons. But they tend to tire out by late evening.

Other students are *night owls*—they wake up sluggish and *drip* out of bed if it's too early in the A.M., and they take a half hour or so to feel alert. They are not nearly as productive in the mornings as they are in the late afternoons and evenings. But they can "burn the midnight oil" with vigor and stay awake until 1:00 A.M. or 2:00 A.M. without any problem.

Which are YOU? Let's find out.

Here is a slightly modified version of a true/false test developed by Professor Rita Dunn of St. John's University in New York. It will help you determine your peak times.

1.   I usually hate to get up in the morning ....T / F

2.   I usually hate to go to sleep at night ....T / F

3.   I wish I could sleep all morning ....T / F

4.   I stay awake for a long time after I get into bed ....T / F

5.   I feel wide awake only after 10:00 in the morning ....T / F

6.   If I stay up late at night, I get too sleepy to remember anything ....T / F

7. I usually feel a "low" after lunch .... T / F

8. When I have a task requiring concentration, I like to get up early in the morning to do it .... T / F

9. When I can, I do my most concentration-requiring tasks in the afternoon ..T / F

10. I usually start the tasks that require the most concentration after dinner ..... T / F

11. I could stay up all night .... T / F

12. I don't like going to school before noon .... T / F

13. I'd rather stay home during the day and go to school at night .... T / F

14. I like going to school in the morning .... T / F

15. I can remember things best when I concentrate on them
    a. in the morning .... T / F
    b. at lunchtime .... T / F
    c. in the afternoon .... T / F
    d. before dinner .... T / F
    e. after dinner .... T / F
    f. late at night .... T / F

CONSISTENCY KEY: PREFERRED FUNCTIONING TIME

Early Morning		Late Morning		Afternoon		Evening	
True	*False*	*True*	*False*	*True*	*False*	*True*	*False*
8	1	5	3	3	7	2	6
14	3	12	8	5	8	4	8
15a	5	15b	9	9	11	5	14
	10		10	12	13	10	
	11		11	15c	14	11	
	12		13	15d		13	
	13		14			15e	
						15f	

(Match your scores with the key above; a fairly equal distribution among all four categories means that the time of day or night at which you study doesn't make much difference.)

Another way to find your optimal study times is to conduct a little chronobiological experiment on yourself. Forgive the scientific mumbo-jumbo, please.

All this means is that you can pinpoint your most energetic hours on your own, without any fancy equipment, and without any know-it-all doctors sticking utensils in your ear, in your rear, or up your nose.

All you need is a fever thermometer.

Yes, a thermometer. Go out and get one for the purpose of this experiment; they are cheap and easy to use (just stick 'em under your tongue). The experiment is simple: take your own temperature at different times during the day, and write down the readings. Your peak hours will be those that have *higher* temperature readings.

Why is that so?

In *The Complete Guide to Your Emotions and Your Health,* Emrika Padus and the staff at *Prevention* magazine explain, "There are a few precious hours each day when all systems are go, your energy is at its peak, and your mind functions at its most alert. . . . When your body temperature reaches its peak, so do a number of other things: energy and alertness, physical performance, dexterity, and overall mental acuity."

In other words, *it is best to reserve your peak times for peak activities, such as exercising and, you guessed it, STUDYING.* Use your peak hours wisely. If you are an early bird, spend your mornings working on your most important study tasks—the ones that are most challenging for you and require the most concentration. If Philosophy 368 is your hardest class and there's a test coming up, hit those books when you are at your mental peak.

Use your nonpeak times for trivial tasks and minor responsibilities—you know, all the stuff that you've got to do sooner or later but doesn't require much brain power. Write those "sorry I haven't written in so long" letters to your friends back home. Run some errands. Do your laundry. Finish up that easy but time-consuming math assignment. Shop for groceries.

> *We all have times when we think more effectively, and times when we should not be thinking at all.*
>
> DANIEL COHEN

This strategy makes the process of learning easier and more natural for you. So never waste your high-energy hours on unimportant activities such as watching TV, chitchatting on the phone, or shooting pool. Save those leisure activities for your nonpeak times.

The beauty of college life is that we all have some say in the making of our daily schedules. Why not take full advantage of this privilege? Accommodate your body clock by reserving peak times for peak purposes. Your grades will sing your praises later.

Optimal Study Is a Matter of Scheduling: Do You Budget Time to Study?

In any given semester, you may be assigned to read through four to six textbooks—a couple thousand pages of learning and memorization, at least. That's a lot of work.

The best way to keep on top of it all is to establish a *sensible* study routine for yourself. Consult your weekly planner from chapter 24, "Time Management," and pencil in specific study sessions throughout the week (in accordance with your peak times, if possible).

Then, stick to your schedule.

Just as professional athletes perform at their best when they are conditioned through routine exercise regimens, we college students also learn best when we have a set study routine going.

The question is, How much should you study?

Many successful students swear by the *two-for-one punch*—a term representing the idea that you should study two hours *outside* of class for every hour you spend *inside* of class. If you are taking fifteen credit hours, you should study around thirty hours per week. Obviously, some classes require more study time and others require less. But in general, the *two-for-one punch* is a good, functional yardstick.

A word to the wise: be realistic in your plans. *Do not schedule ALL of your study hours into your planner at one time.* While time management is an important study aid, it becomes self-defeating when overdone. If you pencil in twenty or thirty hours of study time a week in advance, you may have difficulty sticking with your schedule, get frustrated, and eventually quit managing your time altogether.

A better and more practical method is to schedule only part of your required study time in advance. For example, a night owl could set aside two and a half hours of solid, uninterrupted studying between 10:30 P.M. and 1:00 A.M. each weekday. Other studying can be peppered in at varying times during the week, without following a tightly fixed schedule. The point is to *have a specific amount of time or course material budgeted exclusively for your studies each and every day.*

Optimal Study Is a Matter of Taking Study-Breaks: How Long Do Your Study Sessions Last?

Memory is developed in a fairly predictable fashion. Our brains function in such a way that the first and last items on a list will be more easily remembered

than items in the middle. These are the "primacy" and "recency" theories in action—we naturally remember *beginnings* and *ends* better than in-betweens.

What does this have to do with studying?

Lots. If you want to maximize your recall for the material you study, *don't study continuously.* Take breaks often. It is far better to have six thirty-minute study sessions with breaks in between than one continuous three-hour marathon session.

The key is to create as many beginnings and ends as possible without disrupting the flow of your studies. In his book, *Make the Most of Your Mind,* Tony Buzan suggests, "The ideal study time is between 10 and 45 minutes. This ensures that the beginning and end periods of recall are high, while also making sure that the middle period is not so long that it sags down."

Study breaks should be brief diversions of about two to five minutes. Use this time to take a "mental steambath." Skim through the campus paper, listen to your favorite song on a Walkman, grab a drink or snack, do some stretching exercises, flip through a magazine, or close your eyes and "just chill" for a bit.

This strategy will allow you to remember more of the information with less effort and less monotony. It will also give your mind the opportunity to rest while it absorbs the material it has been fed.

Optimal Study Is a Matter of Environment: Where Do You Study?

Another way to improve your studies is to create a Designated Study Area (DSA) for yourself in your own home. Regardless of where you live, it is important to have a specific area reserved for studying and nothing else.

The advantage of studying at home is that you can tailor your environment to fit your personal needs and learning style. Here are some ideas for creating an optimal study environment:

KEEP THE ROOM TEMPERATURE AT A COOL 68 DEGREES. Studying in slightly cooler temperatures improves concentration and memory.

STUDY FACING A BLANK WALL. Effective study is a result of concentration, of focusing wholeheartedly on the material at hand; arrange your desk so that you face a blank wall or a neutral background—it's all too easy to daydream or lose your train of thought when you're sitting across from a wall checkered with party pics and eye-catching posters or a window facing a swimming pool.

HAVE GOOD LIGHTING. Nothing produces mental fatigue faster than straining your eyes under insufficient light; make sure your DSA is well lit with high-watt soft-light bulbs (they don't produce as much glare on your books as normal bulbs). Also, endocrinologists and psychiatrists have established that natural sunlight has a more positive effect on mood than does artificial light; they suggest that we set up our DSAs next to (but not facing) windows and avoid studying under fluorescent lights.

KEEP EAR PLUGS HANDY. If you live in a noisy environment, put in some ear plugs (to decrease noise levels) or turn on a fan (to muffle and drown out distracting sounds).

ORGANIZE, ORGANIZE, ORGANIZE. Arrange your study area so that anything you could possibly need is within arm's reach; this will allow you to get settled in your DSA and study for long durations without having to get up to hunt for materials and supplies. Have everything on the list below close at hand:

- All of your textbooks and study guides
- All of your class folders and notebooks
- All of your old assignments, quizzes, and tests
- All necessary reference books, such as a dictionary, a thesaurus, an English grammar guide, etc.
- All writing utensils and supplies, such as pens, pencils, highlighter, calculator, ruler, compass . . .

Ah, but you have to take the bad with the good. Studying at home also has its disadvantages.

Dorm rooms, fraternities, sororities, apartments, and other places of residence can be terrible places to study, especially at night. Potential distractors abound: loud roommates, a tempting TV, a phone ringing off the hook, a hot new CD begging to be played, a comfy bed calling out your name, surprise visits from friends, parties in the hallways . . .

If you have a hard time concentrating at home, you still have plenty of other options. Here are some other good alternate places to study:

Libraries
Empty classrooms
Residence hall lounges
Coffee houses
24-hour restaurants
Campus union lounges
Studious friends' places
Church fellowship auditoriums

If you prefer studying in total solitude and silence, consider setting up shop in an empty classroom or in the stacks of your campus library. If you learn best in stimulating environments, try studying on the main floor of a library, in a dorm lounge, or in a coffee-house or a twenty-four-hour restaurant such as Denny's and Village Inn.

The main idea is that you either make or find an environment that supports you in your academic endeavors. As Professor Anita Skeen of Michigan State University says, "The space in which you study is your intellectual home. You need to feel comfortable there, physically, aesthetically, emotionally. Try to find or make it a place you want to seek out when the time comes for reflection and thought."

Optimal Study Is a Matter of "Just Doin' It": Are You a Chronic Procrastinator?

Just sitting down to study is more than half the battle. The problem is that with all the dozens of exciting things constantly vying for our attention, schoolwork is often the first to be "blown off." What we really need are some ways to control our urges to procrastinate.

So here they are. And don't put off reading this section!

1. Manage Your Time
The best way to handle procrastination is to prevent it from developing in the first place. Incorporate some good time-management skills into your daily life, and you'll beat procrastination at its own game. Check out chapter 24, "Time Management," for the entire rundown.

2. Break Down Big Jobs into Small Tasks
When we continually blow off an important task, the source of the problem usually isn't the task itself, but the way we approach it.

For example, reading forty pages of a biology text all at once is a daunting task—even for the most motivated of students. But fragmenting the assignment into a series of smaller minitasks of, oh, five or ten pages per sitting makes it tolerable, manageable, *do*able—even for the slothiest of students.

Nothing is particularly hard if you divide it into small jobs.

HENRY FORD

For any procrastination-inducing task, whether it is a fifteen-page research paper or a hefty reading assignment: *break it down into a series of bite-sized bits, and knock 'em off one by one, step by step.* It's the old divide-and-conquer trick.

And it works every time. The urge to procrastinate usually subsides as goals become easier to attain. Remember what we learned back in grade school, "Life by the yard is hard; life by the inch is a cinch."

3. Pinpoint the Source

Another way to prevent procrastination from interfering with your studies is to *catch yourself in the act.* Next time you find yourself putting off schoolwork, stop whatever it is that you're doing—turn off the TV, hang up the phone, put down that Nintendo joystick—and immediately ask yourself two questions.

First ask, "What excuse am I using on myself to blow off these studies?" Make yourself come up with the specific *reason* for your inaction. Then ask, "Okay, is this a bona fide reason to postpone my schoolwork? Or am I just procrastinating?"

While this may seem like a silly, out-of-the-way exercise, it serves an important purpose: *it forces you to be conscious of and honest about your situation.* If your excuse is justified, fine. But if it's one of those weak "I don't feel like it," "I'm waiting for inspiration," or "It's too nice outside today to study" excuses, you'll know you're really reaching . . .

> *The act of rationalizing our own behavior often motivates us to get off our butts and do what we need to do.*
>
> BILL MOMSEN, *Baylor University*

4. Rev Up Your Engine

To defeat procrastination, we have to understand it—a kind of *know thy enemy* approach to studying. And yes, procrastination should be regarded as an enemy of ours. It can sabotage our academic and personal goals and can leave us feeling, well, less than meritorious.

Consider that *procrastination is inversely related to self-esteem.* The more we procrastinate, the less value we place on our educations. And, education is a focal point of our lives as college students. Perpetually blowing off schoolwork says a lot about our views on our lives and the choices we make in them.

When studying becomes a constant uphill battle, it is time to take on a more radical approach. Here's a little exercise that should help you put the magic back into your studies:

Getting Back to the Basics

So you want to rev up your mental engine without getting burned out? Not a problem. A powerful way to motivate yourself is to simply reevaluate your reason for being at college in the first place.

This exercise attacks procrastination at its roots. As Miguel de Cervantes said, "Take away the cause, and the effect ceases."

On that note, fill in the blanks below:

I believe that going to college is bringing these advantages into my life right now:

_____

_____

_____

I believe that a quality education will provide me with certain advantages in the future; they are:

_____

_____

_____

What I want to be doing five years from now:

_____

_____

_____

How a quality education fits into this picture:

_____

_____

_____

My main professional goals are:

_____

_____

_____

The ways in which a quality education will help me reach these goals are:

_____

_____

_____

Some disadvantages that I would have to endure if I didn't get a quality education include:

_____

_____

_____

List three benefits that you would enjoy by "just doin' it"—buckling down and finishing up the task:

_____

_____

_____

Sources

Buzan, Tony. *Make the Most of Your Mind*. New York: Fireside, 1988.
Deese, James, and Ellin K. Deese. *How to Study*. New York: McGraw-Hill, 1994.
Gross, Ronald. *Peak Learning*. Los Angeles: Jeremy P. Tarcher, 1991.
Pauk, Walter. *How to Study in College*. 3d ed. Boston: Houghton Mifflin, 1984.
Robinson, Adam. *What Smart Students Know*. New York: Crown, 1993.

Chicken Bird   © Ron DiCesare

GETTING THE MOST OUT OF READING

Read, mark, learn, and inwardly digest.

BOOK OF COMMON PRAYER

A textbook is the standard teaching tool for most college classes. Sure, some professors will focus more on lecture material than on reading material. But the bottom line is that we all will be required to read and internalize hundreds upon hundreds of pages of text each and every semester.

Several strategies for college-level reading have been developed since the early 1940s. The good news is, the best of these strategies are proven, practical, and easy to learn. The bad news? Most students never learn anything about them.

But *we* will. We're about to improve our reading skills significantly. The contents of this chapter can catapult our GPAs up a notch or two and make the process of studying textbooks less arduous for us.

Keep in mind that reading, in and of itself, is a rather passive activity. In order to be truly effective in your reading sessions, you have to have an active mind and two active eyes. There must be a conscious purpose behind the act. I ask you: *how many times have you read an entire page—or even an entire chapter—only to realize later that, hey, you can't remember a thing that you just read?*

Read in ineffective ways, and your textbooks will become veritable sleeping pills. If you learn the study system and speed-reading techniques of this chapter, however, you'll (1) absorb textbook information easier, (2) remember it faster, and (3) retain it longer. Let's get started . . .

▲

The SQ3R System

Francis Robinson of Ohio State University developed this study system back in the 1940s to help students study more effectively. SQ3R is a simple five-step plan that we all can use to improve our study habits and make better grades.

S stands for SURVEY

The whole point of the survey is to familiarize yourself with the material before you read it. Most students read their textbook chapters word for word, from beginning to end. But that is not the most efficient way to study. It's best to begin each reading assignment by skimming over the high spots first.

This first step consists of reading

- The chapter title
- The chapter intro
- All section headings and subheadings
- All bold-faced terms and definitions
- *The end-of-chapter summary (most important)*
- The end-of-chapter questions

The survey gives you the "big picture" right off the bat, so that you immediately get to the heart of the chapter and see how all of its individual concepts fit together into an integrated whole. It also provides you with the right mental framework to help you make sense of new information.

Students who survey their textbook chapters *before* they read them comprehend and remember the material far better than students who don't. So always preview your chapters as a first step. This easy ten-minute exercise will save you tons of study and review time in the long run.

Q stands for QUESTION

A terrific way to boost your level of comprehension is to actively form questions from a chapter *as you read it*. One time-tested strategy involves turning every heading into a (who? what? where? when? why? or how?) question.

The heading "TWO PRINCIPLES OF SENSORY PHYSIOLOGY," for instance, can take the form of the question, "What are the two principles of sensory physiology?" The heading "LENGTH OF TIME IN A CHILD'S PREOPERATIONAL STAGE" can become "How long does it take for a child to pass the preoperational stage?" The heading "ACTIVE LISTENING" can become "How can I listen actively?"

As you form these questions, jot 'em down in a separate notebook or in the margins of your textbook. They will be extremely useful to you during exam preparation.

> *Asking a question is the simplest way of focusing thinking . . . asking the right question may be the most important part*
>
> EDWARD DE BONO

This second step, as easy as it is, makes all the difference between passive and active reading. When you read a chapter without actively forming questions, you may often find yourself on automatic pilot—you know, where your eyes just glide over words and your mind just skims over information passively. Not only is it hard to retain information by reading this way, but it's also an ineffectual and boring way to study.

But when you consciously form questions as you read, your mind is very active in the reading and comprehension process. You are, in effect, interacting with your text. This allows you to approach the material with an inquisitive, answer-seeking attitude, which, in turn, maximizes focus and concentration.

R¹ stands for READ

Now that you've surveyed the chapter and formulated a list of target questions, it's time to move on to the main event: *carefully reading the chapter and finding answers to those questions*. As you read each section, find its respective answer and write it down in a separate notebook. All main points of the text should be recorded on paper for later study. Do this for each section before you move on to the next.

R² stands for RECITE

Once you have an answer to a question you've formed, take a minute or two to recite that answer to yourself *in your own words*. Try not to go back to the textbook for help. Take a short break from your reading, close your book, and

quiz yourself. Really do this with your textbooks; it's a very productive exercise! This step prompts you to actively think about the material you've just read—which is exactly why professors use this technique so often in their classes.

You'll notice that teachers either (1) ask the class questions directly from the reading, (2) promote in-class discussions based on the material, or (3) assign written homework on the material. Their rationale for doing this is to have you verbalize—in your own words, not the author's—your knowledge of the subject. It is one of the most effective teaching techniques, and it benefits you in the following ways:

Enhances your memory of the material
Boosts your level of understanding
Gives you immediate feedback on your progress
Gives you practice in answering probable test questions

R³ stands for REVIEW

Many research findings indicate that we usually forget an incredible 90 percent of the material we read within twenty-four hours . . . that is, unless we review the material shortly after we've read it.

It is crucial to have periodic reviews of the main points from your reading (brief ten-minute review sessions are ideal). Cognitive experts say the first review should take place ten to fifteen minutes after you've finished your reading assignment. Successive reviews can be done a day later, a week later, two weeks later, one month later, and so on.

This step is crucial because it transfers information from short-term memory to long-term memory. Too many students read a chapter once, then forget about it until the night before an exam. They then have to refamiliarize themselves with the material, pull late-night cram sessions, and study harder than they need to. Don't fall into this trap! Study smart, and you don't necessarily have to study hard.

The Fourth R, REFLECT

Let's add another R to Francis's system, shall we? Here's a great quote from scholar and Nobel-Prize-winning physicist Dr. Hans Bethe:

There's a world of difference between proficiency and creativity. A student can become proficient by studying his textbooks and lecture notes, but he will never be creative until he attempts to see beyond the facts, tries to leap mentally beyond the given. He must reflect on the facts and ideas, for creativity comes only through reflection.

The message is crystal clear: always take some time to reflect on the material you read! Go beyond the textbook. Talking over the main points of a chapter with a classmate is a great way to reflect on the material.

To Highlight or Not to Highlight?
That Is the Question

Different students mark their textbooks in different ways. When it comes to highlighting a text, there is no best way—no universal standard that's appropriate for everyone.

Whether or not you highlight—and the extent to which you highlight— is entirely up to you. *Highlighting a text is a matter of personal preference.* Reading sessions are effective only insofar as you use a method that brings you the best results.

Thing is, there are tons of different methods.

Some students, for example, take extensive written notes from their texts and don't mark in their books at all. They extract all of the important information from a chapter and write it down in a separate notebook. That way, they don't have to refer to their texts later on. They can simply review their own set of notes and bypass the process of highlighting and rereading highlighted portions of their books.

Other students use a yellow marker to highlight the important points from their reading; when they study for exams, they go back to their texts and concentrate on the highlighted parts. Others use a ballpoint pen to underline the important parts of each chapter, circle key words and phrases, and write down questions and ideas in the margins of their books.

Some students use a combination of these methods. And some don't use any of the above.

Beyond taking some basic written notes from your text (the question-and-answer parts of the SQ3R system), there is no specific piece of advice to give. It's totally up to you to go through some trial and error to find the method that best suits your personal learning style. You may even decide that you learn best by just reading, and not writing or highlighting anything at all.

But if you *do* like to highlight in your books, please refer to the following suggestions:

1. Highlight a Sentence Only *After* You've Read It
Too many students highlight mechanically—that is, *while* they read. This almost always results in overhighlighting, which is a royal waste of time.

After you read a paragraph or section, go back and highlight the chief points. This strategy strengthens your memory for the chapter's main ideas, because your mind reabsorbs the material when you go back to highlight it. It's kind of like giving yourself an immediate review of the most important parts of the chapter.

2. Keep Your Highlighting to a Minimum

Generally, less than one-fourth of a chapter should be highlighted or underlined. Too much highlighting defeats the whole purpose of the exercise: to identify the key points of the chapter and distinguish them from the rest of the text.

3. Use a Yellow Marker, Not a Ball-Point Pen

Highlighted passages are easier to read than are underlined passages. Too many underlined passages create an unnecessary strain on the eyes; this can make you feel tired in a jiffy. Also, highlight with a yellow marker. Avoid using green, orange, or red highlighters; they are harder to read through.

Speed-Reading 101

Pascal once said, "When we read too fast or too slowly we understand nothing." Before we move on, keep in mind that speed is never as important as comprehension. You'll always be better off reading at a slower pace and understanding the material fully than reading swiftly and understanding little.

Still, speed-reading has its place in college. We all have tons of reading to do and not a lot of time in which to do it. If you want to plow through your assignments with greater comprehension, give these five techniques a try.

First, "You Gotta Feel the Need . . . the Need for Speed"

If you want to read faster, read faster. That sounds terribly obvious, I know. But you'll be surprised: making a conscious effort to read faster is usually all it takes to significantly boost your rate of reading.

If you are a particularly slow reader, make a deliberate attempt to read your books a bit more rapidly than usual (experiment right here and right now, if you want). Force yourself to pick up the pace just a notch. This will put a spark in your reading and benefit your studies in two ways:

First, *your mind tends to wander when you read slowly*; this weakens your ability to retain and comprehend information. When you read faster, you're more active and more alert—so you stay in tune with the material. Second,

slow reading is boring reading; and when you're bored, you're more prone to blowing off reading assignments or falling asleep. Rapid reading helps prevent these problems because it stimulates the eyes and mind.

Remember that speed-reading starts with *intent*. If you make a conscious effort to read faster, chances are you will. The next way to step up your reading speed is to make sure you . . .

Stretch Your Sight

It may surprise you to find that while you read, your eyes do not glide along the lines on a page in a continuous, smooth, and flowing manner. Instead, your eyes *hop* across each line in a series of stop-and-go movements called *saccades*.

After each saccade, your eyes actually come to a complete stop, called a *fixation*. This is where your eyes fixate on a group of words, usually one or two at a time, and internalize them before moving on. Amazingly, all of this happens within a fraction of a second, and it occurs thousands of times each time you read a chapter.

Diagrammed, the process looks something like:

[In a] [nutshell,] [this is] [the way] [your eyes] [fixate] [on words]
[while you] [read.]

The trick to speed reading, then, is increasing the number of words you take in per fixation. If you can double the number of words you see at each "eye stop," you can double the speed at which you read. The way to do this is to gradually expand your peripheral vision—which affects the number of words your eyes can fixate on at one time.

But before we get to that, let's take a moment to test the present capacity of your peripheral vision. Focus on the dot above the center mark of each line—do not move your eyes or read horizontally—and see how much of each line your eyes can take in.

•

I

•

wonder

•

how many

•

words you can

•

take in with each

•

eye fixation. The more

•

the better, if you want to

•

boost the rate of your reading.

Average readers can read the first two, maybe three, lines without much difficulty. Expert readers with highly developed peripheral vision can get to the fifth, six, and seventh lines. No matter where you are now, you can take steps to increase your peripheral vision and boost your reading speed.

For example, if your eyes normally fixate at this rate:

[I'll be] [able to] [read] [faster] [with a] [little] [practice.]

you could work at increasing your fixations to

[I'll be able] [to read] [faster with] [a little] [practice.]

and eventually

[I'll be able to] [read faster with] [a little practice.]

The trick here is to imagine a small dot above or in between the group of words you want to see at each fixation:

    •   •   •

[I'll be able to]   [read faster with]   [a little practice.]

By the way, notice the difference between how many stops your eyes make with the above example (only three) and with the example below (seven):

•   •   •   •   •   •   •

[I'll be] [able to] [read] [faster] [with a] [little] [practice.]

If you can increase the range of words you see at each fixation, you will be able to take in more information in less time, and with less strain. Unfortunately, there are no hocus-pocus formulas for increasing peripheral vision. Just like anything else, speed-reading ability comes from practice.

The best and easiest way to get practice is to use this technique on easy reading materials with narrow columns—newspaper and magazine articles are ideal. As you begin practicing this technique, don't force yourself to read too quickly. Let your skills build gradually. Once you get good, then you can apply these skills directly to your textbooks.

Don't Subvocalize

Contrary to popular belief, being a slow reader does not mean you're a slow thinker. If you read slowly, that just means somewhere along the line between kindergarten and college, you developed a habit of *subvocalizing* words as you read them.

Subvocalizing means that, in your head, you "mentally hear" the words you read. For instance, if you read this sentence e x t r e m e l y s l o w l y, you'll notice that you can "mentally hear" the sound of every word. That's subvocalizing—it eats up time like you wouldn't believe.

The mind works much faster than the mouth; and we *think* much faster than we *talk*. When we take time to vocalize or subvocalize every word, we immediately put our mental engines into a lower gear. Naturally, it takes time for our subvocalizations to catch up with our minds. When we control our subvocalizations, we can often double our reading speed without losing our comprehension.

The key here is simply to be aware of the times when you subvocalize. When you notice that you're mentally hearing every word you read, consciously pick up the pace in your reading, and gradually you'll break the habit.

Vary Your Rate of Reading

When it comes to reading textbooks, flexibility is just as important as speed. Advanced students have learned to adjust their reading rate to accommodate the material at hand. For example, *The Great Gatsby* would not be read at the same pace as an upper-level technical thermodynamics textbook.

This makes perfect sense, when you think about it. Books vary in complexity; and so do the individual sections within a book. Reading everything at the same pace is ineffectual.

There are two main components that should affect your reading speed. They are:

1. Your objective for reading
2. The complexity of the material

So, in general:

READ AT A SLOWER RATE WHEN YOU COME ACROSS . . .

- Unfamiliar words and/or ideas
- Technical info
- Abstract concepts
- Bold-faced material

- Poetry, philosophy, and lyrical material
- Key facts and ideas (those you need to remember in detail)
- Complex and/or unusual sentence structures (such as those found in Shakespearean plays)

READ AT A FASTER RATE WHEN YOU COME ACROSS . . .

- Easy concepts
- Familiar material
- Recreational reading
- General info
- Simple examples and vignettes

Remember to be flexible in your reading. Learn to distinguish the important material from the unimportant, the easy-to-grasp material from the hard-to-grasp . . . and adjust your reading speed accordingly. This is a powerful technique, one that will help you get the most out of your texts.

Some books are to be tasted, others to be chewed, and some few to be chewed and digested.

FRANCIS BACON

Eliminate Interference

In order to read both rapidly *and* effectively, you have to be able to "speak the language" of each textbook. In order to read chemistry, you've got to be able to speak the language of chemistry. In order to read economics, you've got to be able to speak the language of economics.

Each textbook has its own language style, complete with its own unique jargon and terminology. But there's the glitch: when you come across an unfamiliar word in your reading, either your reading speed slows down big time, or you begin to pay less attention to the material; that's natural.

As you read your textbooks, you're not going to know the meaning of every word. The problem is, you really break the flow of your reading when you stop at every unfamiliar word to look it up in the dictionary. This is a terrible predicament, which usually makes your mind totally shut off.

What's the solution?

Try circling all of the unfamiliar words you encounter with a pencil or ballpoint pen, then continue reading. When you finish the entire chapter, jot down those circled vocabulary words in a separate notebook. Then look up their definitions and write them down. Finally, go back through the text to see how those words are being used and applied. This will give you a firm understanding of important new vocabulary.

Sources

Ellis, Dave. *Becoming a Master Student*. 6th ed. Boston: Houghton Mifflin, 1993.

Gross, Ronald. *Peak Learning*. Los Angeles: Jeremy P. Tarcher, 1991.

Pauk, Walter. *How to Study in College*. 3d ed. Boston: Houghton Mifflin, 1984.

Robinson, Adam. *What Smart Students Know*. New York: Crown, 1993.

Starke, Mary C. *Strategies for College Success*. 2d ed. Englewood Cliffs, N.J.: Prentice-Hall, 1993.

Making the Grade © Bob Berry

HOW TO
WRITE A-GRADE PAPERS

Composition is, for the most part, an effort of slow diligence and steady persever-ance, to which the mind is dragged by necessity or resolution.

SAMUEL JOHNSON

Writing is one of the most important skills we can develop in college. In many classes, up to 40 percent of the grade will be determined by essays, reports, and term papers. But writing college-level papers is hardly an easy task. In fact, it can be an uphill battle . . . unless, of course, we have a good writing procedure under our belts.

If you have never learned a writing procedure for producing papers, then you may find yourself struggling excessively in your efforts only to earn average grades. But if you learn and follow a proven procedure, lo and behold, you'll generally end up with excellent grades.

The process begins with an idea for a paper and ends with a fat, juicy A. There are obstacles, however, between the idea and the ideal. In what follows we'll learn how to overcome these obstacles with time-tested strategies, common sense, and a little insight into our teachers' expectations.

We all have taken—or are currently taking—an English composition course. English professors in particular offer a wealth of information on written composition—how to avoid common errors in language and grammar

usage, how to write a thesis statement, how to footnote properly, how to produce a bibliography and title page . . . but rarely do they educate students on *how* to write papers effectively. In short, they teach the mechanics of good writing, not the process.

This chapter seeks to fill this educational gap; it is devoted exclusively to the writing process. Most students find the prospect of writing a paper less intimidating when they view it as a series of steps. So the task is broken down into fourteen simple steps that will guide you through every phase of the writing process. Follow the format presented here, and you will produce outstanding papers every time.

▲

The First Phase: Get the Ball Rolling

Step 1: Choose a Topic

Sometimes college professors assign topics for us to write about. But more often than not we are given the freedom to select our own. If your teacher allows you to choose a topic, then keep the following four tips in mind:

- *CHOOSE A TOPIC THAT IS INTERESTING TO YOU.* Personal interest is the most powerful motivating force in writing a paper. You will be spending many hours working intimately with just one topic; so make sure that you have—or can develop—a strong sense of interest in it. Boring topics, even if they're easy to tackle, rarely inspire high quality work.
- *CHOOSE AN ORIGINAL TOPIC.* As a general rule, teachers look for originality, and they tend to reward it with a higher grade.
- *CHOOSE A TOPIC WITH WHICH YOU ARE FAMILIAR.* You can produce an outstanding paper much more easily if you already have some experience with or knowledge of the subject on which you write.
- *CHOOSE A TOPIC THAT ISN'T TOO BROAD OR TOO NARROW.* Make sure that the scope of your topic is appropriate to the length requirement of the assignment.

> HOT TIP: *Choose a topic that you can build on later.* What exactly does this mean? Well, let me illustrate by way of example. ⟶

I was once assigned to write a term paper—with a topic of my choosing—for a business management class. At that time I already knew that I was going to be taking a managerial ethics class the following semester. So I decided to write my term paper on "Ethical Management Issues of the 90s."

The bottom line is that I was able to use the same research material for two classes and build upon the foundation I had laid earlier. In fact, half of my managerial ethics term paper was finished before I even enrolled in the class!

Take it from me, this strategy can save you literally dozens of hours of research and writing. With a little forethought and planning, you can easily double the value of your research. Plus, being aware of this fact gives you incentive to work harder because you realize that your efforts in the present will save you tons of research time and toil in the future. But never use the same paper for two classes.

Step 2: Get Your Teacher's Stamp of Approval

If you know that the topic you have chosen will be acceptable to your teacher, then go to step 3. But if you have any doubts whatsoever, make an appointment with your teacher and talk it over with him or her. Get some feedback and take any and all suggestions to heart before you actually begin working.

Step 3: Make a Date with the Library

After you decide on a topic, it will be time to make a trip to your campus library to do some preliminary research. This is the first major step toward completing your paper. And, thankfully, it's a very easy step to take.

Your purpose during this first visit is neither to hunt for specific data nor to actually begin writing your paper. *Your sole mission at this point is simply to get some basic, general background information on your topic.* Comb through the reference section of the library, scan the computer catalog files, or ask a librarian to help you find a list of sources.

As you locate and peruse these sources, make photocopies and/or take notes of pertinent information. You may choose to take notes on regular notebook paper, or you may opt to take notes on 4 x 6 index cards. Regardless of the method you use, be sure to always keep a running bibliography of your sources.

Record the following information for each source:

- The title
- The name of the author(s)
- The publishing company and location
- The publishing date
- The name of the journal, magazine, etc.
- Applicable page number(s)
- The edition, number, and volume

Here is an example of basic notes taken on a 4 x 6 index card:

(side A)

Providing a panoramic perspective on American extremism from the earliest days of the republic, the book is divided into thematic chapters on race, politics, religion, and economics.

(side B)

—*Extremism in America: A Reader*
—Lyman Tower Sargent
—New York University Press
—New York, NY
—1995

Step 4: Have a "Brainstorming Jam Session"

Now that you have some good background information, the next step is to brainstorm for ideas. Brainstorming is an essential part of the writing process because it helps you tap into fresh ideas, formulate new approaches, uncover new questions, and find innovative solutions. In a word, this step sparks your creative juices.

How do you have a brainstorming jam session?

Easy. Get out a couple sheets of paper (or log on) and jot down every thought related to your topic as it enters your mind; don't hold anything back. Take a full fifteen minutes or so to free associate on paper or screen. Let the right (creative) side of your brain take over and run the show for a while.

The secret of an effective brainstorming session is to let loose mentally; your goal is to generate a constant flow of ideas. So write rapidly and continuously, and don't worry about the quality of your ideas as you write. After you have depleted your creative juices, sit back, relax, and look over all of your ideas. Then x-out the really wacky ones and circle the ones you think you'll be able to use.

Step 5: Make a Tentative Outline of Your Paper

By now you should have a pretty good sense of (1) what your paper will be like, (2) the position you will take in writing it, and (3) several main points that you would like to address. The natural next step is to get organized by sketching a simple outline of your ideas.

A good outline usually follows a standard format such as:

    I. MAIN POINT
      A. Facts and Details
        i. Example

B. Facts and Details
   i. Example
   ii. Example
II. MAIN POINT
  A. Facts and Details
     i. Example
  B. Facts and Details
     i. Example
     ii. Example
  C. Facts and Details
     i. Example
III. MAIN POINT
  A. Facts and Details
     i. Example . . . and so on . . .

Notice that *facts and details* are indexed under *main points* and that *examples* are indexed under *facts and details*. This is the most widely favored structure for formal written composition. Most teachers prefer this format because it categorically satisfies a number of criteria—such as clarity, brevity, and solid organization. This translates into a higher grade for you.

As an example, here is the tentative outline that I used in writing this chapter:

I. INTRO
II. "GETTING STARTED"
  A. Choose a topic
     i. hot tip (research)
  B. Check It with Your Teacher
  C. Go to the Library
  D. Brainstorm for Ideas
  E. Make an Outline
  F. Take a Break
III. "MOVING ON TO THE MAIN EVENT"
  A. Go to the Library Again
     i. list of supplemental sources
     ii. hot tip (get sources early)
  B. Write the Rough Draft
     i. hot tip (introduction)
  C. Take Another Break
  D. Revise Your Draft
     i. use grammar guides
     i. hot tip (strategic words)

IV. "WRAPPING IT UP"
  A. Proofread Your Work
  B. Make Your Final Draft
    i. use cotton fiber paper
  C. Hand It in Promptly
  D. Reward Yourself

Remember that you are producing a *tentative* outline, subject to change. As you do your actual research and writing, you will probably modify it. You may decide to add or delete ideas or change the order in which you present them.

So keep this outline simple. You don't have to spend an inordinate amount of time on this step. Just sketch out a rough outline so that you can develop a sense of direction. Even if you feel like you know exactly how you want to write your paper, go ahead and make an outline anyway. It will be your guiding light as you produce your first draft.

Step 6: Take a Breather

The minute you get this far, stop working and take a well-deserved break. Get away from your paper completely for a full day or so. This will allow the subconscious part of your mind time to work—which, in turn, will help you approach your researching and writing from a clear, fresh perspective.

The Next Phase:
Write Away

Step 7: Gather Your Sources

Very rarely will you be assigned to write a paper that doesn't require any research. In most cases you will need to research a topic in great detail before you can demonstrate expertise through your writing. This will call for subsequent trips to the library to round up a number of sources. *Your job at this point is to extract specific details, hard facts, examples, and ideas from those sources.*

Be sure to cultivate a wide range of sources as you conduct your research. Instead of merely referring to standard textbooks and library books (as most students do), broaden your research and augment your bibliography with some of these supplementals:

- Academic journal articles
- Newspaper articles

- Trade books
- Magazine articles
- Audio-cassettes
- Encyclopedias
- Interviews
- Quotations from experts
- The Internet
- Primary archives

Using a variety of sources is a necessary component of any A-grade paper. Why? First of all, it allows you to draw on and learn from a vast array of perspectives on your topic. This will extend your expertise, which will show through in your writing.

Second, it will make a positive impression on your teacher and boost your grade. College professors favor papers that are inclusive and comprehensively written. You will get a better grade if your work conveys the message that you've researched your topic thoroughly and have consulted an impressive cross section of sources. Remember that credibility is established not only through the written word but also through a visual medium: the bibliography at the end of your paper.

HOT TIP: *Be a bit self-centered and gather your sources from the library as early as possible.* As the semester winds down, students compete for books and journals at their school libraries. Don't get left out in the cold. There is nothing worse than going to the library for research only to find that all the best sources have already been checked out.

Step 8: Write Your First Draft
Okay, now that we've gotten all of the preliminaries out of the way, it is time to make a rough draft. Keep your notes, your index cards, your sources, and your outline handy, and get writing!

At this stage in the process, no one is expecting you to produce an eloquent, Pulitzer-Prize-winning, professionally written masterpiece of grammatical and stylistic perfection. There's no need to set your expectations too high in step 8; in fact, don't worry about grammar guidelines, style, or form at all just yet. Just concentrate on filling in the basics of your outline.

The point of writing a first draft is simply to get your major thoughts down on paper. It doesn't really matter how choppy your writing is right

now, since you'll be setting aside time to polish it up later. For now, just take this cardinal rule of writing to heart: always focus on *what you are going to say* before you focus on *how you are going to say it.*

HOT TIP: *Write the introduction of your paper after you've finished writing the main body and conclusion.* Inevitably your paper will take new shifts and turns as you research your topic in greater depth. You will naturally come up with new ideas, opinions, and arguments as you write your rough draft. In fact, the entire direction of your paper could change during this period. That's why it is best to write the introduction after you already know how your paper has turned out. Blaise Pascal put it perfectly years ago: "The last thing one knows in constructing a work is what to put first."

Step 9: Take Another Breather

Congratulations, you've finished your rough draft. Now a short vacation is in order. Leave your paper alone for a full day or two. This time away will do more than provide a mental reward for your hard work; it will also serve a practical purpose.

You see, it is common to get so wrapped up in the details and specifics of writing a rough draft that you lose sight of the big picture of your work (the overall purpose of the paper). Metaphorically speaking, *you need to step away from the trees in order to see the forest.* After taking an extensive break from your first draft, you will be able to apply a fresher perspective, better judgment, and more objectivity to the next step . . .

Step 10: Review, Revise, and Rewrite

Ah, revision time. Keep in mind that reviewing your work means just that: reviewing your work—looking at it a second time, a third time, and even a fourth time, if necessary. *A terrific way to review is to read your paper aloud.* This will help you judge your paper on its overall readability and smoothness.

Professional writers follow what's called a revision process for editing and polishing up their work. While this may sound complicated, it's really not. A revision process is a simple three-step procedure for ensuring high-quality final drafts. Obviously, the length of your paper will determine the amount of time you will need to spend revising. But, by all means, allocate plenty of time to this cause; grade-wise, it'll always be worth the effort.

The first step of the process is to review your draft and check for content. Does the paper address all of the points in your outline? Are your main arguments

substantiated with supporting evidence, examples, and quotes? Did you explain your topics and subtopics fully? Did you make use of a good cross-section of sources? Does the paper have a distinct introduction, thesis statement, main body, and conclusion?

Next, review your draft again and <u>check for organization and flow</u>. Does your paper read naturally? Are the transitions between sentences and paragraphs smooth? Is the overall structure of your paper clear, straightforward, and consistent? Did you address your main points in a logical sequence?

Finally, review your draft one more time and <u>check for grammar and style</u>. Are there any sentence fragments or misspelled words? Did you cite sources, construct footnotes or endnotes, and use quotations correctly? Are any paragraphs awkwardly structured or hard to understand? Did you misuse big, fancy words in an attempt to sound brilliant? Did you adhere to all of your teacher's writing and structural requirements?

As I mentioned earlier, this isn't a chapter about the mechanics of written composition. There are several resources, however, that you can check out from your school library or buy in a bookstore that will assist you in this regard. Three of the most popular books among college students are *The Elements of Style* by Strunk and White, *The MLA Handbook for Writers* by Gibaldi, and *Webster's Standard American Style Manual*. Any of these would be an excellent investment in your college career, especially if the classes in your major require lots of written work.

HOT TIP: *As you review your paper, look for a few places in which you can interject some of your teacher's favorite words and catch-phrases.* What's the rationale behind this strategy? Well, think about it this way. As a writer, you have to take into consideration your audience. The audience for your paper is a single person (your professor), who plays a dual role (reader and grader).

By *sparingly* using some of his or her language in your writing, you will give his or her ego a positive stroke without coming across as a sycophant. Professors are only human, after all. They want to believe that you pay close attention in their lectures and that their teachings have had an impact on you. On a subconscious level they seek validation to verify their effectiveness as teachers. Provide some of this validation, and you and your paper will be regarded more favorably. Although ideally your paper will stand on its own, it never hurts to write it in a way that gets you on your teacher's good side.

The Final Phase:
Wrapping It Up

Step 11: Get an Objective Opinion
Now it's time to have a friend or classmate proofread your paper for coherency, readability, and proper mechanics. Often an objective, neutral third party will be able to offer some ideas for improvement and catch any piddly grammatical mistakes that you may have missed. Always be open to constructive criticism, and make modifications as you see fit.

Step 12: Print Out a Beautiful Final Draft
When it comes to college-level papers, teachers grade on presentation as well as content. If you hand in a sloppy, handwritten, Coke-stained paper on crinkled pages, you won't have a prayer for getting an A—regardless of how highly original, intelligently written, thorough, and grammatically flawless your work may be. To most teachers, the physical appearance of a paper is a reflection of its quality.

To make your paper stand out and look like a class act, follow your teacher's written guidelines to a T. Also, print out your work on standard-size (8½ x 11) 20 or 24 lb. 100 percent cotton fiber paper. Why bother? Your paper will not only look good; it will *feel* good in your teacher's hands. The Southworth Company of West Springfield, Massachusetts, reports that "letters written on cotton fiber paper receive more attention than those written on wood fiber papers."

Step 13: Hand in Your Masterpiece
Always submit your paper on or before its due date. If you turn in your paper late, your teacher will either deduct points from your grade, consider you a disorganized student, or refuse to accept your paper at all. To avoid the intense pressures of a deadline, try to complete your paper two or three days earlier than necessary.

Step 14: Go Out and Celebrate
Completing a college-level paper is not an easy job. You've put in a lot of hard hours to finish your work, so go out and reward yourself. You've earned it.

Let's grab some drinks,
Let's have some fun.
Because at last,
This job is done.

STEWART JONES, *Montana State University*

Term Paper Checklist and Time Line

Nothing happens by itself. . . It all will come your way, once you understand that you have to make it come your way, by your own exertions.

BEN STEIN

FROM "THE FIRST PHASE"

1. Did you choose a topic that:
    - is interesting to you?... Y / N
    - is original? .... Y / N
    - is suitable for the assigned number of pages?............................. Y / N
    - can be applied to more than one course? .... Y / N
    - is acceptable to your teacher? .... Y / N

    finish by this date: _____

2. Did you conduct preliminary research to collect background information on your topic? .... Y / N

3. Did you have a brainstorming jam session? .... Y / N

4. Did you make a tentative outline for your paper? .... Y / N

    finish by this date: _____

FROM "THE NEXT PHASE"

1. Did you gather and utilize a good variety of sources? .... Y / N

    finish by this date: _____

2. Did you write your first draft? .... Y / N

    finish by this date: _____

3. Revising your first draft:
    - did you check it for content?.. Y / N
    - did you check it for organization and flow?............................... Y / N
    - did you check it for mechanics and grammar? .... Y / N
    - did you read it aloud? .... Y / N

    finish by this date: _____

FROM "THE FINAL PHASE"

1. Did you have a friend proofread your work? .... Y / N

    finish by this date: _____

2. Did you follow all assigned guidelines? .... Y / N

3. Did you print out your paper on cotton fiber paper? .... Y / N

4. Did you turn in your paper on time?... Y / N

    finish by this date: _____

THE PAPER'S DUE DATE: _____

Sources

Fry, Ron. *How to Study Program*. Hawthorne, N.J.: Career Press, 1991.

Green, Gordon W. *Getting Straight A's*. Secaucus, N.J.: Lyle Stuart, 1985.

Myers, David G. *Psychology*. New York: Worth, 1986.

Pauk, Walter. *How to Study in College*. 3d ed. Boston: Houghton Mifflin, 1984.

Robinson, Adam. *What Smart Students Know*. New York: Crown, 1993.

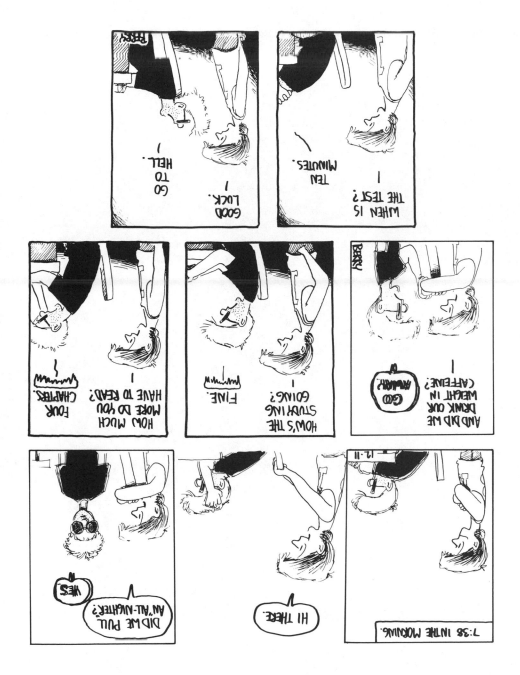

Making the Grade © **Bob Berry**

TIME MANAGEMENT

To choose time is to save time.

LEONARD BACON

As college students, our lives are saturated with things to do: Study smart. Party hard. Exercise regularly. Eat right. Get involved on campus. Try new experiences. Meet new people. Spend time with the family. Nurture friendships and relationships. Get a good amount of rest . . .

But there's a problem: we have only twenty-four hours in a day to do everything we want and need to do. And if you think about it, that's not a lot of time . . . *or is it?*

Think about how you manage your time. Do you fall prey to all-nighters? Do you cram for exams and stress out over deadlines? Do all of your responsibilities seem to pile up on you at once? Do you always feel "pressed for time"?

Yeah? You do?

Welcome to college life.

By now you're probably no stranger to time pressure. It is part and parcel of every college experience—and it afflicts all of us. The good news is, many

of your day-to-day time pressures can be alleviated with some basic time-management skills. That is what this chapter will provide for you.

The purpose of time management is to

- Organize your efforts so that you get as much done as possible every day
- Establish a balance between a *structured* lifestyle and a *flexible* lifestyle
- Provide a means of identifying specific goals
- Assist you in achieving these goals
- Help you avoid time traps and time conflicts
- Help you track your efforts so that you can evaluate your own performance
- Help you do what you need to do, when you need to do it
- Make darn sure that you have plenty of time for fun

The bottom line is that when you have more control over your time, you have more control in your life. And managing your time with a custom-made weekly schedule may be just what you need.

▲

The College Success Time Management System

One of the best lessons that anyone can learn in life is how to use time wisely.
WILLIAM A. IRWIN

A weekly planner is a weekly planner is a weekly planner, right?

WRONG!

The College Success Time Management System is unique, different from every other planner you may have seen or used in the past. It has been designed specifically to fit the college student lifestyle and serves as the foundation of this time management chapter.

The system facilitates effective time management by helping you organize, prioritize, and fulfill your daily responsibilities. Best of all, it actually *assists* you in reaching your academic goals.

In other words, this system was developed to give you more of what you have the least of: TIME.

And speaking of time, let's begin by putting it to good use . . .

Using the System

The College Success Time Management System provides a simple, yet complete, process for managing your time. At first glance it may look a little complicated,

especially if you've never used a planner before—but don't worry. This system is easy to learn and even easier to use on an ongoing basis. Once you get started, you immediately begin to add more organization and control into your daily life.

Setting up the system is a breeze. Here's how:

First: Use the Weekly "To Do" Lists

Keeping a weekly "To Do" list will help you manage your time effectively. Each week has its own "To Do" list for you to use. Plenty of spaces are provided. In them, write down the individual tasks, commitments, and plans that you have for that week.

Do not depend on your memory to keep track of all the things you need to do. Life is hectic enough the way it is, don't you think? The last thing you need is to try to keep all your commitments in your head. So jot 'em down.

Second: Prioritize Your "To Do" List

Some of your weekly tasks will be more important than others, and some tasks will take more time than others. To make optimal use of time, it is best to structure these tasks in an organized way. If you work on them in a random, arbitrary fashion, you'll invariably run into time problems.

The solution? *Prioritize your list.* Isolate the most important tasks and focus your energies on them first. Get them out of the way, and worry about the minor ones afterward.

You can easily prioritize your list by determining each task's level of importance. Notice the Priority box (marked *P*) next to each space in the "To Do" list. Place the appropriate letter in this box, beside the task you have written down.

A— *TASKS OF HIGHEST PRIORITY.* These tasks are *essential* to your personal goals and must be done, no matter what!

B— *TASKS OF SECONDARY IMPORTANCE.* These tasks are important to do, but only after your A-tasks have been completed.

C— *TASKS OF MINOR IMPORTANCE.* If you don't get these tasks completed this week, fine. You can carry them over to the next week without a problem.

Third: Check Off Finished Tasks

Once you have completed a task, check it off in the "done" box (marked "D"). This simple act of completion has a positive effect on you both mentally and physically. It has been scientifically proven that checking things off from a list releases endorphins into your body. It's nature's way of rewarding you for tackling your tasks.

Fourth: Fill in Your Weekly Schedule

Sometime before the school week begins (Sunday night or Monday morning is usually best), take some time to fill out your schedule for the upcoming week. *Write down all of your daily commitments*—class times, lab times, work hours, club meeting times, regular exercise times, commuting times, and so on. This will give you a bird's-eye view of your entire week.

Once you know how much time has already been spoken for, you can easily see how much time remains for you to allocate toward your academic goals and leisure time activities. Creating a record of your weekly commitments keeps you in touch with *how you actually spend your time*. This is the essence of effective time management. Through this system, you will be able to identify pockets of time throughout the week that can be used more productively.

Fifth: Write Down Your Weekly Goals

Let's face it. We've got a lot of academic responsibilities in college. One of the best ways to handle these responsibilities and do well in them is to *set our own academic goals*.

In chapter 9, "Goal Setting," we learned the psychological benefits of writing our goals down on paper and seeing those written goals frequently. Simply stated, goals are most easily reached when they are specific, measurable, and written down, and when we are reminded of them regularly. This planner was developed on this powerful psychological principle.

Open up the planner and take a look at a weekly schedule. On the bottom portion of each day's section, you will find two spaces—one is labeled *G1*, the other is labeled *G2*. In these spaces you are to write down your *first* and *second* Academic Goals.

Let's say one of your goals is to get a B on Friday's English test. Simply write "B on English test" in the space provided. Write down this goal each day from the time you begin preparing for the test until the day you actually take the test.

Why do this?

Written objectives are a form of self-motivation. They help solidify your goal in your mind and give you a specific, visual target to shoot for. Your chances for attaining your goals greatly improve when they are recorded in this manner.

Sixth: Calculate the Time You Spend on Your Goals

It is always a good idea to keep track of how much time you apply toward the goals you set. Time-management experts call this "time tracking." They say it is a great way to measure your own performance because it eliminates ambigu-

ity from your weekly study habits. Ideally, the actual amount of time you spend on your goals gauges the level of commitment you have for them.

Time tracking also gives you a double shot of realism. First, you can't trick yourself into thinking that you worked really hard on a project when you see that you spent only three hours on it. Second, you can't chastise yourself for "being lazy" or "not working hard enough" on a project if you see that you have studied over ten hours for it.

With the College Success Time Management System, time tracking can be done in a snap. On the right side of each day's section, you will see two columns, *G1* and *G2*—representing Goal 1 and Goal 2. *For every half hour of time that you allocate toward a goal from 7:00* A.M. *to midnight, place an X in the appropriate box.*

If you work on your goal between midnight and 7:00 A.M., *write down* those amounts in the appropriate boxes. At the end of the day simply add up the Xs (and the late-night time, if applicable) and VOILA! You've calculated the time you spent on your goal for that day.

Eventually, you will take your test or finish your project or whatever your goal may have been. You can then tally up your daily totals to come up with your <u>Weekly Total</u>. This amount represents the TOTAL amount of time you spent on that goal.

Why is this information valuable? Well, let's say that your goal is to get an A on Friday's algebra test. You begin studying for it Monday and record your study times in the planner. Friday, you take your test. Your test grade: B +.

As you look back on your planner, you discover that you spent a total of five hours studying for that algebra test. The test before, you studied four hours and received a B. This is valuable information. You begin to realize that if you study six or seven hours, you may be able to bring your *next* test score up to an A!

This method gives you a kind of yardstick measurement of your own performance. *It gives you an understanding of how effectively you study in given time frames.* Time tracking can be a major determining factor in your success in school.

SIDE NOTE: Time tracking is meant to give you a *close estimate* of how much time you spend on your academic goals—not a perfectly exact, to-the-minute calculation. So if you study an hour and twenty-five minutes on a goal, round up. If you study for an hour and seven minutes, round down. There's no need to be too precise. A good estimate is more than adequate.

Seventh: Fill in the "Due Today" Section

Jot down all tests, projects, and assignments in the "DUE TODAY" section as soon as you know of their due dates. This planner uses a *week-at-a-glance*

format, which means all of your weekly responsibilities can be conveniently laid out in front of you via this section. One glance at your weekly schedule gives you a picture of your entire school week. You will know exactly what you have to do and when to do it.

A Final Note

To get the most out of this system, make a concerted effort to use your planner on a daily basis. Photocopy the blank sample pages and use them each and every week.

It may take a little effort to budget your time effectively, but, oh, what a return you'll get from this investment. Not only will you be more productive every day; you will also have more time to do the things you *want* to do.

Make time for your planner, and it'll make time for you.

** THE WEEK OF:_____ **
WEEKLY "TO DO" LIST

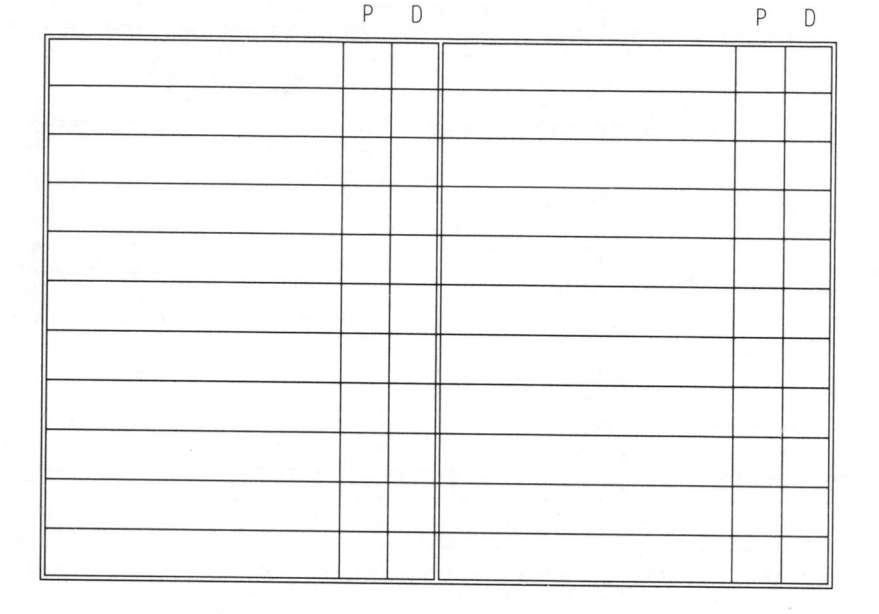

MISCELLANEOUS EVENTS & PERSONAL NOTES

MONDAY _____ G1 G2	TUESDAY _____ G1 G2	WEDNESDAY _____ G1 G2
7AM———————	7AM———————	7AM———————
8————————	8————————	8————————
9————————	9————————	9————————
10———————	10———————	10———————
11———————	11———————	11———————
NOON——————	NOON——————	NOON——————
1PM——————	1PM——————	1PM——————
2————————	2————————	2————————
3————————	3————————	3————————
4————————	4————————	4————————
5————————	5————————	5————————
6————————	6————————	6————————
7————————	7————————	7————————
8————————	8————————	8————————
9————————	9————————	9————————
10———————	10———————	10———————
11———————	11———————	11———————
12-7AM—————	12-7AM—————	12-7AM—————
——————G1 __	——————G1 __	——————G1 __
——————G2 __	——————G2 __	——————G2 __
G1: _____total __	G1: _____total __	G1: _____total __
G2: _____total __	G2: _____total __	G2: _____total __
* DUE TODAY *	* DUE TODAY *	* DUE TODAY *
1.	1.	1.
2.	2.	2.
3.	3.	3.

THURSDAY _____ G1 G2 FRIDAY _____ G1 G2 SATURDAY _____

THURSDAY			FRIDAY			SATURDAY	
7AM			7AM			AM	
8			8				
9			9			PM	
10			10				
11			11			EVENING	
NOON			NOON				
1PM			1PM				
2			2			TIME SPENT ON GOAL1:	___
3			3			TIME SPENT ON GOAL2:	___
4			4				
5			5			SUNDAY _____	
6			6			AM	
7			7				
8			8			PM	
9			9				
10			10			EVENING	
11			11				
12-7AM			12-7AM				
	G1	___		G1	___	TIME SPENT ON GOAL1:	___
	G2	___		G2	___	TIME SPENT ON GOAL2:	___
G1: _____ total	___		G1: _____ total	___			
G2: _____ total	___		G2: _____ total	___			

* DUE TODAY *	* DUE TODAY *
1.	1.
2.	2.
3.	3.

** WEEKLY TOTALS **	
GOAL 1:	_____ hrs
GOAL 2:	_____ hrs

Igmee   © David Estoye

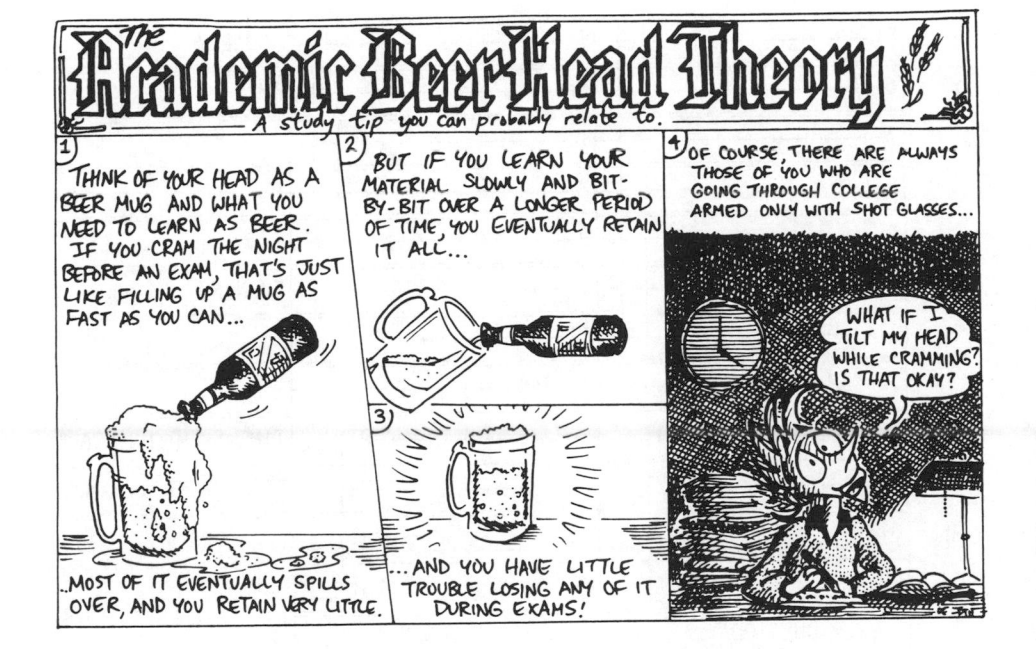

HOW TO
ENHANCE YOUR MEMORY

Memory is the diary that we all carry about with us.

OSCAR WILDE

For most classes our grades are determined by how well we can remember academic material. Preparing for tests, for example, is just a big exercise in memorization. It only makes sense that being an effective student warrants a good memory. This means you need to have good memorization techniques to support you throughout college.

For the most part, learning in school is based on facts, formulas, theories, principles, statistics, and history. Week in and week out we listen to lectures, read textbooks, take exams, do case studies, and conduct lab experiments. My point? *These are all primarily left brain activities—those that require analytical thinking and logical reasoning.*

This aspect of our educational system is all well and fine, except for one thing: the right side of the brain—the hemisphere devoted to creativity, visualization, and emotion—is largely neglected. This makes the process of memorizing information doubly difficult for us; we are essentially using only the left sides of our brains. We are so focused in on the analytical aspect of learning that we all but disregard our creative natures.

But the minute we engage both the left *and* right sides of our brains, memorizing academic material becomes infinitely easier. The methods presented here add a creative element to the process of learning—which is the key to building a powerful memory. There are literally dozens of memorization techniques out there, but only a select few seem to be appropriate in an academic setting. The five techniques in this chapter have proved to be most effective for college students.

The basis of all memorization is association. You can remember something you *don't* know simply by associating it with something you *do* know. The best way to master this concept is to apply it several times, with different techniques. This chapter has several exercises to illustrate its points and to show how your memory is improving. The exercises will allow you to experiment with your memory, so that you can choose the techniques that work best for you.

Before we go any further, a word of caution: always make sure that you fully understand the material you intend to memorize *before* you attempt to memorize it. Memorizing information without understanding it is just as useless as understanding information without being able to remember it. So be sure to have a solid foundation for the material before you apply any memorization techniques. You will benefit most from this chapter if you treat it as a knowledge *supplement,* not a knowledge *substitute*.

Okay, I'll get off my soapbox. Let's begin by learning a couple of standard methods for enhancing your memory . . .

▲

Standard Methods

Memory is the treasurer of the mind.

UNKNOWN

The Common-Sense Technique

The best piece of wisdom regarding memory was offered by Samuel Johnson back in the 1700s. "The true art of memory is the art of attention." As a starting point to building a powerful memory, we must enter every study session ready to focus our attention on one thing and one thing only: the material at hand.

The Mnemonic Technique

Using a mnemonic device is an excellent way to recall lists, groups, or sequences of information. This memorization technique is so effective and easy to apply that it has become a regular part of our daily language. For instance, when you see GPA, IRS, SAT, ASAP, CEO, or PMS, chances are you instantly know what each stands for and what each means; these are *acronyms*—mnemonic devices in action.

On a more academic level, maybe you learned all of the colors of the light spectrum with the acronym

ROY G. BIV (Red Orange Yellow Green Blue Indigo Violet)

Or perhaps you learned all the musical notes in the treble clef with the sentence:

Every Good Boy Does Fine (E G B D F)

Or maybe, just maybe, you learned how to set goals with:

SMART (Specific, Measurable, Attainable, Realistic, Timely)

At any rate, it's plain to see how mnemonic devices can help you recall information easily and quickly, and for the long term. Can this technique be applied directly to your courses? You bet.

Let's say the professor of your nutrition class requires you to remember that these six foods are rich in zinc: Beef, Oysters, Lamb, Almonds, Turkey, Cashews.

How can you memorize these six otherwise unrelated foods?

Simple. *The trick is to use the first letter of each word as a mental cue and construct an acronym.* For example, you could play around with the order of these six words until you come up with an acronym such as "COBALT" (as in the color) or "CATBOL" (as in a *cat's bowl*). If, during an exam, you are asked to "list the six foods that are rich in zinc," your mind will automatically think along these lines: "Zinc . . . okay, a cat's bowl . . . a cat's bowl . . . CATBOL. Ah ha, got it. Cashews, Almonds, Turkey, Beef, Oysters, Lamb."

Or, *you could simply construct a sentence—again, using the first letter of each word as a cue.* Come up with a crazy, funny, totally ludicrous sentence with those letters, such as "Cats And Turtles Barf On Lisa." Remember that the sillier and more visual the sentence is, the easier it will be to remember. Use this technique and, like a computer, your brain will respond to those mental cues and provide you with the information you need.

The Recitation Technique

Another terrific memory technique involves reciting aloud the information you want to remember. If you have formulas, concepts, principles, definitions,

or vocabulary words to memorize, it really pays to open up your mouth and vocalize the material as you study it.

Why?

When you say the material out loud, you are simultaneously engaging all three of your primary senses. Your visual (sight), auditory (sound), and kinesthetic (physical movement) senses are all being stimulated and applied directly to the subject matter. In other words, you are using more of your brain; you are seeing the information, hearing the information, and applying a physical element to the learning process—all at the same time. This absolutely proliferates your ability to memorize information.

Visualization Methods

The human memory would be worthless without the capacity to make mental pictures.

JOSEPH SHORR

The Pegging Technique

On campuses all over America, the Pegging Technique is often hailed as the best memorization method for college students. Before we actually learn how to apply this system, though, let's take a moment to test out your present ability to memorize new information.

Below is a list of fourteen words. Start at the top of the list and work your way down. Take as much time as you want, but *read each word only one time*. Once you have gone through the entire list, stop and immediately go to the next page.

pencil
swan
lips
car
hand
gun
cliff
skate
cat
Bo Derek
chop sticks
beer
ski mask
heart

In the spaces provided, write down as many of the words from the list as you can *in the correct order*.

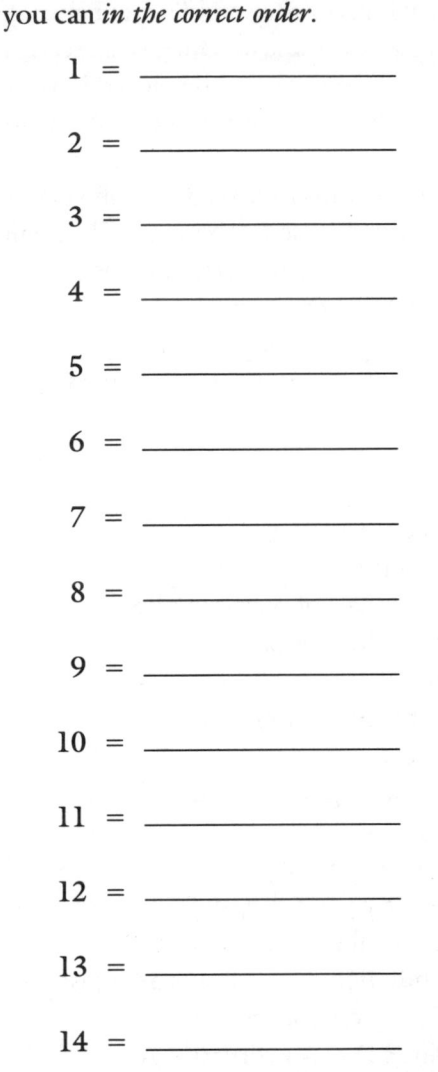

1 = _____

2 = _____

3 = _____

4 = _____

5 = _____

6 = _____

7 = _____

8 = _____

9 = _____

10 = _____

11 = _____

12 = _____

13 = _____

14 = _____

Well? How many did you get right? Two? Three? Four? Discouraged?

Don't be. This test serves only to reveal the deficiencies in the standard learning methods of college students. You see, the most common way for students to memorize data is through *rote memorization*—which is the tedious process of mentally repeating information over and over again until it gets etched into memory.

There are three major problems with rote memorization. First, memorizing information in this fashion is extremely time consuming. Second, it is an ineffective method for promoting long-term retention of new information. And third, mindlessly repeating information is a cumbersome, monotonous, absolutely boring way to learn.

Instead of absorbing data via the rote method, you can make use of the *principle of visual association*—making a visual link (in your mind's eye) between something you don't know and something you do know. Once you create a visual association in your mind, that image will be permanently etched in your memory. This will allow you to memorize information easier and faster than you ever have before.

While the written description of this concept may seem a bit confusing, it will all come together once you see it illustrated in some examples. You will find in the next section the 1–2–3 Peg List. *Commit this list to memory, and I guarantee it will serve you throughout your entire college career.*

This is an extremely valuable technique we're learning, so take a good ten minutes (or however long you need) to learn this list backward and forward . . .

1–2–3 PEG LIST

1	=	PENCIL	looks like a pencil
2	=	SWAN	looks like a swan
3	=	LIPS	looks like a pair of puckering lips
4	=	CAR	four speed, four door, 4 x 4
5	=	HAND	five fingers
6	=	GUN	six-shooter cowboy gun
7	=	CLIFF	looks like a cliff
8	=	SKATE	rhymes with eight, figure-8
9	=	CAT	nine lives
10	=	BO DEREK	star of the movie *10*
11	=	CHOPSTICKS	looks like a pair of chopsticks
12	=	CAN OF BEER	12-pack, 12 fluid ounces per can
13	=	HOCKEY MASK	the bloody hockey mask worn by Jason in those *Friday the 13th* movies
14	=	HEART	Valentine's Day is February 14th

(This list was developed by several students from the University of Southern Maine.)

The 1–2–3 Peg List is fairly easy to learn because there is an intellectual component involved—each number is logically related to its peg word in a particular, concrete way.

In terms of remembering these "pegs," be sure to visualize the image of each word in your mind; for instance, really imagine how a swan resembles the number 2. Form as vivid, clear, and colorful a mental picture of each peg word as you possibly can. Once you associate the image with its respective number, it will be locked away in your memory bank.

And Remember . . .

As you visualize each peg word, hold its image in your mind for five to fifteen seconds before moving on to the next. This will give your mind enough time to form a neural pathway for each word, which will make the new association a permanent part of your memory. *Mental consolidation* is the term used to describe this psychological phenomenon.

And Now . . .

Now we're ready to move on to the next step: actually putting the pegging technique to use. After you have visualized each of the words on the 1–2–3 Peg List (and maybe had a review or two), retake the memory test in the spaces below.

1 = _____

2 = _____

3 = _____

4 = _____

5 = _____

6 = _____

7 = _____

8 = _____

9 = _____

10 = _____

11 = _____

12 = _____

13 = _____

14 = _____

I'll bet your score improved dramatically. In fact, if you took the time to clearly visualize each word, you probably got a perfect score without any difficulty.

You can see how the principle of visual association can really enhance your memory for new material. But learning the 1–2–3 Peg List is only the first step; it's just a way to introduce the pegging concept. What we really want to learn is how to apply this newfound knowledge directly to our classes . . .

The Next Step   Let's get practical and say you have to memorize a speech on Neanderthals for a sociology class. There are ten key points that you want to address in your speech:

cave
moon
smoke signals
fire
boat
skull
boulder
fish
spear
tree

How can you memorize these key points and give a flawless speech without referring to flash cards or notes? Simple. Just link together—through visualization—the ten key words with ten pegs from the 1–2–3 Peg List.[1]

Number	Peg Word	Key Word
1	pencil	*cave*
2	swan	*moon*
3	lips	*smoke signals*
4	car	*fire*
5	hand	*boat*
6	gun	*skull*
7	cliff	*boulder*
8	skate	*fish*
9	cat	*spear*
10	Bo Derek	*tree*

Pegging Tips   When you mentally link together two visual images, be sure to keep these five tips in mind; they will help make your visualizations much more vivid and memorable.

- Magnify, exaggerate, and colorize the images as much as possible.
- Imagine lots of physical action taking place—running, screaming, exploding, shooting, kicking, singing, etc.
- Include yourself in the visualization whenever possible.
- Engage all primary senses in your imagination—visual (sights), auditory (sounds), and kinesthetic (physical movement).
- Make your mental images as crazy, bizarre, ludicrous, silly, sexual, or absurd as you can (remember that normal everyday, mundane images do not stand out in your mind and are much more difficult to remember).

Now then, here are some examples of how you could create visual associations between what you want to remember (key words for the speech) and what you already know (numbers and peg words). Remember to take ten seconds or so to close your eyes and visualize each example vividly in your mind. Paul Gauguin hit the point accurately when he wrote, "I shut my eyes in order to see."

You could remember that point 1 is *cave* by imagining your family eating dinner in a cave in a huge yellow mountain that's made completely of pencils.

You could remember that point 2 is *moon* by visualizing a big swan wearing a silver space suit, walking around on the moon.

You could remember that point 3 is *smoke signals* by picturing an enormous pair of ruby-red lips sucking on a cigarette and blowing out smoke signals.

You could remember that point 4 is *fire* by envisioning your car engulfed in flames and imagining yourself screaming and running toward it with a fire extinguisher.

You could remember that point 5 is *boat* by visualizing the Jolly Green Giant holding a sail boat—with you in it—in his gargantuan right hand.

You could remember that point 6 is *skull* by picturing yourself aiming an AK-47 assault rifle at a skull, pulling the trigger, and watching the skull explode into a million white pieces.

You could remember that point 7 is *boulder* by imagining Wile E. Coyote standing on a cliff, waiting to push a gigantic boulder down onto the Roadrunner.

You could remember that point 8 is *fish* by envisioning yourself wearing huge ice skates, skating on a pond, playing ice hockey against a team of giant-sized skating fish.

You could remember that point 9 is *cat* by visualizing yourself throwing a spear at a big black cat and hitting it dead center. $\longrightarrow$

> You could remember that point 10 is *tree* by picturing Bo Derek sitting naked on a thick tree limb, singing the "Save the Rain Forest" theme song.

Pegging This Information Is as Easy as 1–2–3   Now let's see how well you can remember all the points of your speech. Fill in the blanks.

Number	Peg Word	Key Word
1	_____	_____
2	_____	_____
3	_____	_____
4	_____	_____
5	_____	_____
6	_____	_____
7	_____	_____
8	_____	_____
9	_____	_____
10	_____	_____

Pretty amazing, isn't it? Without use of the pegging technique, it would be virtually impossible to fill in most of these twenty blanks in the amount of time we spent.

The best part of all is that each association took only ten seconds or so to visualize and lock away in memory—which is why this pegging technique is much more time efficient than rote memorization. It is also more fun, because you are allowing your imagination to run free as you memorize important material. The information that was once random and impersonal is now organized in a way that has meaning for you.

More good news: This method works equally well in reverse—you can use the key words from your speech to remember the exact numbers of the points you want to address. See for yourself:

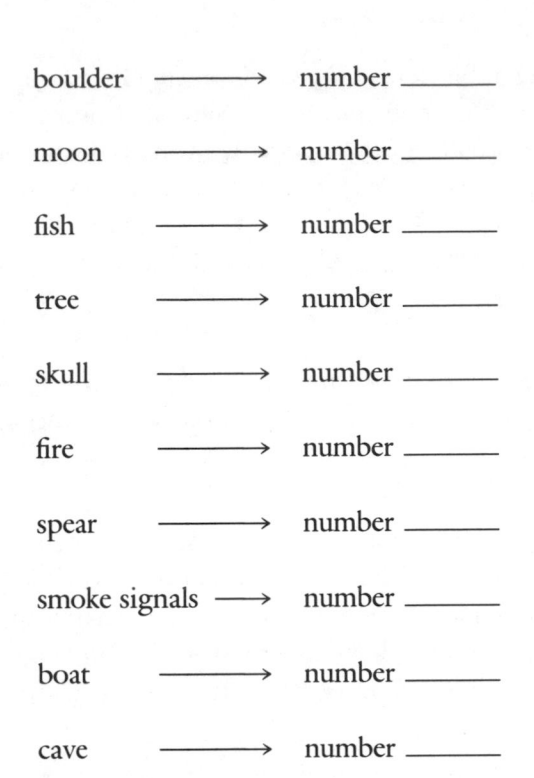

boulder ⟶ number _____

moon ⟶ number _____

fish ⟶ number _____

tree ⟶ number _____

skull ⟶ number _____

fire ⟶ number _____

spear ⟶ number _____

smoke signals ⟶ number _____

boat ⟶ number _____

cave ⟶ number _____

FYI: If you need to, you can extend the 1–2–3 Peg List simply by adding on more numbers and pegs. For example, you could peg a birthday cake to the number 16 ("sweet sixteen" birthday parties), a bottle of liquor could be pegged to the number 21 (legal drinking age in most states), a shiny quarter could be pegged to the number 25 (a quarter is worth 25 cents), and so on.

The Tell-a-Tale Technique

Another visual method for memorizing sequences of information is the Tell-a-Tale Technique. The name of this technique says it all, really—*you simply make up a crazy, wacky, ludicrous story that directly involves the information you want to remember*. Then, through visualization, you play out the story in your mind as vividly as you can. This method is especially popular among college students because it is like creating and watching your own "mental movie" with the material you need to learn.

Let's say that for an American history final exam, you have to remember that Abraham Lincoln was assassinated in 1865. Recalling the 1–2–3 Peg List, we know that 1–8–6–5 can be identified visually as: *pencil-skate-gun-hand*.

With this sequence of information you can make a story that is creative, chronologically accurate, and most importantly, easy to remember. You could memorize this date by creating and imagining a scenario such as the following (at each "***" close your eyes for ten seconds and vividly imagine the scene taking place in your mind):

Abe Lincoln is quietly sitting at his desk in the Oval Office. He is using a huge purple *PENCIL* to draw a goofy picture of himself delivering a presidential speech on roller *SKATES*. *** Suddenly, a masked assassin crashes into the room through the office window! *** He is holding a big black *GUN* in his quivering *HAND* and is screaming "I must kill the president!! I must kill the president!!" *** The masked man approaches Abe and pulls the trigger .

Or maybe you want to remember that your friend Karen's birthday is 9–22–76. Again, simply use the pegs from the 1–2–3 Peg List to serve as mental cues, and develop a wacky story . . .

Karen is taking a nice, leisurely walk on a mountain in Arizona when she spots a cute little *CAT* meowing nervously. *** Soon, *two* vicious *SWANS* magically appear out of thin air and ferociously chase the kitty to the edge of a steep *CLIFF*. *** Not knowing how else to stop the onslaught, Karen pulls out a huge machine *GUN* from her backpack and blasts a thousand bullets into the air . . . ***

Okay, are you ready to try one on your own? Do this exercise—create a zany story with these four words in this order:

policeman, glasses, candle, rain

Remember to visualize a story vividly in your mind. Envision colorful, exaggerated images and imagine lots of physical action taking place. Creating stories like these is a constructive and fun way to remember sequences of information.

Side Note: Keep in mind that you can associate *any* word with a visual image—even abstract words such as *deformative, organization, schizophrenia,* and *metaphony*. How do you create visual images with abstract words?

The key is to break down the word into syllables, and form visual images from those syllables with sound-alike words. For example:

DEFORMATIVE ⟶ DE-FORM-A-TIVE
"The *form of his* face became abnormal after the car accident."

ORGANIZATION ⟶ OR-GAN-I-ZA-TION
"Our church's huge wooden *organ is asian*-made."

SCHIZOPHRENIA ⟶ SCHIZ-O-PHREN-I-A
"For her birthday party, I put on two silly *skits of* my *friend Miah*."

METAPHONY ⟶ MET-A-PHONY
"At a Halloween party, I *met a phony* Madonna."

Try some of your own. Make visual images from these abstract words:

OXFORD $\longrightarrow$ OX-FORD

" _____ . "

SUPEREROGATION $\longrightarrow$ SUPER-ER-O-GA-TION

" _____ . "

DOGMATISM $\longrightarrow$ DOG-MA-TISM

" _____ . "

As you can see, this strategy will allow you to use the Tell-a-Tale Technique with even the most abstract of words.

Notes

1. Tony Buzan, *Make the Most of Your Mind* (New York: Fireside, 1988).

Sources

Buzan, Tony. *Make the Most of Your Mind*. New York: Fireside, 1988.
Lorayne, Harry, and Jerry Lucas. *The Memory Book*. New York: Dorset Press, 1974.
Myers, David G. *Psychology*. New York: Worth, 1986.
Pauk, Walter. *How to Study in College*. 3d ed. Boston: Houghton Mifflin, 1984.
Starke, Mary C. *Strategies for College Success*. 2d ed. Englewood Cliffs, N.J.: Prentice-Hall, 1993.
Trudeau, Kevin. *MegaMemory*. Niles, Ill.: Nightingale-Conant, 1991.

College   © Dan Killeen

HOW TO
ACE YOUR EXAMS

It is not enough to have a good mind. The main thing is to use it well.

RENÉ DESCARTES

A, B, C, D, P, F, W. It's amazing how these harmless-looking little letters can have such incredible impact on our lives. On the surface they look like mere characters from the alphabet. But on a deeper level they translate into keys for our future: a college diploma, excellent job offers, future earning potential, happy parents, self-respect, an open door to graduate school, scholarships . . . Success in college depends on our ability to take tests, since they are the standard way for teachers to evaluate our performance.

How hard is it for you to ace your exams? If you have ever studied your heart out for a test but still failed to get an A, then keep reading. It's an interesting phenomenon: many of the brightest students on our campuses make only average grades, while many less-than-brilliant students—who don't work particularly hard—ace their classes, virtually every time.

What's their secret?

Well, if you want to find out for yourself, do what I did: conduct an experiment. Go up to all the straight-A students you can find and ask them their secrets of success. Chances are, you're not going to get answers like

"nonstop studying," "innate ability," or "good luck." You will generally find that these academic dynamos know and apply some good test-taking skills. Basically, that's it. Simple.

It stands to reason that if they can do it, we can too. Obviously, a high intelligence and an impeccable work ethic helps, but they are by no means the only requisites for high grades.

This chapter is all about acing your exams. First, we'll learn twenty general test-taking strategies. Next, we'll move on to the three predominant forms of college testing: multiple-choice questions, true/false questions, and essay questions.

Basic studying and preparation for any exam is up to you, of course. But you can supplement your studies with time-tested strategies—and improve your grades. And don't worry, they're easy to learn and apply. So let's check 'em out.

▲

Top Twenty Test-Taking Tips

1. Be Prepared. Ah yes, the old Boy Scout motto we've all heard a million times before. The phrase may be simplistic and overused, but, hey, good advice is good advice. If you plan your time well, study smart, and apply the strategies you've learned in the other academic chapters, you'll be A-bound at every test. Scout's honor.

2. Catch Some Z's. Even if you have to cram till the wee hours of the morning, it's important to get *some* sleep before the exam. A couple hours of REM sleep will prevent you from drawing blanks or freezing up during the test. Despite what many studyholics believe, sleeping is *not* a waste of study time—your brain subconsciously reviews all the material you have learned while you're off in la-la land.

3. Watch Your Watch. Always bring your own watch to your exams. Never rely on a clock being on the wall. There may not be one; and besides, it's inconvenient to raise your head and look around the room every time you want to check the time. Many top students place their watches on top of their desks, where they can be referred to easily and often.

4. Eat Smart. Nutrition specialist Judith Wurtman describes how some foods produce mental alertness, while others dull the mind and spawn mental

and physical sluggishness. She provides a detailed explanation of all the hows and whys in her wonderful book, *Managing Your Mind and Mood through Food.*

In a nutshell, Wurtman suggests that you eat foods higher in protein and lower in carbohydrates. Around test time, it's best to indulge more in "brain foods" such as lean meat deli sandwiches, peanuts, fresh poultry and fish, and green, leafy veggies. Moderate your intake of "high-carb" foods such as cereal, pasta, potatoes, bagels, dates, and bean-based foods; they make you feel groggy. Plus, give the ol' heave-ho to foods high in fat. Save those jumbo pizzas and Chinese buffets for *after* the test.

5. Never Miss a Review Session.   And never miss the class period directly before the exam. Teachers provide the most vital information about their tests during these times. They also tend to give helpful hints and valuable insight at the end of the session, during the Q & A period.

6. Snag Those Old Exams.   Some teachers arrange for students to check out tests from previous semesters at the campus library. If this system is not available to you, don't fret. Many fraternities and sororities have test files with old exams dating back to when the houses were founded. Often you will be able to find your teacher's old exams (or at least similar ones) in them. If you're not in the Greek system, buddy up with someone who is.

7. Test Yourself before You Get Tested.   Days before the exam, make up practice test questions for yourself. Here are some ideas:

- Make flash cards with terms on one side and definitions on the other.
- Use your text's appendix or end-of-chapter exercises to help you form sample test questions.
- Get involved with a study group and brainstorm for possible test questions.
- Use the asterisked or underlined portions of your class notes to help you form sample test questions.
- Buy a supplemental study guide for the text and work through it.
- Refer to earlier quizzes and assignments.

8. Review Strategically.   *The night before the exam, review the material immediately before you go to bed.* Make sure the test information is the last thing on your mind before you drop off to sleep. If you argue with your boyfriend or watch an hour of Letterman and *then* go to bed, you'll impair your memory for the material. This is a phenomenon called *retroactive interference,* which refers to the disruptive effect that new experiences have on the recall of prior learning.

The morning of the exam, do another brief review of your notes as soon as you wake up. This will help reinforce your memory and strengthen your understanding of the material.

9. *Wear Loose, Comfortable Clothing.* It's hard to think straight when your clothes are tight and cut off your circulation. If you want to be loose and comfortable during the exam, wear loose and comfortable clothing! Throw on whatever you feel most relaxed in, even if you have to stroll into the test room in your planet-and-star PJs and bunny slippers.

10. *Don't Overload on Caffeine.* You have to stay alert and focused during an exam in order to ace it. But what if your brain's fried from too much studying and you're tired from lack of sleep? What should you do then? Guzzle down a six-pack of Jolt? Pop a couple of NoDoz? Slam a pot of coffee?

No, definitely not.

True, caffeine *is* a stimulant; it increases the adrenaline level in your blood stream. But you can have too much of a good thing. If you are already anxious about a test and you infuse your body with caffeine, you get a double shot of adrenaline—which will make you restless, jittery, nervous. And there's no way you can concentrate when you're bouncing off the walls.

11. *Don't Pig Out before the Exam.* The quantity of food you eat influences your test-taking performance. When you scarf down a huge meal, your body expends most of its energy in your stomach and digestive tract (that's why you often feel tired after large meals). Filling up with food just before your exam causes your body temperature and blood sugar to drop—meaning that less energy will be distributed where it's needed most: up in your noggin.

12. *Arrive at the Test Site Early.* There's nothing that raises a student's anxiety level more than rushing to get to an exam on time. If at all possible, be at the test site a full half hour early. Find a good seat, relax, familiarize yourself with the environment, and calmly look over your notes one last time.

13. *Be Antisocial.* Once you're in the testing room, sit alone and don't listen to the other students' patter: how impossible they think the test is going to be, how hard and long they studied for it, how worried they are about flunking. Their negative talk may psych you out and cause you to worry needlessly.

14. *Check the Water before You Jump In.* As soon as you are handed your exam, briefly skim over it before you put your nose to the grindstone. Ac-

quaint yourself with its format. Then read and follow the directions carefully, and check for missing pages.

15. *Do the Easy Questions First*.   While you're skimming the exam, find the easy questions and answer them first. You'll build confidence and momentum and will take those positives with you into the harder, more demanding questions. Often, answers to the difficult problems will come to you naturally as you work on the easier ones.

16. *Budget Your Time*.   Time is an either/or entity. Either you control it, or it controls you. To ace your exams, you have to be in control of time; that means budgeting it carefully.

As soon as you receive your test, determine roughly how much time you have to spend on each question or each major section. Allot more time to those questions that are worth the most points. Then pace yourself. Monitor your work periodically to stay within your time constraints.

17. *Prime Your Mind*.   *It is vital to "deep breathe" before and during your tests.* And, no, this isn't some weird, booga booga metaphysical gambit. It is sound advice based on physiology and neurological functioning. And most students know nothing about it.

You see, your brain comprises only 2 percent of total body weight, yet it utilizes 25 percent of the body's supply of oxygen. For your brain to function at its peak, it must be provided with an ample quantity of oxygen.

But there's a problem. *Taking exams (especially the BIG ones) can create lots of anxiety*. When you are anxious or nervous during an exam, your breathing pattern changes: your in-breaths become quicker and more shallow; and your out-breaths become less frequent and less complete. This causes a buildup of carbon dioxide, which limits the amount of oxygen available to your brain. The result? Possible tension headaches, an inability to concentrate, light-headedness, or an overall jittery feeling—none of which will help you ace your exam.

But you can counteract the effects of anxiety by oxygenating your brain. Maintain a good breathing pattern throughout the test: in through the nose, out through the mouth, in through the nose . . . you know the routine. Just be sure to keep your breathing rhythmic, slow, and deep. Oxygen is energy, and the more you have the better.

If, in the middle of the exam, you feel your concentration start to wane, put your pen down, close your eyes, and take a couple of slow, super-deep breaths. This will revitalize your brain and have a calming effect on your nerves—both of which will help you ace your exam.

18. *Use All Your Test Time.* Let's face it. Taking a test isn't exactly our idea of a good time. In fact, it can be an outright miserable experience. It's normal for us to want to get it over with as quickly as possible, bolt out the door, head straight for home, and double-fist a couple of tall cold ones.

But restrain the temptation to leave before the exam is officially over. If you've finished your test and there's extra time left, <u>use all of it</u>. Double-check your answers: proofread for spelling and grammar, reevaluate and recalculate your solutions, and <u>make sure</u> you didn't skip over any questions.

19. *Do All Extra Credit.* Treat every extra-credit opportunity as if it was a requirement.

20. *Don't Cheat.* I'm not a college administrator, and I'm definitely not your dad, but I would agree with them on one thing: no exam is worth compromising your principles and jeopardizing your education. Even bombing a test is a better option.

Multiple-Choice Questions

Multiple-choice questions test your recall. The best way to answer them is to narrow down your options by using a process of elimination. On your test sheet, place an X next to the options you know are bogus.

IN 1988, MAURICE ALLAIS RECEIVED WORLDWIDE RECOGNITION FOR:

xA. launching into outer space on the space shuttle *Discovery*
 B. winning the Nobel Prize for Physics
xC. starring in Andrew Lloyd Webber's Broadway hit, *Phantom of the Opera*
 D. winning the Nobel Prize for Economics
xE. developing the world's first plutonium-powered pacemaker

Here are some other helpful hints:

- Middle options (B, C, and D) are usually better choices than first and last options (A and E).
- When two choices are *similar* to each other, one of them is usually the correct answer.
- When two choices are *opposites* of each other, one of them is usually the correct answer.
- Your first hunch or "gut feeling" will be correct more often than your second or third guesses.

- Choices with unusual, unfamiliar-looking words are generally poor options.
- When options are numerical, the highest and lowest numbers are often poor choices; second-to-last highs and lows are more often correct.
- "None of the above" options are rarely correct.
- "All of the above" options are often correct.

True/False Questions

A true/false question is the most simple and straightforward way to test for knowledge and understanding. You either know the right answer or you don't. There are no in-betweens.

Most likely, you are going to run into several questions for which you don't know the answer. When this happens, make an educated guess and move on. Here are some general guidelines that will help you up your total score:

- *Longer* statements are true more often than not.
- Trust your first intuition; second guesses are usually inaccurate.
- True answers are slightly more common than false.
- Qualified statements containing words like "usually," "often," "generally," and "some" are usually true.
- Absolute statements containing words like "always," "never," "none," "all," and "every" are usually false.
- Statements with unusual, unfamiliar-looking words are commonly false.
- If *any* part of the statement is false, the entire statement is false.
- Statements with lots of facts have a tendency to be false (e.g. "In the year 1906, Oscar Wilde wrote *Kipps,* H. G. Wells wrote *De Profundis,* and Belasco produced *The Girl of the Golden West*.").
- Statements that give *reasons*—and contain the words "because," "since," "reason," and "on account of"—are often false (e.g. "The nativist approach to language development was rejected because the critical-period hypothesis was proven valid.").

Essay Questions

These are the kingpins of all test forms. An entire exam grade can be determined by just one or two of these questions. So we'll cover them in greater detail.

Essay questions test more than mere recall. They test our ability to reason

and express ourselves intelligently; they require explanations, opinions, and creativity. It's not easy to ace essay exams, that is, unless you have a system for writing them.

Good news is, there *is* a system. A great one.

That said, it's important to realize that getting a good essay grade is all a matter of being persuasive. We have to demonstrate to our teachers that we are well-informed about the topics at hand, and that we deserve an A on our exam.

But there's a catch.

Let's say you know everything there is to know about Shakespeare's *Hamlet*. All well and good, but if you can't persuade the old English prof of that fact through your writing, all of your knowledge—and all of the time you spent *obtaining* that knowledge—isn't going to do your grade a bit of good.

Don't be fooled into thinking that essays are graded objectively. They aren't. They *can't* be. It's impossible to be objective in a subjective format. Your grade is based on the *teacher's interpretation* of your writing—not simply on the quality of your work.

The truth is that if your teacher doesn't like what he sees, he is not likely to give your essay a high grade—even if it's jam-packed with facts, great ideas, and thorough explanations. Herbert Spencer put it best back in the 1800s: "Opinion is ultimately determined by the feelings and not by the intellect."

An essay needs to have both substance *and* style in order to earn a high grade. Substance *should* be the only important thing in any test, but it isn't. Essays are evaluated subjectively. If you can push your teacher's subjective hot buttons—without pandering transparently to his or her likes or dislikes—and provide a well-written essay, you'll do well every time.

Here are six terrific strategies to help you do that:

Read the Question Carefully

Commonsensical as it is, you have to *fully* understand the question before you begin writing. Read the question slowly, intently. If you misread it and get off track in your writing, you'll never recover. Also remember that you have the right to ask the teacher for clarification if you need it. Unless he or she is a big-time jerk, you'll get the assistance you need.

Mark Your Mission

Make sure you answer the question that is asked instead of a question you want to answer. In other words, don't explain when you are asked to compare

and contrast. Don't <u>illustrate</u> when you are asked to <u>critique</u>. Be totally clear on what the question is asking of you. <u>Underline the key verbs of the question</u> and keep them in mind as you . . .

Formulate a Game Plan

It's important to stop and think about what you're going to write *before* you write it. The first three minutes of each essay are crucial to this end.

As you read the question, *do a quick-and-dirty one-minute brainstorm*. Immediately jot down the ideas and key words that come to mind in the margin of the test or on a piece of scrap paper.

Then, *make a mini-outline of your answer*. No full sentences, just headings and subheadings written with abbreviated words and shorthand scribbles (you're the only one who is going to read it). This should take two minutes, tops.

Now you're all set to write a complete, well-structured essay without a lot of bulk or rambling—exactly the kind of work organization that teachers love.

The mini-outline:

- allows you to plan the major points you want to bring out in the essay
- helps you arrange them in the right order
- prevents you from getting stuck or blanking out in the midst of your writing

It's much better to spend a few minutes formulating a game plan for your essays than to "wing it" and haphazardly write down facts and ideas as they enter your mind. As Jenny Jones of UCLA said, "Success is not arbitrary—you've got to have a method to your madness."

Restate the Question Carefully

There is a persuasive element to writing A-grade essays. Obviously you have to be concise and intelligible in your writing; that's a given. But there's another way to add to your essay's appeal: make direct references to the teacher's question.

In your first paragraph, rephrase the question as a topic sentence. For example, if the question requests:

"EXPLAIN THE DIFFERENCES BETWEEN *DELUSIONARY FEARS* AND *LEGITIMATE FEARS* FROM A TYPICAL COLLEGE STUDENT PERSPECTIVE."

Your topic sentence could look something like:

"There are major differences between delusionary and legitimate fears, particularly from a typical college student's perspective."

Address the question exactly as the teacher asked it. Don't use too many of your own words just yet. Stroke your teacher's ego a little first. Give him exactly what he or she wants.

Remember that the first paragraph sets the tone for the rest of the essay. It's also the first thing your teacher reads. This fact alone makes it a major determining factor in your grade. Psychologists call this the *primacy effect*— which describes the tendency for information presented *first* to have the most persuasive influence. Make the first part of your essay shine, and you're half-way home.

After you write the main body of the essay, follow this same strategy in your conclusion. *Make another direct reference to the teacher's question and link it to the answer you provided in the main body*. You could start out like this:

"From a college student's perspective, the differences between delusionary fears and legitimate fears are pivotal indeed . . ."

The conclusion is the last thing your teacher reads, which makes it another major determining factor in your grade. This is a principle called the *recency effect*— alluding to the fact that information presented *last* is also highly influential.

To persuade the teacher that you deserve an A, you have to start smart and finish strong. Your first paragraph should assure the teacher that you are addressing his or her question directly; your main body should validate this assertion; and your conclusion should reassure him or her that you *did* address his or her question directly. This strategy gives your essay a huge psychological edge.

Technically, you'll earn most of your points in the main body. But the overall impression of your essay is always made at the beginning and at the end because those are the places where your teacher's concentration peaks. So remember: for each essay, <u>assure</u> first, <u>prove</u> next, and <u>reassure</u> last.

Be a Literary Emily Post

Since essays are graded subjectively, following some simple rules of etiquette will really help you boost your grade:

- Write on just one side of each sheet of paper.
- Leave about a two-inch margin on each page.

- Don't cram your words close together; leave plenty of space between them.
- Write neatly; use a good pen (and have an identical back-up pen handy).
- If you have to cross out a mistake, use a straight, single line instead of a random scribble.
- Break down your essay into a series of short three- to four-sentence paragraphs instead of long, five- to eight-sentence paragraphs.
- Don't try to dazzle your teacher with big, fancy words or complex sentence structures; be brief, to the point, clear, and concise.

These tips allow you to make modifications easily. But more importantly, they add to your essay's readability and overall attractiveness—and, at the same time, they project authority and confidence in your writing. If your essay is sloppy, difficult to read, or hard to understand, there's no way your teacher is going to reward you with a high score—no matter how much information it contains.

Keep in mind that grading essays is to a teacher what doing homework is to us: A MAJOR DRAG. Making that job as easy and enjoyable as possible will prompt him or her to grade your essay more favorably.

Proofread Your Work

Double-check your essay after you've written it. Make sure it doesn't have any misspellings or sentence errors. Many professors are hard-nosed about grammar and spelling. They will deduct an entire letter grade if they find three misspelled words or sentence fragments in your essay. Beat them to the punch and correct any mistakes. A brief rereading of your work can literally make the difference between an A and a B or a B and a C.

Sources

Buzan, Tony. *Make the Most of Your Mind*. New York: Fireside, 1988.
Green, Gordon W. *Getting Straight A's*. Secaucus, N.J.: Lyle Stuart, 1985.
Myers, David G. *Psychology*. New York: Worth, 1986.
Pauk, Walter. *How to Study in College*. 3d ed. Boston: Houghton Mifflin, 1984.
Robinson, Adam. *What Smart Students Know*. New York: Crown, 1993.
Silver, Theodore. *Study Smart*. New York: Villard, 1992.
Starke, Mary C. *Strategies for College Success*. 2d ed. Englewood Cliffs, N.J.: Prentice-Hall, 1993.

Chicken Bird © Ron DiCesare

INDEX

A NOTE FROM ME TO YOU

I want to hear from you!

If you have any ideas that pertain to *anything* from this book, write out a quote and send it to:

Richard C. Newman
College Success
P.O. Box 780016
Wichita, KS 67278

Please include your name, phone number, and college, along with the name you would like to have next to your quote. Your words of wisdom may be published in an upcoming college life book. By responding, you are agreeing to have your quote published.

Thanks, and happy writing!

ABOUT THE AUTHOR

Richard C. Newman is currently an MBA student at the University of Kansas. He is both the youngest author ever to be published in the *International Journal of Comparative and Applied Criminal Justice* and the youngest representative ever to be hired by the Wandling Midwest Agency of the Equitable Financial Companies.

In his years as a student, Richard has run the full gamut of college experience. He has lived in a dormitory, a fraternity, at home "with the folks," in an apartment with a roommate, and in a single apartment. He has achieved average grades, Dean's List grades, and---using the techniques in his book---straight A's.

Richard was born in DeKalb, Illinois, and was raised in Wichita, Kansas. He enjoys sports, writing, sparring, and playing drums for a rock group. He currently resides in Lawrence, Kansas.